# THE GR AMERICAN DRUG DEAL

A New Prescription for
Innovative and Affordable Medicines

## PETER KOLCHINSKY

EVE LEX A PR ESS

Published by Evelexa Press

Boston, Massachusetts

Cover design by *the*Book Designers

Book design by Alex Head / The Draft Lab

Cover Image: shutterstock.com

Author photo by Bryce Vickmark

Images created by Erin Clutter

ISBN: 978-1-7330589-1-9

Printed in the United States of America

*For those struggling in America's healthcare system.*
*We can and should do better for you.*

# CONTENTS

# PART 1

# THE BIOTECH SOCIAL CONTRACT

# 1

## A WORTHY CAUSE

**Of all the bones in your body, your hip might just be the worst one to break.**
Fracturing this vital joint can necessitate replacement surgery followed by
months of slow and often excruciating recovery. For seniors, especially,
it can disrupt important routines, lead to isolation from social networks,
and ultimately tip the balance between good and poor health, beginning a
downward spiral toward death. Still, we can only be grateful, for without
surgery people would remain immobilized and racked with pain.

The procedure and tools have improved since hip replacement surgery
was first performed in the 1940s, but, in essence, the method is the same:
The patient is put under anesthesia, and the surgeon cuts into the skin and
removes old bone, implants an artificial joint made of metal or ceramic,
sews up the patient, and prescribes antibiotics and pain medication. Many
patients require opioids for severe pain, which come with a risk of addiction.

Hip replacement surgery costs around $40,000 (not counting any
extended nursing or rehabilitation, which is often needed),[1] and around
400,000 such procedures are performed in America each year, double the
rate from 15 years ago.[2] For the sake of argument, let's ballpark the overall
cost of hip replacement in America at $16 billion in 2019—and that cost is
likely to climb as our population grows and ages. Hospital costs consistently
climb faster than inflation and the growth of the broader economy, aver-
aging 4-5% per year over the last decade.[3] Not only will the number of hip

replacements double again in the next couple of decades, but the costs likely will too. Today's $16 billion in hip replacement spending could become $50 billion in the next several decades. As things stand, hip replacement surgery and the associated inconvenience, pain, and growing costs are our future, our children's future, and our grandchildren's future.

And yet scientists know a lot about how bones work, how they become weaker, and how they can be strengthened. For decades, scientists have been testing molecules to determine how to reverse bone loss to prevent fractures. Because of the high cost of making new drugs—far more than an academic laboratory can afford—researchers and investors have created and funded companies to develop some of these molecules into medicines that prevent bone damage, with some success, particularly for patients with osteoporosis and rheumatoid arthritis. If not for these breakthroughs, the rate of hip replacement surgery would be even higher than it is.

Now imagine that later this year, a company comes out with a drug that strengthens bones so effectively that a person's risk of fracturing their hip is cut in half. This drug would spare 200,000 Americans the agony and impairment of hip replacement surgery and save society $8 billion. After a couple of decades, with the cost of surgery over $60,000 and twice as many people at risk of fracture, society would be saving closer to $25 billion per year. Tens of millions of people—our grandchildren and their children—would live longer, fuller lives, thanks to this miracle drug.

What's that worth to America? Such a drug would be one of the highest-selling medicines ever, pulling in many billions in US sales and much more on a global basis until its patent expired—a jackpot for the company and a boon for humankind. As inexpensive generic versions of that drug continued to keep the rate of hip surgeries down for the rest of time, the savings to society would likely reach trillions of dollars. Yet down the road, no one would talk about the cost of that common, affordable bone-building drug. It would be a gift from a long-forgotten era, paid for by a long-forgotten generation, like all of our generic drugs today.

· · ·

When I was a student, history was a difficult subject for me, as my youthful ignorance blinded me to the lessons I needed to draw from the past. I preferred science because each discovery seemed to fit neatly into an interlocking, logical framework, and whatever didn't make sense held a secret to be discovered through experimentation. Science promises to operate on the basis of true and false, black and white, which can feel the same to a teenager as right and wrong. History is comparatively messy.

When I was a teenager, my father suggested that biotechnology would change the world for the better, setting me on the path I've been on ever since. I trained as a virologist, partly because I thought viruses were fascinating, but mostly to learn the language and methods of science that would allow me to distinguish between data I could trust and data that would mislead me. Around the time the human genome project was nearing its stunning conclusion, I joined the biotechnology industry to help scientists turn their breakthroughs into novel medicines and diagnostics.

As a biotechnology investor, I'm on the receiving end of a fire hose of knowledge. Our office buzzes with excitement as we learn about creative ideas for combatting diseases with chemicals, antibodies, and cutting-edge technologies such as gene therapies and antisense oligonucleotides. My team is accountable to our investors, and the biotechnology companies in which we invest are accountable to us and their other shareholders, yet really all of us are accountable to the patients who our products must ultimately serve for any of our work to matter.

Since 2002, I've observed and participated in the evolution of the biotechnology industry. I've seen ideas that existed only in patents and small companies' slide decks become marketed drugs that cured millions of people of hepatitis C, saved the lives of children born with spinal muscular atrophy, and helped patients with cancer survive their diagnoses. And I've witnessed thousands of other ideas collapse under the weight of all we don't yet know about disease. But each success remains a permanent step forward. We've made the present healthier than the past, and the future will be better still.

For too long my utopian view of the biotechnology industry omitted the perspective of patients who couldn't afford their medications. I'll confess that for many years their plight was more of an abstract problem for my team and other investors. When considering how many patients might someday benefit from a new drug, we would assume that the total would be less than 100% of those who needed it, shaving down the percentage out of deference to what we simply saw as unfortunate realities. Not all patients would even know they had the disease that the drug was meant to treat. Not all patients who suspected they had this disease would consult their physicians. Not all physicians would know the drug existed or think to prescribe it. Even when it was prescribed, not all patients would fill their prescriptions, maybe because they couldn't be bothered or because their insurance wouldn't cover the drug. Even if their insurance covered the drug, the copayment might be too high for the patient to afford. And even once a patient started taking the medication, they might not continue taking it, either because they didn't think it was working for them or due to side effects, or, again, because the copayments became overwhelming. When the law permits, drug companies usually offer to help pay these copayments, and yet some patients still go without, perhaps because they do not realize they are eligible for copayment assistance or even can get drugs for free.

America's healthcare system makes it hard for some patients to access drugs that could help them. But I certainly didn't see how this troubling fact was the biotechnology industry's fault, and I didn't spend much time dwelling on what could be done about it. As I saw it, our byzantine health-care "system" (a word we use when we don't know exactly who does what) wanted to save money by denying patients access to expensive treatments. Drug companies just needed to be savvy enough to get around those defenses by making sure that patients and doctors knew how their drugs could help, negotiating with insurance companies to get their drugs reimbursed, and providing copayment assistance to circumvent financial deterrents. The outcome was that most patients did eventually get the treatments they needed. But I failed to see that the growing outrage over those left behind by this bureaucracy could pose an existential threat to innovation.

In 2014, there was an especially loud outcry from politicians, the media, and the public over what they saw as the high price of newly launched hepatitis C drugs. For almost eight years, I'd been immersed in the science of how the virus reproduces in people's livers, trying to predict which companies were on the right track to curing it, and supporting some of them with investment. With breakthrough drugs coming to market, millions of patients would finally be cured. But the list price for the first of these drugs was $84,000 (which came out to $1,000 per pill), and instead of celebrating our collective triumph over a devastating disease, society accused the industry of price-gouging. Some defended the price, pointing out that it cost less than the prior standard-of-care on a per-cure basis. The drug was inarguably less expensive than the cost of untreated hepatitis C, which leads to liver failure, cancer, and death. Others noted that, since this cost was paid upfront for a cure, the cost of hepatitis C drugs was a bargain compared to the $25,000 *per year* cost of HIV medications that must be taken indefinitely to manage a disease we still don't know how to cure. The entry of another comparably effective hepatitis C drug towards the end of 2014 and the subsequent drop in prices as two (and, later, more) companies competed to cure patients helped calm the turmoil. Still, the public's fury had been palpable, belying a deep mistrust of the pharmaceutical industry that could and would be triggered again.

That moment came in July 2015, when a small, newly formed company called Turing Pharmaceuticals bought from another company the rights to sell an old drug that treats very rare infections and jacked up its price by more than 5000%. The resulting outrage extended to other companies that had raised prices on old drugs, then to companies that were raising prices on newer drugs, and finally to any company selling a high-priced drug. The industry responded by condemning Turing's heinous price-jacking of an old drug but otherwise defended high drug costs with standard explanations of how expensive it is to develop a drug. Some executives vowed that their companies would take only modest price increases, in some cases under 10% and in some cases no more than inflation.

When politicians started talking about price controls, industry representatives responded with statements that amount to "patients need to be able to afford drugs, *but* Congress should not pursue policies that would undermine innovation." The problem is the word "but"—it is tone-deaf.

"But" implies that patients bankrupted by medical bills or unable to afford treatment are unfortunate but unavoidable casualties of innovation. That "but" should have been an "and," and it should have been followed immediately by "here's how."

> *Patients need to be able to afford drugs, **and** Congress should not pursue policies that would undermine innovation. Here's how...*

I believe in that "and," and this book is the "here's how..."

In listening to the industry's response, what surprised me was what *wasn't* being talked about. No one was extolling the benefits of the mountain of off-patent, inexpensive generic drugs that continue to help humanity and always will. What makes drugs affordable to society in the long run is precisely the fact that they are typically easy enough to manufacture that, once their patents expire, the same drugs can be made by dozens of different companies that then compete on price. That's not the case for the rest of healthcare. Doctors and hospitals do not go generic. Surgery will only climb in price. For all the outrage over companies raising the prices of their branded drugs year after year, that is the norm for land values, housing costs, and the prices of many other products. And yet, while apartments in New York City will not suddenly turn into affordable housing overnight, that's essentially what happens when drugs like Lipitor go generic.*

When you pay a high and growing price for an apartment forever, that's called rent. When you pay a high price for an apartment for a defined period of time and then you own it, that's a mortgage. Those expressing outrage at the high price of branded drugs were, in a way, thinking of a mortgage payment as if it were rent. Rent is an expense. A mortgage is an investment. No one was making this point.

---

\* You may have heard about the dangers of high cholesterol. Cholesterol-lowering drugs like atorvastatin (formerly known as Lipitor, which generated around $13 billion per year in revenues for Pfizer at its peak and is now the 3ʳᵈ most highly prescribed drug in America) have contributed to a 50% decline in death from both heart attacks and strokes throughout the developed world over the last few decades. When Pfizer's patent on Lipitor expired and generic versions entered the market, the price quickly dropped by 95% of the initial cost and has remained negligible ever since.
Michael Rosenblatt, "The Real Cost of 'High-Priced' Drugs," *Harvard Business Review*, Nov. 17, 2014, https://hbr.org/2014/11/the-real-cost-of-high-priced-drugs.

Another response I didn't hear: High drug prices aren't the reason patients are unable to afford medications—high out-of-pocket costs are. The only way patients can be expected to afford branded drugs is if they have insurance, and by that I mean insurance that offers proper coverage of healthcare costs instead of the patchwork of gaps many patients fall through today.

America's safety net is failing. There are people in America who don't have enough food, yet it's not because food is too expensive. There are people in America who don't have access to clean water, yet it's not because clean water is too expensive. And there are patients in America who are denied available treatments, but it's not because those treatments are too expensive. In every case, it's because of how we fail to compassionately and thoughtfully distribute the resources we do have.

The whole point of healthcare reform and the crux of the Affordable Care Act (aka Obamacare) was to extend health insurance to more Americans, ideally to everyone, to protect them from the unforeseeable costs of illness and accidents.

How come then, in response to a patient not being able to afford a treatment, the public's first thought was "drug prices are too high" instead of "hey, isn't that what insurance is for?"

I think that drug developers failed to account for the consequences of their successes. Innovators achieved one breakthrough after another, spending huge amounts of money to develop drugs that physicians and patients badly wanted for many diseases, but then neglected to inspire the public to see the value and long-term cost-effectiveness of these advances. Innovators left that part of the narrative to middlemen—the insurance companies—who took the easier path of casting drug companies as price-gouging villains. So as insurance plans balanced their own budgets by cutting back on the amount of coverage they offered, causing patients' out-of-pocket costs to rise and many to forego insurance, the public blamed drug companies. In retrospect, the drug industry should have made a case for the value of their products and helped patients lobby for the kind of insurance policies that would make these breakthroughs affordable to them. If America could be inspired to pay to send people to the moon, it can be inspired to find a way to pay for curing hepatitis C and cancer without bankrupting patients.

Yet, over the course of 2015 and 2016, I watched as the drug industry failed to make a clear case that:

1. Patients would be able to afford medicines if insurance companies and Medicare were forbidden from imposing high out-of-pocket costs,* relegating the question of drug costs to a question of what society can afford, not what any one sick patient can afford.

2. In terms of what society can afford, high drug prices are usually temporary. The vast majority of drugs go generic after 10-15 years and stay inexpensive for the rest of time, permanently upgrading our standard of care.

3. The prices paid for genericizable drugs are a mortgage, a cost-effective investment that benefits our society, the cost of which should be borne by the entire society—which is what insurance is for, to avoid disproportionately burdening the sick and poor.

4. The small percentage of drugs that can't be "genericized" (i.e., drugs with a recipe that is too hard to copy) must be regulated so that their costs drop over time as if they had, in fact, gone generic.

As 2016 came to a close, I began to see that the biopharmaceutical industry and society are engaged in a kind of symbiotic relationship, a powerful but delicate one that I came to call the Biotech Social Contract (a term others had used but in different ways). This contract is the central tenet of this book and the basis of all of my arguments.

---

* Medicare is a US federal government-run healthcare insurance plan run for older Americans. Not to be confused with Medicaid, which is a group of state-run plans that cover very poor people. Those who make too much income to qualify for Medicaid (which isn't hard since the threshold is under $20K/individual) or are too young for Medicare either get private insurance (typically through whatever company they work for, though self-employed people can also purchase private insurance) or go uninsured (about 13% of Americans have no insurance; they tend to earn too much for Medicaid but are too poor to afford private insurance and are more likely to risk going without insurance if they are younger and feel healthy, though that leaves them vulnerable if they do fall ill).

I define the Biotech Social Contract as follows:

> The drug development industry's commitment to developing new medicines (and other technologies) that **will go generic without undue delay** is *reciprocated by* society's commitment to providing **universal health insurance with low/no out-of-pocket costs** so that patients can afford what their physicians prescribe.

As long as those conditions were met, patients would get the medicines they needed and society would continue to enjoy a growing armamentarium of inexpensive, generic medicines that would improve human health for the rest of time thanks to the ingenuity of the thriving collective of scientists, clinicians, executives, investors, and others at the heart of the biotechnology industry.

But that's not what anyone was talking about.

## The Biotech Social Contract: An Analogy

Here's how I've come to think about the injustices of how we, as a society, have come to pay for medicines.

Imagine that a community, where, on average, five homes catch fire each year, decides that it needs a fire station. It will cost $20 million to build the fire station and then $1 million/year to maintain it. So the town decides to take out a ten-year loan for $20 million and raise taxes on every one in town to generate the extra $1 million/year in operating costs as well as to cover 80% of the payments on the long-term loan. To cover the extra 20% of the loan payments (let's say $500,000/year for 10 years, allowing for interest), they plan to charge $100,000 to each family that calls for help during the first ten years after the fire station is built.

In ten years, everyone will continue to enjoy the services of the fire station for the rest of time for merely the cost of the modest fire station operating tax. That's good for everyone except those families unlucky enough to need the fire station's help during its first decade; they were hit with bills of

$100,000 each and some of them were driven into bankruptcy and ended up homeless.

Part of the town management committee's rationale for having the $100,000 copayments was that it would discourage people from calling the fire station for help. Indeed, a few people who could not afford the copayment decided against calling the fire station. While that left them homeless and living in their cars, at least they didn't have the extra $100,000 of debt.

Of course, that's not actually what a town would do. But, sadly, it's how we currently pay for drugs.

In this analogy, fire represents being diagnosed with a disease, let's say cancer, and building the fire station represents developing a drug. The bank that loaned the town money represents the company and investors funding drug development. The town is the insurance company, taxes are the premiums it charges all its members, and the $100,000/family charge represents patients' out-of-pocket costs for the drug. Paying off the loan represents the fire station going generic. A smart and compassionate populace would agree to raise taxes enough to fully service the loan payments. It would fully spread the cost of building the fire station across all the residents over ten years without hitting people whose homes burned down with a sudden $100,000 bill. All families would be treated fairly, whether they needed help from the fire department in its first decade, three decades later, or never.

## This Book's Origin Story

The rancor of the 2016 presidential election left me searching for reassurance that our country had dealt effectively with greater adversity, so I went back to America's beginnings. That year, I read Ron Chernow's biography of Alexander Hamilton. Like many of America's founders, Hamilton appreciated the significance of what they were doing, shaping a nation that would be ruled according to the world's best practices gleaned from hard lessons learned over millennia, ranging from Greece and Rome to then-modern England and France. Their work culminated in the US Constitution, possibly the most intentional and deliberated social contract ever written. With its checks and balances, the Constitution attempted to reconcile the many conflicting priorities of the original thirteen states—some industrial, others engaged mostly in farming, some densely populated, others sparsely so. Everyone had to give something up, but the question was whether they appreciated how much more they stood to gain by foregoing their individual liberties as states and submitting to a contract binding them all as a single nation.

Each state's legislature had to ratify the Constitution. If even one state held out, it could all fall apart. Debates raged all over the country, in the pages of every newspaper and in every tavern. There was a serious risk that the Constitution would not be ratified and the opportunity to forge a nation would be lost, potentially forever. That was their moment and there might not be another.

Hamilton fought for the social contract he believed in. He had helped shape the Constitution, knew its workings, and was intimately involved in deliberating the many scenarios it was designed to handle. Together with fellow founders James Madison and John Jay, over a period of about two years, Hamilton published 85 essays in support of the Constitution, exploring its advantages and defending it against its opponents' arguments. These were later aggregated into a compendium called The Federalist Papers. He was tireless, earnest, opinionated, analytical, and passionate. The fact that the Constitution was ratified and we now live in the United States of America is due in part to Hamilton's conviction that this was the future worth fighting for. His efforts to overcome the arguments of many skeptics were successful.

You may see where I'm going with this. From my vantage point, the public's mostly misdirected outrage against high drug prices and patients being unable to afford medicines is a threat to what I view as humanity's epic endeavor to solve disease through science and technology, improving life for generations to come. There is a social contract between the drug development industry and society that hasn't been spelled out, which leaves it even more vulnerable to misunderstanding and mischaracterization than the written Constitution.

Mixed in with arguments about high drug prices was anger that drug companies were advertising their products directly to consumers, ignoring the fact that no patient can get a drug if their physician doesn't know about it. People seemed to resent that some drugs were too similar to other drugs and therefore not innovative, overlooking that it was precisely the launch of multiple, similar cures for hepatitis C that sparked a price war that saved society billions of dollars.

I saw the constructive contract between society and its innovative biotechnology sector about to be torn to shreds. Nobody was reconciling the two sides by explaining both how patients could afford their medicines and how society could get value for its money. Yes, certain reforms are necessary. We need universal health insurance (not necessarily the same as a single-payer system) and limits to what patients have to pay out of pocket. We need to do something about drugs that can't or don't go generic, which I see as the real threat to society getting its money's worth over time.

These simple and effective ideas elicit many questions that start with "But what about…?" What about the high cost of the EpiPen? What about doctors prescribing drugs that patients don't need and wasting society's money? What price, if any, is too high for a drug? This book offers a single, internally consistent framework for answering these questions and many others.

So it boils down to this. I'm a scientist and investor, I love my work, and I admire the integrity and intentions of most people in my industry. I'm inspired to see companies having to constantly hustle to think of something new because they know that they will only get to collect revenues from their successes for a finite period of time. That creativity and drive is healthy and productive for society. I'm distressed and saddened by the anger directed against my professional community for injustices that are a result of America's broken health insurance system. I am frustrated by my industry's inability to defend itself against the facile arguments of critics who either don't realize or don't want to acknowledge that patients can't afford drugs because insurance companies don't want them to. And yet I am embarrassed by the real abuses of my industry, particularly the growing share of drugs that cannot go generic, and I therefore suggest reforms, some novel, that will keep the biotechnology industry vibrant for the long run.

I'm not alone in these concerns. It won't come as a surprise that there is widespread agreement in the drug industry on the need to reform the US insurance system. But many of my colleagues and peers also agree with the need for the reforms of the drug industry that I call for. I wish I could tell you that insurance executives acknowledge the harms of their policies and are calling for reforms to make healthcare accessible to all patients, but they aren't. So it's up to the rest of us to reshape the system.

In answer to your presumed outrage—I share it. I believe that patients should be able to afford what their physicians prescribe, and this book lays out how to do that while ensuring that the drug industry continues to expand our generic drug mountain. I hope that this book inspires policymakers to eliminate out-of-pocket costs for patients while ensuring that all drugs go generic without undue delay, and I hope that you will do what you can to see that these key tenets of the Biotech Social Contract come to pass.

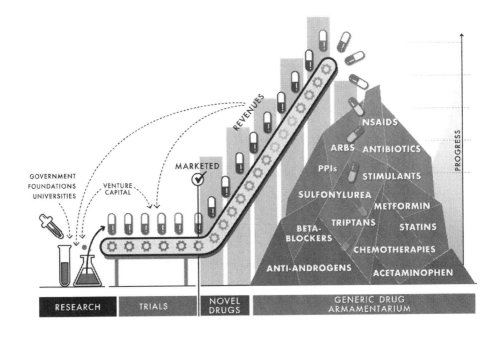

# 2

## GENERIC DRUGS: A MOUNTAIN OF PROGRESS AND ITS UNSUNG HEROES

This year over 100 million prescriptions will be written in the US for lisinopril, a drug for high blood pressure, heart failure, and other cardiac problems. It's inexpensive (a few dollars per month), and year after year it ranks as either the most or second-most commonly prescribed medicine in the country. Since keeping blood pressure under control is so critical, it is not an exaggeration to say that lisinopril has saved millions of lives around the world and has improved the quality of life for tens of millions more.

But there are no lisinopril commercials on TV or ads for it in the newspaper. Unless you're taking it, you've probably never heard of it. Seems strange that such a widespread and beneficial resource is so anonymous, doesn't it? Before we get into why and what lesson we can take from that, let's rewind the clock a bit.

Lisinopril came on the market in 1987 as the branded drugs Prinivil (invented and sold by Merck & Co.) and Zestril (sold by AstraZeneca under license from Merck).* Both were billed as new-and-improved versions of a similar drug, enalapril, which helps regulate the amount of fluid in the body

---

* It's unusual and confusing that the same drug was marketed under two brand names, but it's not important. The Zestril brand dominated so I will refer to branded lisinopril as Zestril going forward.

by blocking an enzyme called ACE. But lisinopril proved to be more effective in controlling blood pressure than enalapril.[4] (Enalapril itself was developed as a better ACE inhibitor than captopril, the first drug in this class, which has a spectacular origin story, having been derived from the venom of a poisonous snake, but turned off patients with its strongly metallic taste).

Fast-forward to 1999. Zestril racks up $1.2 billion in sales for Astra-Zeneca.[5] US physicians have prescribed Zestril some 22 million times, making it the top ACE inhibitor on the market and placing it in the top 20 of all prescribed drugs.[6]

But then, in 2002, something amazing—but also very common—happens: The patent expires, lisinopril goes generic, and other companies are free to bring competing drugs to market, which drives the price down—way down. These generics have the same chemical formula as the original drug, Zestril, and are sold in the same dosages and forms. Lisinopril generics are the same as the branded drug in every way, except one: They can't call themselves Zestril. Generics like this are inexpensive because they are composed of commodity chemicals, and the price is a function of the cost of manufacturing, which is miniscule compared to the cost of inventing. Companies that make generics simply follow the instructions in the inventors' patents, conduct minimal, inexpensive clinical trials, and demonstrate to regulators that their version is the same as the original. Having taken negligible risk and invested so little to launch the generic, these companies can afford to charge very little for their product. The generic's label (the instructions for doctors and patients about how the drug should be used) is the same as the brand's, and the two products are considered interchangeable. So even if you're prescribed Zestril, a pharmacist can give you the cheaper generic.

The result? These days, lisinopril can be bought for a small fraction of the price of the original, branded versions. Physicians now prescribe five times as much of the generic version of the drug than they did back when it was branded,* helping millions more people keep their blood pressure under control and lead healthier lives.

---

* Prescription rates are higher now not necessarily because the drug is less expensive, though that helps, but because America's population has increased and aged and, with the rise of obesity due to changing lifestyles, the rate of heart disease has climbed.

And that's how it's supposed to work. The US government issues patents to allow inventors—in this case, Merck and its licensee AstraZeneca—to profit from their invention for a defined period of time, typically 10-15 years after launching the drug. These temporary monopolies incentivize and fuel inventors and investors to develop new drugs. Companies that succeed in creating something new and beneficial can recoup their R&D costs, reward their investors, and plow some of those profits into future projects. This system keeps the biotechnology innovation engine churning and—importantly—prevents companies from milking cash-cow drugs indefinitely.

Furthermore, this system creates a mountain of low-cost therapies that is the core of the Biotech Social Contract,* which says, "Yes, prices will be initially—and temporarily—high on branded drugs. But after the patent expires, society reaps the benefits of the cheap, effective generic versions for the rest of time."

I will often talk about drugs going generic (or not going generic), so I'll define what I mean by that term and variations of that term. Once the patents expire and generic companies start making generic copies of a drug and the price competition causes the price to drop, the branded drug is said to "go generic," to have "gone generic," or "to have been genericized." The hallmark of "genericization," by which I mean the process of a drug going generic, is steep price erosion resulting from many competitors entering the market, each fighting for market share by offering a lower price than the others. But what everyone really cares about when they talk about a drug going generic is that its price drops by a lot, regardless of how—usually it's through competition, but that may not be the only way, as I'll discuss in Chapter 8.†

---

* Social contracts can be explicit, such as when Americans gave their representatives the power to govern them within the democratic precepts of the Constitution and the Declaration of Independence. In other instances, social contracts become implicit agreements between company and consumer. Google's memorable motto, "Don't be evil" (now "Do the Right Thing"), became an implied promise to the user that, "In exchange for using our services, we won't do anything monstrous with the power you've given us."

† For all society cares, what matters about genericization is not that a drug's price drops due to competition, but just that the price drops when the patents expire. Which is why we'll talk in Chapter 8 about ways of simulating, through novel regulations, the genericization of a drug that would be ungenericizable by competitive means and would otherwise enjoy a natural monopoly (i.e. competitors can't make a copy of the drug due to reasons that are partly scientific and partly legal).

So, with all these generic drugs competing with each other for market share, how can the consumer be sure they are getting the best price? That's another key component of this system, when it is working as it should. If a doctor writes a prescription for Zestril, in almost all cases, the pharmacy that fills the prescription doesn't actually have to give the patient the expensive Zestril-branded version of lisinopril. The pharmacy can give the patient a generic version of the drug for a lower price. Most patients don't even need to comparison shop—their pharmacy does it for them!

In fact, if insurance is paying for the drug, as is most often the case, the insurance company requires that the pharmacy fill the Zestril prescription with a generic version to save the insurance plan money. And since the pharmacy is paid a fixed amount by the insurance company for the generic, it's in the pharmacy's interest to source the product from whichever manufacturer sells it for the lowest price. What insurance plans save by making pharmacies shop for the least expensive generics helps reduce the cost to consumers of their insurance plans.

Even if a patient is paying out of pocket for the drug, pharmacies compete with one another for customers, who often buy other products each time they come to refill their prescriptions. Pharmacies can't afford to lose their customers to another pharmacy that sources even cheaper generics and can sell them for less. So they have a strong incentive to comparison shop to be able to offer the lowest prices they can, benefiting everyone. In this way, savings from the constant price war among generic manufacturers and pharmacies are passed along to the consumer.[*]

There are many hundreds of generic drugs like lisinopril.[7] Not all of them were billion-dollar blockbusters, and not all of them are equally ubiquitous. Many, like drugs for rare forms of cancer, are rarely used but no less essential to those who need them. These drugs represent decades of research, clinical trials, and medical practice. Together, they make up a metaphorical mountain of inexpensive, generic pharmaceuticals used to treat high blood pressure, high cholesterol, diabetes, migraines, inflammation, chronic pain,

---

[*] Like with any marketplace that relies on competition and comparison shopping, there can be inefficiencies. For example, when a town has only one pharmacy, it might not have a strong incentive to source the cheapest drugs. However, with many patients now getting their drugs from online pharmacies, local pharmacies have to try all the harder to keep their customers.

depression, schizophrenia, heartburn, hypothyroidism, infections, prostate enlargement, insomnia, ADHD, Parkinson's disease, and cancer, as well as preventatives for heart attacks and strokes.

Though generics account for a whopping 90% of all prescriptions written in the US,* people outside the medical field rarely think about this mountain. These represent just a glimpse of the medicines that biotechnology can produce for humanity if we continue to fuel and incentivize the biopharmaceutical industry. Society tends to take these drugs for granted, yet they serve more than just the patients who take them. When lives that would otherwise have been cut short are rescued, our loved ones remain with us to enrich our lives. Musicians, painters, and authors live on to create new works. Scientists survive their illnesses to make new discoveries.

Today, as we focus on the diseases that remain untreated, we can lose sight of this mountain of available drugs and forget to honor yesterday's innovations. Despite their benefits, some of these drugs may have been derided back when they were launched because of their prices or frowned upon as "me-too" drugs, only incrementally better than similar drugs. Yet even after these medicines go generic and disappear from public consciousness, they continue to pay dividends with even incremental advances compounding on themselves, prolonging life and health in a modern age, which is actually not so far removed from a time when a simple abscess could prove deadly.

## Origin Stories

Behind each generic drug is a story of risky and expensive innovation. The story of lisinopril starts with a chemist named Arthur A. Patchett. He and his team—Elbert E. Harris, Edward W. Tristram, and Matthew J. Wyvratt—created a very special chemical that has helped millions live longer, healthier lives.[8] But you won't find much about them on the Internet,

---

* In 2018, the US spent $271 billion on branded drugs and a comparatively modest $76 billion on generics. Unlike almost any other aspect of healthcare, drugs constantly go generic, which keeps total spending on retail drugs a fraction of total healthcare costs (9.4% in 2018), about the same as it was in 1972.

nor are their names listed on a bottle of lisinopril generic pills. Seems strange, doesn't it? Imagine a publisher bringing to market an inexpensive copy of *Pride and Prejudice*, the copyright to which long ago expired, and deciding not to put Jane Austen's name on the cover. Not even Merck, let alone Patchett, is mentioned on a bottle of lisinopril generic pills, which only credits the company that manufactured that particular generic itself. Imagine if every copy of *Pride and Prejudice* were merely stamped with the name of its publisher.

Of course, Arthur A. Patchett and his team didn't develop lisinopril alone. They and those like them are overlooked in part because developing a drug and bringing it to market is a massive project that requires huge sums of money and hundreds, even thousands, of people, including pharmacologists, clinical researchers, lawyers, accountants, consultants, and technicians. Today, an estimated 4.7 million people are directly or indirectly employed in the discovery, development, and commercialization of pharmaceuticals—and that's just in the US. For every success there are many failures, years of research and millions of dollars of investment poured into molecules that never make it past the initial development phases into human trials.

If a candidate drug seems promising, researchers and chemical engineers have to figure out how to manufacture it at scale, develop tests to ensure batch-to-batch consistency, and come up with packaging that will deliver the right dosage.

If it makes it to human trials, then the real costs pile up. Enrolling a single patient in a drug study is extremely expensive; $200,000 per patient is now common for cancer studies. That money goes to hospitals, physicians, nurses, laboratories that run tests, experts who serve on safety and ethics boards tasked with overseeing the trials, and vendors that keep clear and honest records of how the trial is conducted so that the results can be trusted.

And then there's the unquantifiable human cost of developing a drug. Patients risk much—even their very lives—in order to participate in a clinical study, hoping to benefit from a new discovery and to help other patients like themselves. Many of these patients do so knowing that there might be no benefit or that they'll end up in a control group and given a placebo. These patients shoulder the risk that an experimental drug may actually harm them and understand that, whether the drug proves effective or not, their sacrifice advances the pursuit of knowledge. Despite the amount of time and resources that have gone into getting a drug to this phase, most drugs that enter human testing fail those trials, either because they are deemed unsafe for patients or turn out to be less effective than predicted, leaving inventors, investors, and, most poignantly, patients disappointed.

The small minority of drugs, those that do manage to navigate all of these obstacles and make their way into medicine cabinets as branded drugs, must one day shed their brand names and join the growing mountain of generics. And, again, that is as it should be. But perhaps we should find ways to appreciate and celebrate the Arthur A. Patchetts of the world. If their inventions are destined to do great things, perhaps they deserve to be recognized, though they didn't do it for the fame. Doing so will remind us not to take for granted the mountain of generics that is their legacy and gift to future generations.

My point is not that specific people or companies should demand or are even entitled to more recognition than they received—some inventors are quite modest—but the fact that we do not ascribe inventorship to generic drugs allows us to blindly enjoy their benefits while forgetting all it took to bring them into the world. These drugs are successful products of human ingenuity and labor, and what we take for granted we also risk thoughtlessly discarding.

## Drugs Are Special Because They Can Go Generic

Every new drug's story begins differently, but most of those stories will end the same way. It is the destiny of nearly all new drugs to become as affordable and accessible as Zestril.* These include better treatments or even cures for cystic fibrosis, HIV, hepatitis C, lung cancer, and multiple sclerosis.[9]

---

* There are some drugs that won't, or cannot, quietly go generic—this is a problem we'll address in Chapter 8

Even the medicines we haven't yet discovered for all the healthcare problems we haven't yet solved will, thankfully, someday go generic.

In a *Wall Street Journal* op-ed, I argued that because human biology is essentially unchanging, many drugs we use today will work as well in a century.[10] Some may even work better with improved diagnostics, delivery technologies, and insights into drug combinations. Thus, the scientific progress we achieve in our lifetimes will also benefit future generations.

Therefore, whenever a debate about drug prices breaks out, it is important that we take into account what society is trying to achieve by supporting the biopharmaceutical industry. Despite the headlines and Wall Street fanfare that heralds a new drug's approval, the purpose of the industry, as a whole, is not simply to invent new drugs to help those in need today, nor is it to generate short-term profits during the 10- to 15-year life of the patent, though companies must to survive. Its greater purpose—even though currently most people in the industry are not conscious if it—is to expand humankind's generic drug armamentarium, the vast, inexpensive toolkit of medicines and know-how that make up our standards of care.

Altruism doesn't have to be part of the motivation of every, or even any person who works in the drug development industry, just as no one cell in your body needs to know your reason for being for you to feel that you have a purpose. Individuals are also motivated by their own personal goals, such as putting their kids through school, affording a nicer home, or even becoming rich and famous. But the rules to which the drug industry is subject—such as the FDA's requirement that companies prove their drugs work and typically beat standard of care, that insurance companies only pay for new drugs that are better than generics, and that patents eventually expire—requires that the enterprise as a whole achieve a noble goal: improving human health with new drugs that will someday go generic.

By comparison, the tobacco and fast food industries—and everyone who works for them—sustain themselves only by keeping customers smoking and eating french fries.

Still, I'm not making any argument about the inherent nobility of the average scientist over the average tobacco executive—that would be easy, but it's not necessary. I'm simply making the argument that we should not lose sight of the fact that the ultimate product of the drug industry—our generic armamentarium—is an unalloyed positive for humanity, and we should preserve its operation to expand this valuable, inexpensive resource.*

When it comes to our healthcare system, drugs are unique.† Unlike a doctor's visit, an MRI for a sprained knee, a hip replacement, a routine mammogram, nursing care, home healthcare, and all the other healthcare services and procedures, drugs are manufactured goods that become less expensive over time once they go generic. Collectively, service-related costs account for the vast majority of healthcare spending, over 70%, far more than what we spend on drugs. They typically require the time and effort of expensive, highly trained professionals, including doctors, surgeons, nurses, and technicians, whose salaries climb each year. These services require land, which is in short supply (especially near cities), and buildings, such as clinics and hospitals, that are expensive to build, equip, maintain, and sanitize. And, again, those costs rise each year. Healthcare services never go generic; their costs will continue to climb over time. Furthermore, unlike services, drugs benefit from economies of scale, which means that the higher the number of patients that need a generic drug, the less expensive it is to treat each one.

Well, you might be thinking, if this mountain of generics is so important, why not just make all drugs go generic right now?

---

* How? By paying for branded drugs via insurance that makes those drugs affordable to the patients who need them. Once we see it as a priority to continue to invest in creating more generic drugs by continuing to pay for branded ones, it won't be hard to find the few tens of billions of dollars we need to cover the cost of branded drugs for the patients currently struggling with out-of-pocket costs by cutting back on less worthy spending elsewhere, including elsewhere within healthcare.

† Many new diagnostics and medical devices are similar to drugs in that they cost a lot to develop and are patentable. They can cost a lot once they get on the market and then become inexpensive when their patents expire because many companies are able to make them and compete with one another on price. But because most diagnostics and medical devices are used in hospitals or as part of visits to the doctor, their costs are bundled in with other costs, which obscures their prices. For example, the costs of cancer tests or artificial knee implants are not widely known and have not attracted much public scrutiny. Therefore, I have chosen to keep this book focused on drugs and drug prices. However, the principles of this book apply to all medical innovations, including diagnostics and medical devices. In fact, I would argue that flaws in the way that diagnostics and medical devices are paid for, which have a lot in common with how antibiotics are paid for, impede important progress we should be making in the discovery and development of better diagnostics, medical devices, and antibiotics (because companies and investors know that, even if they create something useful and valuable, insurance plans are likely to put up roadblocks to paying for them).

Let's explore that option, the numbers behind it, and the effects it would have, good and bad. Imagine that all currently branded drugs immediately went generic, through government-mandated price controls, invalidation of their patents (aka "march-in rights"), or some other means. Branded drug spending could fall by as much 90%, resulting in a one-time 6.7% reduction in healthcare spending. That works out to about 1.2% of US GDP.* Within a few years though, healthcare costs would revert to previous levels due to the rising costs of hospitals, surgeries, and other non-genericizable services.[11] Meanwhile, without revenues from branded drugs to incentivize and fund new development, our mountain of generic drugs would cease to grow—the conveyor belt would grind to a halt. In exchange for a modest and temporary savings in our collective budget, we would have destroyed the drug industry's innovative core, the system that incentivizes the creation of new treatments for migraines, bone fractures, cancer, diabetes, and countless other diseases that send patients, young and old, to hospitals each year. As overall costs continued to grow, the public would realize what Congress and insurance companies already know: the bulk of healthcare costs stem from hospitals and services, none of which will ever go generic.[12]

## We Need to Celebrate When Drugs Become Generic

*An earlier version of this section was originally published in* Stat *in February 2019, with Jessica Sagers, PhD[13]*

In January 2019, readers, archivists, and creatives in the United States celebrated a special holiday: the largest Public Domain Day in 21 years.[14] The

---

* According to IQVIA, in 2018 the US spent a net $344 billion on all drugs, of which branded drugs represented 78.7% of all drug spending, which comes to $271 billion. The US GDP was $20.5 trillion and the US spent $3.65 trillion on healthcare in 2018, which means that the US spent 1.3% of GDP on branded drugs and that made up 7.4% of all healthcare spending, so a 90% drop in branded drug spending due to all drugs going generic would save 1.2% of GDP and 6.7% of all healthcare costs. (IQVIA Institute for Human Data Science, *Medicine Use and Spending in the U.S.: A Review of 2018 and Outlook to 2023* (Parsippany, NJ: IQVIA, 2019), https://www.iqvia.com/-/media/iqvia/pdfs/institute-reports/medicine-use-and-spending-in-the-us---a-review-of-2018-outlook-to-2023.pdf?&_=1557542013851.)

legal ownership of hundreds of works of classic literature, including well-loved Robert Frost poems like "Nothing Gold Can Stay" and "Stopping by Woods on a Snowy Evening," was transferred into the hands of the people.

From that day forward, all works of literature published for the first time in the United States in 1923 became free for creators to share and innovate upon. New compilations of classic poems will be printed, with younger artists lending more diverse perspectives to introductions and illustrations. The opportunity to choose between multiple editions of classic texts will bring down prices, increasing accessibility. Creative parodies, such as 2009's *Pride and Prejudice and Zombies*, will abound. Film and television will incorporate relevant material. If you first heard Percy Shelley's "Ozymandias" and Walt Whitman's "When I Heard the Learn'd Astronomer" while watching "Breaking Bad," you have the public domain to thank.

But you don't have to wait for Public Domain Day to learn what's coming. The literary and artistic community can consult Open Knowledge Foundation's Working Group on the Public Domain and the Public Domain Review, as well as Twitter accounts (for example, @publicdomainday) to learn when copyright protections will expire.

But when it comes to drugs, no such luck.

For starters, specific information on drug patent expirations is suspiciously difficult to find. A few websites, including GoodRx and Drug Patent Watch, compile lists of drugs that should, in theory, go generic within the next few years, but there is no definitive, trustworthy resource available to the public.

As for an actual event dedicated to celebrating drug patent expirations? There's nothing even close.

All of that should change. Like the literary and artistic communities, the biotech community should develop information resources on patent expirations, though there could be some significant hurdles (access to this information may be impeded by lawsuits and pay-for-delay settlements, for example).

And why not have a Public Domain Day for drugs? Why shouldn't we show innovators that they are appreciated, while also applying some pressure to companies that are considering tying up patent expirations in complicated legislative battles that delay the entry of generics (see Chapter 13)?

Creative Commons and the Internet Archive sponsored a public-domain-themed bash in San Francisco to celebrate Public Domain Day, featuring keynote speeches by Harvard and Berkeley intellectual property law professors accompanied by lightning talks and panels devoted to the newly available works.[15] Imagine a similar event celebrating the drugs whose patent protections are set to expire in the upcoming year, perhaps with their creators recounting stories about how they were developed, physicians giving their clinical perspectives, and patients sharing how these medications changed their lives.

Celebrating and upholding patent expirations and the advent of generics is only a step toward a healthcare system that is cost-effective for society and affordably meets patient needs—but it could be a significant and memorable one.

# 3

---

# BRANDED DRUGS: AN INVESTMENT—NOT AN EXPENSE

How many times in the past few months—or even days—have you heard that drug prices are too high or read that drug price controls are needed? How often have you seen a politician or member of the media portray pharmaceutical companies as price-gouging profiteers intent on wringing every possible dime out of their customers?

I will be the first to admit that branded drugs carry high price tags, but are they too high? Are the profit margins of these companies outrageously bloated? And do they serve a purpose other than lining executives' pockets? I've introduced you to the Biotech Social Contract and the mountain of generic drugs that is its result—and we'll dig deeper into those topics later—but for now, let's take a closer look at branded drugs, those strangely named products that are advertised incessantly on television and receive so much media attention and draw considerable political ire.

What society pays in total for branded drugs is an investment, incentivizing and attracting society's talent and capital to the biopharmaceutical industry to fund and research new cures and treatments that will eventually add to the generic drug mountain.

But even if temporarily high prices for branded drugs are necessary to expand our generic drug armamentarium, I don't think we should allow anyone's child or aging parents to be denied the medication they need on account of cost. The branded drug investment should be borne by the whole of society, not just the vulnerable minority of current patients.

Branded drugs can be made more affordable—without imperiling bio-pharmaceutical innovation—by ensuring that health insurance properly covers patients, sparing them the euphemism of "cost-sharing," which refers to all the out-of-pocket costs insurance companies demand of patients (e.g., copays and deductibles) on top of regular monthly premiums. The real reason why some new drugs are unaffordable to some patients lies not with branded drug prices themselves but with the intentionally poor design and distribution of healthcare insurance in our country, which I'll explore in more detail in the next chapter.*

## Higher Spending Does Not Mean Higher Prices

In 2014, drug spending jumped 10%. It appeared that drug prices were skyrocketing, and people weren't happy. But here's the thing: drug prices weren't actually skyrocketing. Yes, list prices grew a reported 13.5% from 2013, and many people understood that to mean that actual drug prices were up by that amount. But they weren't taking into account the drug rebate system—and that's understandable; it is both byzantine and unfamiliar to most. Rebates are like discounts, except that companies pay them back to insurers, but they are confidential and some insurers negotiate more effectively than others for greater rebates. Taking into account 2014 rebates, the *net* price of drugs grew 4.3% from the prior year, higher than inflation but hardly headline-worthy.

Digging a little deeper, we find that in 2014 nearly half (4.6%) of that 10% increase in drug spending was driven by the launch of those

---

* Sneak peek (since we'll discuss more in Chapter 4): whenever a patient can't afford a drug prescribed by her physician, it's because her insurance company doesn't want her to. And that's if she even has insurance. Except for the very wealthy, no patient can be expected to access modern medicine without the benefit of insurance. The same applies to access to branded drugs. Universal health insurance is essential to the Biotech Social Contract.

long-awaited, blockbuster cures for hepatitis C, which generated $12.3 billion in sales. And recall that multiple companies launched competing products within a short time, eroding those prices quickly—even before any of the drugs came close to their patent expiration.

Had no one invented the cure for hepatitis C, drug spending would have grown only half as much as it did in 2014. But in this alternate reality, America would have been on the hook for tens of billions of dollars a year in spending to care for millions of patients with chronic hepatitis C progressing to liver failure, cancer, and an early death.

Moving forward to 2019, a May report from IQVIA pegged the growth of *net* prices (what drug companies actually get after discounts and rebates) at 0.3% from 2017 to 2018.[16] That's well below inflation. Furthermore, net prices are projected to stay close to flat through 2023, thanks to a slew of new generics and biosimilars (which are like generics of types of drugs called biologics—discussed in detail in Chapter 8) that are on their way to market.

Yes, total spending on drugs did go up from 2017 to 2018, by around 4.5%, but not because of *net* price increases. It went up for two legitimate (and encouraging!) reasons: new drugs were approved and more patients got the treatments they needed. To the extent that prices of some drugs increased that year, like most years, they were nearly entirely offset (all but 0.3%) by other drugs going generic.

## Healthcare in the US vs the Rest of the World

Here's a complaint you've no doubt come across: Healthcare is more expensive in the US than anywhere else in the world, including comparably wealthy European countries and Canada, but our outcomes lag far behind, with lower life expectancy in the US than in some other countries.[17]

There is plenty of evidence to support that assertion and a good deal of research that refutes it, but what's clear is that, even as one can see when a drug has cured a patient of cancer, the link between drug spending and disparities in health at the level of entire populations is very hard to characterize."[,18] For example, healthcare outcomes are influenced by many factors that have nothing to do with pharmaceuticals, including obesity, gun violence, suicide, and how infant mortality is recorded. At the same time, the US makes the most use of generic drugs—more than any major healthcare market.

Generics make up 90% of prescriptions filled in the US, compared to 17% in Switzerland, 30% in France, 47% in Spain, and 80% in Germany.[†,19] It's true that Americans pay more for branded drugs, but those in other countries continue to pay for branded drugs longer than we do in America. Europeans were still spending more money on older, far less effective treatments for hepatitis C when America was already far along in curing its population with newer treatments.[20]

That said, there is certainly a difference between how Americans pay (or can't afford to pay) for drugs and how people in other developing countries do it. We'll get into that in much greater detail when we discuss health insurance (see Chapter 4).

## Drugs as Precious "Infrastructure"

Increasing infrastructure investment is one of the last areas of bipartisan agreement in the US.[21] We know that we need infrastructure—we need functional roads and water and sewage treatment facilities. Most agree that infrastructure spending creates jobs, too.[22] This holds true for the drug industry. We need (or will eventually need) the things that the biopharmaceutical industry creates as well. And the sales of branded drugs make all of that possible by supporting millions of highly trained people employed directly or indirectly in the discovery, development, and distribution of these medicines.

At less than a tenth of total healthcare spending, branded drugs repre-

---

* On the contrary, the US enjoys faster approvals of innovative drugs, giving many US patients access to important medicines, such as cures for hepatitis C, years before they are used widely in Europe.

† To be fair, some European countries employ their own price control schemes to extract discounts from the brand manufacturer after a drug goes generic rather than relying on competition among many generics manufacturers, but the effect of using such price controls is that they don't find out how much lower their prices could have been for a given generic had they encouraged competition, as is the norm in the American generics market.

sent 1.3% of the US GDP.* Compare that to the 2.4% of GDP spent by the US government on roads, drinking water, and wastewater infrastructure, and few would consider those to be unworthy investments. But it's the differences in how we pay that make clean water feel affordable to all while drugs feel inaccessible to some.

Because health insurance plans, including Medicare, require out-of-pocket copayments as high as 20% of the price of a drug, vulnerable patients disproportionately carry the burden of supporting the biopharmaceutical workforce and building our common stockpile of generic treatments.[23] We don't fund development of other important infrastructure in this way—we don't pay for the security of a police force or fire department by charging ruinous copays (or any copays) to those who call for help.

---

## QALY-based Pricing: Precision Without Accuracy

Health economists around the world propose calculating the benefit a drug offers and paying a price that is proportional to that benefit.† This kind of value-based pricing scheme typically assigns a value called a Quality Adjusted Life Year (QALY) to estimate the reduction of life and quality of life associated with a patient having a particular condition. Calculating the

---

* According to IQVIA, in 2018 the US spent a net $344 billion on all drugs, retail, and non-retail drugs, branded and generic. Based on list prices, the total was $479 billion, but one has to subtract $135 billion (~28%) for rebates, discounts, and other pricing concessions. Generic drugs made up 90% of all scripts and about 22% of all spending; branded drugs represented 78.7% of all drug spending, which comes to $271 billion. The US GDP was $20.5 trillion in 2018, which means that the US spent 1.3% of GDP on branded drugs and 1.7% of GDP on all drugs. The US spent $3.65 trillion on healthcare. All drug spending as a % of total healthcare spending is $344 billion/$3.65 trillion = 9.4%. For just branded drugs as a percent of healthcare spending, it's $271 billion/$3.65 trillion = 7.4%. See: http://fortune.com/2019/02/21/us-health-care-costs-2/. For GDP spent on roads, drinking water, and wastewater infrastructure, see: https://www.cbo.gov/publication/52463

Erik Sherman, "US Health Care Costs Skyrocketed to $3.65 Trillion in 2018," Fortune, Feb. 21, 2019, http://fortune.com/2019/02/21/us-health-care-costs-2/.

Chad Shirley, "Spending on Infrastructure and Investment," *Congressional Budget Office* (blog), March 1, 2017, https://www.cbo.gov/publication/52463.

† Health economists would also take into account money saved on fewer work days missed, fewer hospital procedures, doctor's visits, etc. In this case, I'm referring to how health economists determine how much more society should spend on a drug net of all those savings given a particular QALY-based benefit.

QALY of living with a particular condition relies on asking a person what chance of death they would accept for a total cure.[*] If someone said 30%, then it means they consider each year of living with that condition as having 0.7 QALYs. In the US, the Institute for Clinical and Economic Review (ICER) assumes the value of a QALY gained is $100,000-$150,000 (net of all savings).[24] ICER's approach suggests that it isn't worth developing a drug if doing so can only be justified by charging a net price higher than that.

The trouble is that you get a different QALY value when you ask different people how they perceive a condition. Someone who is otherwise healthy but who has just been in a car crash might think that being paralyzed would be a fate worse than death and therefore assign that condition a very low QALY value. But an already paralyzed person who may have found joy and purpose in living with those disabilities would assign a higher QALY. Indeed, the same person might assign different QALYs at different times in their life. So which perspective do you take into account when telling innovators how society would value a cure for paralysis? Undervaluing the benefit might disincentivize investors from funding a company to pursue such a breakthrough.

Consider also that the value of a drug that cures paralysis would not only restore QALYs to those people who are paralyzed, but it would reduce in all healthy people the low level of fear of ever ending up paralyzed, whether from falling from a horse, playing sports, skiing, car crashes, or some other trauma. Similarly, thanks to all of the progress we are making in treating cancer, someday soon parents will know that their daughters will never die of breast cancer and their sons will never die of prostate cancer. That peace of mind isn't captured in any models.

Once they have assigned quantities to every variable of a disease and its treatment, health economists can be quite precise in calculating the value of a biomedical innovation by using QALYs (though they don't take future genericization into account). But given all the subjectivity in their work,

---

[*] This is referred to as the Standard Gamble, but there are other ways of estimating a QALY value for a particular condition.

Wikipedia Contributors, "Quality-Adjusted Life Year," *Wikipedia, The Free Encyclopedia*, accessed Nov. 25, 2019, https://en.wikipedia.org/wiki/Quality-adjusted_life_year.

their conclusions can't be considered accurate. Should we really trust health economists to decide what any breakthrough is worth to everyone for the rest of time? I strongly agree with those who say that we shouldn't.[25]

So many advances—from the car to the Internet to statins—were at first under-appreciated; society simply isn't good at anticipating what kinds of innovation are possible, much less what kinds of innovation might transform our lives. Rather than risking our collective myopia setting the upper ceiling on what society should be willing to pay for a breakthrough, I would rather that we not set it, since we don't really know what it should be.

## The Fair Price Conundrum

So just how do we establish a drug's cost-effectiveness, whether or not it has been "worth it" to produce and whether or not it was "worth it" for the patient? Even a supposedly small medical breakthrough that will someday go generic—think back to lisinopril's modest advantages over enalapril— offers society high value for low cost when that advantage is permanently embedded in our armamentarium and compounded indefinitely.[26]

Others have proposed the notion of a biotech social contract but defined it entirely differently, putting the emphasis on keeping branded drug price increases in check while they are patent-protected.[27] But genericization without undue delays is the key provision of the Biotech Social Contract as I define it, and the industry has, for the most part (though we will explore exceptions in Chapters 8, 9, and 13), honored that provision for decades. As long as a drug ultimately will go generic, it's not all that critical to the long-run price/value assessment whether it starts off at a lower price, climbs, and then goes generic, or if it starts off at a higher price, stays flat, and then goes generic.

A drug's cost-effectiveness is linked to its cost today, its cost in the future, and how much it helps society save in other costs over time. A patient with elevated cholesterol who skips treatment to save money in the short term, should he suffer a heart attack, might end up costing himself, his family, and society more later. In such a case, the patient should want preventative treatment, and society should want him to get it. But it's not only about the money.

Take, for example, the macabre bit of trivia that smokers save taxpayers money on Medicare and Social Security by dying younger and more quickly than non-smokers. If it were only about money, we ought to be encouraging smokers to keep lighting up.

But that's not who we are. We value well-being, which means that the benefits of healthcare are unquantifiable, at least in America. We have not come to terms with how or whether to put a price on life.* We believe that paying whatever it takes to treat or prevent pain, disability, and untimely death is the right thing to do. Not every country can afford that luxury, but putting money over life in a country as wealthy as America is heartless and contemptible.

Yet we know that our inability to say "no" to effective medications on the basis of cost makes us vulnerable to price gouging and other unfair practices. And we know that drug companies know this too, calling into question whether they are charging a fair price, even as we struggle to define what fair is.

Some argue that pegging prices to the cost of drug development is fair. They call for pharmaceutical companies to disclose what it cost them to develop each drug. Others propose charging for a drug only if it works, although in practice we often do not know if a drug is working for a specific patient. Both of these suggestions are more or less feasible to implement, but they're not as simple—and maybe not as fair—as they might seem at first blush.

Greater transparency from pharmaceutical companies might sound reasonable and might even help make drug development more efficient. But if drug prices are to be based upon transparency, we need to be clear that they should factor in all R&D costs and other expenses across the entire industry that led to the breakthrough—all the related drug development

---

* Not entirely true. The EPA set the value of a statistical life at $10 million in 2016, FDA just under at $9.5 million, and the Department of Agriculture at $8.9 million. So they don't agree on the value of a life, except that it's pretty high.

Dave Merrill, "No One Values Your Life More Than the Federal Government," *Bloomberg*, Oct. 19, 2017, https://www.bloomberg.com/graphics/2017-value-of-life/.

programs that fell short and all the invested capital lost on entire companies that quietly failed. I suspect that, in the end, that kind of holistic transparency would not serve to expose some vast imbalance between what went into a drug's development and the price tag it carries on the pharmacy shelf. On the contrary, it would likely confirm what can already be discerned by simply looking at the overall industry's bottom line: The industry's overall 10-20% profit margin is not egregious and doesn't support claims of systemic price-gouging. We'd likely end up right where we are and should be, with prices of branded drugs—generally speaking—reflecting the cost of running the industry as a whole (see Chapter 11).

Despite the evidence, some still believe that the industry's profits are too high. It has become a popular pastime of politicians and pundits to talk about slashing big pharma profits. That might make for a splashy tweet or headline, but let's get into the numbers on this. Let's say that some price controls are put in place, to the tune of a 20% drop in US branded drug prices. That alone would cut the biopharmaceutical industry's profits in half. Leaving aside the facts that companies and labs would go out of business, thousands would lose their jobs, and innovation would grind to a crawl, what impact would that have on patients' ability to afford medications? Is a 20% reduction in the price of a $30,000 cancer treatment going to make it affordable for a patient who has to pay a 20% copayment out of pocket? If a patient can't afford $6,000 but with a 20% discount will "only" have to pay $4,800—does that make it affordable? What about patients without insurance? Instead of $30,000, they would have to pay $24,000. Without proper insurance, cutting 20% from drug prices makes them "more affordable," but not actually affordable.

If the goal of price controls is to allow patients to afford the direct costs of a branded drug, then the price cuts would have to be much deeper. But the profit numbers tell us that there isn't actually room to reduce branded drug prices by an amount that would make a significant difference for individuals who need them—not without destroying the industry completely.

This is not to say that individual companies couldn't be more efficient or that some executive salaries aren't excessive. There are inefficiencies in every industry and every company, but shareholders are already motivated to push companies to cut any obviously unnecessary expenses. Taken as a whole, it does not appear that the pharmaceutical industry is engaged in some kind of systematic, widespread price-gouging or profiteering.* The numbers simply don't bear that out. And, equally importantly, price controls would not result in branded drugs suddenly being vastly more affordable to the people who need them.

So, here we are. Many Americans can't afford the new, name-brand medicines that their physicians prescribe for them, and that is indeed outrageous. But if the answer isn't more transparency, top-down price setting by Congress or some federal agency, or other, more obscure international price-pegging stratagems that have been proposed (discussed in Chapter 10), what is the answer? How do we fuel innovation and invest in our society's health without denying treatments to people who need them but can't afford them? In what direction should our outrage be directed, and how do we fix this?

---

* Indisputable price-gouging—like price-jacking of an old generic drug—does happen, but on a comparatively small scale. These practices, and others I'll discuss, can and should be eliminated (I argue for ways to end this practice in Chapters 8, 9, and 13, and the FDA has already implemented some fixes), because such tactics don't benefit society and therefore should be discouraged.

# 4

## AMERICA'S HEALTH INSURANCE SYSTEM BREAKS THE CONTRACT: A CALL FOR REFORMS

I've described the drug industry's end of the Biotech Social Contract and the central yet underappreciated role of valuable generic medicines. But what about society's end of the deal? That's where health insurance comes into play. For society to bear the cost of new drugs and other healthcare fairly, everyone in America must have health insurance, and that insurance must actually cover the treatments that doctors appropriately prescribe.

But, unfortunately, that's not what we have today. I'd go so far as to argue that what we have today—a patchwork of government-run and private insurance schemes that often offer inadequate coverage—is not actually insurance at all. Through these programs, the sick subsidize the costs of the healthy, and that's a problem. At the core of the problem is a trick insurers play on sick and vulnerable Americans that causes them to choose between denying themselves the care they need or bearing a disproportionate share of the cost.

It's a con game, really, and it is built on the premise that unless a patient is responsible for a share of his or her healthcare costs—through copayments or deductibles—they will seek out unnecessary treatments and services. That's how insurance companies justify copayments and premiums, but there is mounting evidence that patients cannot discriminate between frivolous spending and life-saving treatments, which means that a lot of people can't pay for treatments they need, so they don't get them, or they endure severe financial hardship if they do.[28]

The out-of-pocket costs borne by the sick are enormous. In 2018, Americans paid $61 billion in deductibles and copayments for drugs and another $310 billion for physician visits and other services—and billions more in premiums.[29]

Many people who have insurance still can't afford healthcare, which means they aren't truly insured against the costs of illness. Adding insult to injury, insurance companies have even found ways to get patients to pay more for drugs than biopharmaceutical companies charge, keeping the difference for themselves. And millions are entirely uninsured.

But I'm getting ahead of myself. Let's take a step back and understand what insurance is supposed to be, how it is supposed to work, and what the main forms of healthcare insurance are in America.

## How Insurance Is Supposed to Work

Insurance spreads individual risk across many people, sometimes all of society, and it works by having large numbers of people contribute small, regular payments, called premiums, into one pool from which an individual can draw upon to make large payments, as needed, should something catastrophic happen. You don't use insurance for things that are regular and predictable, such as paying for lunch every day. But you can insure yourself against just about anything else that is unexpected or for which timing is unpredictable and that cause us some degree of anxiety—from disastrous events like floods, fires, and car accidents to less-devastating inconveniences like malfunctioning appliances and damaged sports equipment.

To both reduce our anxiety and keep insurance premiums minimal, society seeks to prevent catastrophes from happening. In the case of fires, we create standards and regulations designed to reduce risk and employ fire marshals and inspectors to enforce them. It costs builders more to meet these standards, which leads to higher housing costs, but the alternative—cheaper houses that catch fire more often, more spent on fire departments, and everyone praying that the fire trucks don't get stuck in traffic—is worse.

In some cases, individuals also have a role to play in mitigating risk and helping to prevent something catastrophic from happening to them. To reflect that and encourage individuals to behave responsibly and not expose themselves to unnecessary risks simply because they have insurance, insurance often requires individuals to participate in the costs that ensue from a catastrophe. This is called a deductible.

For example, if you have car insurance and are in a minor car accident, you might have to pay the first $500 for repairs, and your insurance plan will cover anything above that. The idea is that this deductible will incentivize you to drive carefully, if not for your own safety, then to avoid incurring the cost associated with an accident. And if your car does suffer minor damage, maybe a ding in a side panel, the deductible might nudge you to just leave it be.

Insurers often work with individuals to help them reduce their risk. For example, flood insurance companies might educate homeowners about sensors that automatically shut off water to the house when they detect flooding. A company might even offer financial incentives to the homeowner for having sensors installed, like money back or discounts on premiums.

Some insurance plans are nice to have, such as insurance on an expensive pre-paid vacation that refunds you if weather turns bad. Other types of insurance, such as home insurance, are optional but feel necessary. Still other types, such as car insurance, are mandated by law.

Why might the government mandate that people buy insurance?

In all but one state, you can't own a car without car insurance (hello, New Hampshire). What makes this good policy is that, even if you don't care about your own well-being, if you're at fault in an accident with another car, the victims have the right to the assurance that your insurance plan will pay their medical bills and repair their car.

Health insurance is increasingly becoming a legal requirement. In Massachusetts, every resident must be covered by a health insurance plan. This isn't quite the law of the land throughout America, though that's what the Affordable Care Act (ACA, aka Obamacare) attempted to do by offering people both subsidies to help them afford insurance premiums, as well as levying a financial penalty on those who don't buy insurance.

The logic behind mandating health insurance is two-fold.

First, when people get extremely sick, the only alternative to dying may be going to the emergency room (ER). Letting someone die in the waiting room because they don't have health insurance and can't afford care is unconscionable. That's why ERs are not allowed to turn away anyone who desperately needs help. But treating patients in the ER is incredibly expensive. ERs are equipped with a lot of modern technology and staffed around the clock by highly trained medical professionals. Just as it's more cost-effective to prevent fires than to put them out, it is far more cost-effective for society to keep people healthy than to treat them in the ER. Better to make sure that everyone can afford to seek routine medical care than to let minor problems escalate into major ones.

The second reason for mandating health insurance is that, eventually, something medically catastrophic is going to happen to each of us. While not everyone drives a car and not everyone owns a home in a flood plain, everyone is human and will someday fall ill. But if people wait until they're sick to buy health insurance, it's like buying fire insurance when your house is on fire. If people were allowed to do that, they'd have been freeloading on the security funded by everyone else's insurance premiums. If that were allowed, everyone would do it, and the result would be that the only people paying for insurance would be the sick. With the costs of our healthcare system funded only by the sick, instead of being spread out over the whole population, each sick person would be charged a very high price for their care. At the end of the day, such insurance isn't even insurance.\*

Some people might try foregoing insurance for the same reason that someone buying a TV might skip the warranty: they think they can just save up money and pay for whatever they need when the need arises. When it comes to healthcare catastrophes, the problem is that at least some of these people still won't be able to afford the emergency treatment.[†] Does that mean it will be denied them? Of course not. In these cases, society provides the backstop, which is morally sound but also means that everyone should buy into the system.

In 2013, uninsured patients paid about \$25 billion out-of-pocket for health-care, but hospitals and physicians logged \$85 billion worth of services for which

---

\* Consider the extreme case of people only buying fire insurance when their homes are actually on fire. If ten people a month need it, then the payments only these ten people will make must be enough to pay for all ten to have their homes rebuilt. In other words, each will pay the cost of rebuilding a house. So they aren't really insured. To put this in more quantitative terms, imagine an island of 1,000 families on which there are ten home fires a year on average; if each of them pay \$2,000 a year, they collect \$2 million each year with which to rebuild ten homes for \$200,000 each. But if only 800 islander families buy insurance, of which eight experience a fire, and the other 200 don't buy insurance until their home is on fire and two of them experience a fire, then only 802 families will pay insurance premiums but still ten families will need to have their homes rebuilt at \$200,000 each. So now that \$2 million cost is spread across only 802 families, which means their premium has to be nearly \$2,500/year. Basically, when 20% of the population freeloads, it increases the costs for everyone else by 25%. If half the population doesn't buy insurance, then it doubles everyone else's cost. Of course, it might seem more fair to just refuse to allow someone to buy insurance at the last minute while their house is burning and therefore just let them become homeless (if they can't afford to rebuild their home from their own savings or from a bank loan), but when it comes to health insurance, America doesn't consider it conscionable to turn someone who is desperate and suffering away from care just because they can't afford it–ERs will accept anyone.

† Let's say that the average person will have modest healthcare costs each year but experience a medical emergency that costs \$50,000 once every 40 years. (I'm just making these numbers up to illustrate a point.) That means that if everyone saved up \$50,000 over 40 years to pay for their own emergency, then some people would not have saved enough because they would be unluckier than average, experiencing an emergency earlier than average or one that costs more than average or maybe even have more than one emergency in that time. So to be safer and have a buffer against bad luck, everyone would need to save up \$100,000. But that just means that the very unlucky who have an early, more expensive emergency or three emergencies will not have saved enough. So only the rich will feel that they have enough to cover the cost of even the worst luck, while everyone else will have to save a large portion of their income for self-insurance or else living in a state of anxiety that they might get even unluckier than they have planned for. The result would be that most people would have over-saved for healthcare and robbed themselves of other joys of life. That's why it's far more efficient to have everyone share their collective risk in an insurance pool and know that they can contribute to average costs regardless whether they themselves might end up being among the unlucky ones who need an above average amount of help. Of course, this means that those destined to live very healthy lives pay more than they would have if they had just covered their own costs, but who can ever be that sure of their own health?

they weren't able to collect payment from a patient, also known as "uncompensated care." Healthcare providers can't be expected to bear those kinds of losses, so in 2013, federal and state governments paid $53 billion to offset uncompensated care.[30] And where did that money come from? Taxes—so society still paid.

What about the remaining $32 billion in uncompensated care? Hospitals and physicians can't absorb losses like that and stay in practice, so those losses are offset by charging higher prices to everyone else who does pay—in other words, by the rest of society. The solution, then, is clear: If our healthcare system is to provide expensive emergency care to uninsured and desperate patients—as it inarguably should, morally speaking—then it is already functionally insuring those people but in the most expensive and least efficient way possible. Let's do it properly by requiring that everyone enroll in insurance and contribute what they can afford.

## Insurance for Pre-existing Conditions

Until relatively recently, not everyone could qualify for health insurance. Companies could refuse to cover a patient's pre-existing conditions. That resulted in America watching as patients suffered from their diseases because they couldn't afford to pay for treatment themselves and had no insurance, either because they had chosen not to get health insurance while they were healthy, or because they'd lost their insurance due to a job change or move and were denied a new policy because of a pre-existing condition. The ACA changed that by outlawing denial of health insurance on the basis of a pre-existing condition. The ACA also barred health insurance companies from charging higher insurance premiums to people who were already sick. That's great for patients. And since insurance falls apart if people can sign up for it only when they need help, the ACA attempted to have everyone participate.

The whole point of insurance is that the costs of helping people who need it are covered primarily by all the people who don't need it. Those unclear on the concept might grumble, "But why should I pay if my house hasn't had a fire in 30 years?" Those are the lucky people. Insurance is something you buy and hope you never need. If it were only bought by the people who knew they would need it soon, it wouldn't be insurance.

## Spreading the Costs Around

If having insurance is mandatory, then the cost of buying that insurance is functionally a tax. Like many taxes, that cost is not spread evenly. Only people who buy things pay sales taxes, and those who buy more pay more. Those who own homes pay real estate taxes, but those who rent seemingly do not. Renters may not realize it, but their rent is influenced by the landlord's real estate taxes and insurance costs, so renters indirectly pay those costs. People who make above a certain threshold of income pay income taxes. We try to spread costs across the population in such a way that everyone can afford a certain minimum living standard, which is meant to include safe neighborhoods, clean water, and schools good enough to give children a chance to realize their full potential. That America has fallen woefully short on one or more of these in some communities does not mean that we shouldn't continue to try to live up to our ideals.

Just as taxes are spread unevenly, the premiums paid by people for a necessary type of insurance should be, can be, and are spread unevenly, with some people even getting insurance coverage for free or at a subsidized price. Funding should be gathered *as fairly as possible* from everyone who can afford to pay in order to cover those who need help.

Some call this scheme utopian, claiming that there is no one solution for "as fairly as possible." One could say the same thing about how taxes are imposed; does that mean that we should dismantle the tax system and bring our society to ruin until we agree on the perfect system of taxation?

There is no one way to spread costs in a way that will make everyone happy, but that shouldn't stop us from ensuring that everyone in America has access to preventative care and the security of health insurance to be able to afford it, not simply the last resort of going to an ER. The bickering over costs should come after we have secured access to decent healthcare as a right for every American. While that statement might trigger a brawl in Congress, both liberal and conservative politicians have supported policies that acknowledge healthcare as a right, whether it was called Romneycare in Massachusetts, Obamacare nationally, or expansions of state insurance plans for the poor (Medicaid) across many red and blue states.

We already offer health insurance subsidies to families with lower incomes, so I'm not proposing anything unprecedented. I'm calling for a shift in the current balance.

## A Byzantine Patchwork Leaves Some Patients Without a Safety Net

For people who can't afford private health insurance, the government (federal and/or state) offers three main types of health insurance plans. Those living well below the poverty line are covered by Medicaid, which is administered by states and funded by a combination of state taxes and federal subsidies, which are themselves funded by federal taxes. Older Americans (65+) are covered by Medicare, which is paid for by taxes and administered by the federal government, like Social Security. The third type is for veterans of the armed services (with the exception of those who have been dishonorably discharged). The Department of Veterans Affairs administers this type of insurance, which is also funded by federal tax dollars.

That leaves a lot of Americans who aren't veterans, are not poor enough to qualify for Medicaid, and are not old enough to qualify for Medicare. If they work for a company, even a small one, odds are that they get health insurance through their employer. It is important to note that this insurance isn't provided to the employee for free; it is a part of their compensation. If employers didn't provide health insurance to their employees, they would have to pay higher salaries, so that employees would be able to afford to buy health insurance on their own. But since income is taxed and health insurance benefits are not, it's cheaper for both the employer and employee for a company to directly pay for health insurance than it would be to pay a higher salary and have the employee buy that insurance.*

---

* A change in the tax code that taxed health insurance provided by employers might decouple health insurance from employment, causing people to shop for their own insurance. While that might appear to create a free market for insurance with more people shopping around, I actually think that the complexity of insurance in America would cause more people to fall victim to loopholes in plans that claim to be comprehensive and cheaper than others and later, when a person falls ill, turn out not to cover treatment. That already happens now, and at least some companies know that their employees will hold them accountable for weak insurance and therefore might shop around for a better plan. But if insurance and employment were decoupled, people might choose to band together into insurance buying groups, which then mimic what companies can do by negotiating for better coverage on behalf of many customers. One way or another, when it comes to a complex marketplace, people usually do better to work together to negotiate collectively rather than try to cut through the complexity on their own.

So, what about the people who don't qualify for any of the three main government plans and are not employed by a company that includes health insurance as part of its compensation package? Today, those people have the option to buy health insurance via state-run exchanges through which various insurers sell policies. Under the ACA, the government also provides subsidies to help individuals and families with lower incomes pay premiums and other costs. Today, the average cost of health insurance coverage for an individual qualifying for subsidies is around $2,500/year.[31] Without these subsidies, a family of four with an income of $50,000 would pay around $17,000/year for health insurance; with subsidies that family would pay closer to $3,000/year.* A family of four that earns less than $100,000, which is 400% of the $25,000/year poverty line for a family of that size, can get subsidies that would reduce the cost of health insurance to about $10,000. But if that family were to make just a bit more, crossing over the 400% mark, then they would be ineligible for all subsidies, and they would have to pay around $17,000. That means that a family of four is technically better off making $100,000/year than $105,000/year. It's especially in these income zones, in which the subsidy math gets strange, where healthcare can feel particularly unaffordable.

The ACA attempts to help everyone, but it is imperfect and leaves some families, such as those living in cities where the cost of living is higher, still struggling to pay for health insurance. Some who are eligible for subsidized coverage might not even realize it. The system is complex, wordy, and inaccessible to millions, especially those who are functionally illiterate. Others understand their options perfectly but still feel that they can't afford to purchase insurance. So, they just take their chances.

Altogether, around 13% of Americans fall through the cracks in the system by not having health insurance. These people will not be turned away at the ER, which means that they are still partaking in America's health system, but in the most expensive way possible—both for themselves and for society as a whole. When an uninsured person receives an ER bill, the

---

* The Kaiser Family Foundation runs a remarkably comprehensive, thoughtful, and useful website that offers a lot of useful information about how healthcare in America works and features a calculator that lets anyone see what health insurance would likely cost them if they paid for it themselves, including what subsidies they would get given their income level and size of their families.

"Health Insurance Marketplace Calculator," KFF, updated Oct. 31, 2019, https://www.kff.org/interactive/subsidy-calculator/.

amounts due are often huge, in part because they reflect inflated list prices of procedures, medicines, hospital stays, and personnel costs. If you're insured, your insurance company negotiates a lower price for these expenses. The fact is that our healthcare system wasn't designed for people without insurance.

Many people without health insurance who get care from a hospital can, if they push back on their bill, get it reduced and may be able to pay it off over time with an installment plan (kind of like insurance premium payments after the fact). Hospitals will also often sell their uncollected debts to collectors at a discount, and those collectors will then try to extract payment from patients. The cost of all this bureaucracy and billing is staggeringly large. It is estimated at roughly $500 billion, coming in at 2.4% of GDP, proportionately twice what Canada and Germany spend administering their healthcare systems.[32] That's almost twice what America spends on branded drugs. Consider that for all the outrage over drug prices, the savings from streamlining billing and bureaucracy to the level of, say, Germany, would be greater than if every single currently branded drug went generic. Bureaucracy never goes generic.*

As a society, we have inflicted this failure on ourselves. Every American should have health insurance. Massachusetts has mandated this, and now only 2.8% of residents lack insurance.[33] Given the way politicians are talking, it is—one would hope—only a matter of time before we achieve universal coverage or something much closer to it than what we currently have. Some taxes will go up, but it will result in savings elsewhere. If everyone is "in the system," hospitals and physicians would no longer need to increase prices elsewhere to offset costs for uncompensated care. Bureaucracy would be reduced, billing streamlined. More people would feel financially able to seek out preventative care, which would result in fewer of the most expensive type of doctor visits. Fewer ER visits means fewer lost days

---

* Think of it–$500 billion of society's money is spent on employing millions of administrative workers to send bills, remind patients of bills, explain bills, correct billing errors, and threaten patients who can't pay with bankruptcy. We need some people to do this, for sure. But if our insurance system were more straightforward and we employed fewer people for this kind of work, then we could spend the same money employing them to do something else for society: teachers, nurses, artists, builders... just about anything besides medical billing paperwork.

of work, and fewer families bankrupted by illness. I would consider that a general upgrade to the integrity of our social fabric, wouldn't you?

## Not Just Some Insurance, but *Enough* Insurance

But even with universal health insurance in America, the devil will be in the details. And that "skin-in-the-game" con I raised at the beginning of this chapter, supposedly intended to ensure that patients do not seek unnecessary treatments, is at the heart of where our insurance system isn't holding up its end of the Biotech Social Contract.

The notion that patients should pay for a portion of their healthcare through deductibles and copayments is called "cost-sharing." Most reasonably healthy people can afford these out-of-pocket costs, because they don't use many healthcare services or take branded medications. Lisinopril or a statin might cost someone no more than $10 per month, for example. Of patients with some sort of insurance, 91% pay less than $500 per year in out-of-pocket costs.[34]

But many people struggle with out-of-pocket costs, especially when they have complex medical conditions requiring frequent visits to the doctor and multiple medications. These are the patients for whom cost-sharing really means that they have inadequate insurance coverage. Approximately 2% of patients with insurance pay more than $1,500 per year in out-of-pocket costs, some much more.[35] 2% may not seem like a lot, but that's millions of people, most of whom have modest incomes and arc unable to afford needed treatments. Their dilemmas are what disproportionately drive outrage over drug prices.

The ACA sets a limit on the out-of-pocket costs private insurance plans can impose on patients in a given year, but many families with private insurance still struggle to meet them.* For example, the annual out-of-pocket limit for a family of four with a $50,000 income is $6,500—a

---

* For patients covered by Medicare, there is no out-of-pocket maximum, but most Medicare patients also qualify for programs like Medigap or Medicare Advantage, which cap out-of-pocket costs. For some patients, those caps are still too high.

significant sum relative to total income, and that's on top of the insurance premiums they pay.

There are three main reasons why insurance companies impose cost-sharing on their policy holders. Let's take a close look at all three.

## Reason #1: Preventing Over-Utilization of Care

As mentioned earlier: The theory is that if patients have to pay for a portion of a treatment, it will discourage them from seeking more treatments than necessary and running up more costs than necessary. This is called "over-utilization" of care, and it applies to both doctor visits and medications. This is fine—in theory—but the problem is that in practice, these out-of-pocket costs, if unaffordable, can cause patients to abandon treatments that they actually need or avoid going to see their doctor when they should, which leads to worse outcomes and more expensive treatments down the road.[36]

When a car insurance deductible discourages a car owner from fixing a ding in the door, there's a risk it will rust. When a patient is discouraged by out-of-pocket costs from taking cholesterol-lowering medication, there's a risk of a heart attack.

Insurance companies already have checks in place to prevent over-utilization in case a physician prescribes an expensive drug too liberally. One such check, called a "step edit," rejects paying for a branded drug unless a patient has failed to benefit from or can't tolerate one or more other cost-effective, typically generic treatment (i.e., the patient must step through a generic).[37] Insurance companies also commonly impose a requirement that physicians get "prior authorization" (PA) before the payer will agree to cover a drug.[38] This process requires that the physician submits paperwork to the insurance company documenting the diagnosis and prior treatments that the patient has received, sometimes with evidence for why the branded drug for which the PA is being sought is medically necessary. Insurance companies will sometimes impose a PA requirement on a new drug to make it harder for physicians to prescribe (since no one likes paperwork) and so the PA can be considered a mechanism for ensuring that physicians have skin in the game, likely seeking a PA only for patients they strongly feel need the new drug.

So why then, when a patient has met the step-edit requirements and an insurance company has issued a PA, does the insurance company still impose a copayment for the drug or make the patient pay for it out of her deductible? Towards what decision is that insurance company nudging the patient? To abandon the treatment that both the physician and insurance company agree is appropriate. That's heartless. Yet that's what happens.[39] A patient comes into a pharmacy to fill a prescription, maybe a drug for diabetes, an asthma inhaler, or heart-failure medication; the pharmacist looks up the patient's insurance and reports what the copayment will be; and the patient just walks away without the medication. Clearly, reducing inappropriate utilization is not the only purpose behind cost-sharing.

## Reason #2: Lower Premiums

The second reason is that cost-sharing allows insurance companies to offer lower premiums to everyone, most of whom are healthy. That is lousy in both theory and practice, since the whole point of insurance is to have the currently healthy members of society subsidize the cost of treating the currently sick, not the other way around.

Lower premiums make an insurance plan look more attractive to new, typically healthy subscribers, except that what insurance companies are now selling is no longer insurance (unless you can afford the out-of-pocket costs). Increasingly, subscribers need to read the fine print and estimate what costs their plans would saddle them with should they develop one or more chronic illnesses.

Imagine that a college lured students with low tuition and then charged them a copayment for entering each class.* The administration might even say that the copays are intended to prevent inappropriate attendance. The trouble is that poorer students who thought they were signing up for an

---

* Actually, something like this is happening at colleges across America.

James Yang, "Those Hidden College Fees," Nov. 3, 2016, https://www.nytimes.com/2016/11/06/education/edlife/those-hidden-college-fees.html.

affordable education would miss classes because they can't afford the copayments and then drop out without an education or degree.

If insurance is supposed to actually make it possible for people to afford treatment when they get sick, then many Americans who think they have insurance will someday discover that they don't.

## Reason #3: Pharmacy Benefit Managers Get Paid

The third reason is the existence of Pharmacy Benefit Managers (PBMs), a type of insurance company that extracts a profit whenever a patient gets a drug, even if the patient pays for that drug out of pocket. This profit comes from a rebate that the drug company pays to the PBM, essentially a kickback, and it's entirely absurd. Imagine getting into a minor car accident and discovering that your mechanic must pay $50 to your car insurance company even if your total bill is $400 and you pay it all out of your $500 deductible. That means that you've paid the mechanic $350 for the actual repairs and, despite all the insurance premiums you already pay, your insurance company manages to extract $50 more from you through your repair bill. Before you get too angry with your car insurance, I'll reassure you that this isn't how it works (and when it happens, it's a crime).[40] But health insurance does work this way. We'll take a much closer look at PBMs in Chapter 7.

## Combating Out-of-Pocket Costs

For now, suffice it to say that drug companies are aware that insurers erect barriers (in the form of high out of pocket costs) between patients and the drugs their doctors prescribe. This has created a bit of an arms race between drug companies and insurance companies.* For example, drug companies commonly give patients with private insurance coupons to offset their

---

* Many drug companies have created programs that provide free drugs to patients who lack insurance. Yet, many patients don't realize that such programs exist, assume that they won't be able to afford a drug, and don't bother getting a prescription filled. Physicians are often too busy to explain the details of copay assistance or free drug programs to each patient. These barriers to access create their intended result: some patients don't fill their prescriptions.

copayments.* In response, insurers sometimes institute a 'copay accumulator,' a rule that says that the coupon doesn't count toward the patient's deductible. The result? When the coupons run out, if the patient's out-of-pocket spending—not counting the coupons—don't meet or exceed the deductible, the patient will have to keep paying his share before insurance kicks in. It's not enough that a physician prescribes a medicine—the insurer wants to see the patient strain to pay for it before contributing to covering the rest of the cost.

Not every out-of-pocket cost is egregious. Insurance companies imposing a small copayment for doctor visits can discourage people from going too often with minor complaints, while still making it affordable for everyone to get annual checkups. But prescription drugs are a different story. A patient can go to a doctor on his or her own initiative, but patients can't legally get a prescription drug unless a doctor prescribes it!

Insurance companies set low copayments for inexpensive generic drugs and higher copayments for branded drugs. That differential makes a certain amount of sense: the high copayment encourages patients to choose the generic version of whatever branded drug their doctor prescribed, if one is available. But why should there be a copayment, however small, for a generic drug? And why are there large copayments for branded drugs for which there are no generic substitutes?

Copays and deductibles not only make filling a prescription difficult or impossible for many, they force many patients who initially filled the prescription to stop taking their medications as prescribed, leading to worse outcomes and higher long-term costs. Even small copays and fees—as low as $1 to $5—reduce a patient's adherence to treatment and cause patients to avoid necessary care. The higher the copay, the greater the reduction, which sometimes has terrible consequences (e.g., diabetes without insulin treatment is lethal).[41]

---

* Payers want the deterrent effects of copayments partly because they worry that a pharmaceutical company has inappropriately marketed a drug, encouraging physicians to prescribe it to patients who don't need it. When this does happen, the government should prosecute and punish companies, but it's inappropriate to cast suspicion on every doctor-patient interaction that results in a prescription for a high-priced drug and then, via cost-sharing, coerce patients into second-guessing their physicians.

Approximately 50% of patients who fail to adhere to their prescriptions do so in part because of copays. High deductibles push many patients to cut out valuable preventative services (e.g., consulting a doctor about a skin infection before it becomes a dangerous abscess). Greater cost-sharing is also associated with increased ER visits.[42] Low-income patients are often the most vulnerable. Indeed, the very term "cost-sharing" disguises what could be more aptly described as an institutionalized failure to insure.

## If Not Out of Pocket, Where Would the Money Come From?

In 2018, Americans paid roughly $2.6 trillion in private insurance premiums and taxes that fund Medicare and Medicaid (I'll refer to all these as "premiums").[43] That year, Americans paid $61 billion in out-of-pocket costs for drugs, which are harder to bear when one is sick and often older. Americans' total personal income stood at approximately $17.5 trillion in 2018.[44] Grab a calculator: Eliminating all out-of-pocket costs for medicines would only require either a 2.3% increase in all premiums or a 0.35% increase to the total tax rate Americans pay.

Maybe most people, if they need one prescription or only need generics, can afford to pay some out-of-pocket costs. So instead of getting rid of all of them, we could cap them to reduce the burden on those hardest hit, like patients with multiple chronic diseases. Such caps would require shifting less than $20 billion to premiums or general taxes.[45] This means we're talking about either increasing premiums by 0.76% or adding 0.11% to Americans' overall tax rate. These increases are modest considering the security that all Americans would gain knowing that when they need a drug, they will be able to afford it (which is the whole point of insurance). Would making drugs more affordable increase utilization? We know that patients currently can't access treatments they need, so I hope it would. Inappropriate utilization of drugs is already managed in other ways, including equipping physicians with software to remind them of medical guidelines.

Patients also paid over $300 billion out-of-pocket for healthcare services in 2018 (doctor's visits, surgeries). Some of these costs make sense when the goal is to make a person consider whether they really need to see a doctor, so let's estimate that helping the hardest hit patients would require shifting the most burdensome third of those costs (approximately $100 billion) to premiums and taxes. That would require either increasing premiums by 3.8% or adding 0.57% to the overall tax *rate*.

I've assumed here that eliminating or reducing out-of-pocket costs would result in a direct shift of that money to premiums. But that's not necessarily true. For example, the Congressional Budget Office calculated that one proposal for reducing patient out-of-pocket costs would result in a $10 billion increase in Medicare spending on drugs over 10 years. But that drug spending would be offset by a $20 billion reduction in spending on healthcare services such as hospital and physician care.[46] So reducing out-of-pocket costs could actually ultimately reduce our insurance premiums.

---

In a speech delivered to insurance company executives in early March 2018, former FDA Commissioner Scott Gottlieb hammered home the point. "Patients shouldn't face exorbitant out-of-pocket costs and pay money where the primary purpose is to help subsidize rebates paid to a long list of supply chain intermediaries, or is used to buy down the premium costs for everyone else," he said at the national health policy conference of AHIP, the insurance company lobby. "After all, what's the point of a big copay on a costly cancer drug? Is a patient really in a position to make an economically based decision? Is the copay going to discourage over-utilization? Is someone in this situation voluntarily seeking chemo?"[47]

Indeed, this "skin-in-the-game" approach only works when informed customers can comparison shop, but most sick patients have neither the medical training nor often the composure to truly understand their options. At some point, a nudge to not overuse healthcare that the patient doesn't need becomes a shove away from healthcare that the patient does need, and that is horrendous. For all the outrage over drug prices, imagine what the debate would look like if patients could count on their insurance plans to pay in full for whatever drug their physicians prescribed. Once patients are fully insured, then the discussion about whether drug costs make sense would be had between industry and society, as it should be.

Some have argued for a biotech social contract that places responsibility on drug companies to make sure that patients have access to their drugs.[48] This stance ignores the role of insurers' cost-sharing mechanisms. Drug companies can't make branded drugs affordable to Americans who don't have insurance or who have poor insurance. If we cut the cost of most branded drugs in half tomorrow, decimating the drug industry, there would still be many Americans who wouldn't be able to afford to pay Medicare's required 20% copay for their medicines. So if the drug industry is to keep making new medicines, as I hope we all agree it should, it cannot support itself by charging prices that most patients can afford. Just as the fire department offers everyone security but its service would be unaffordable if only those who need its services paid for it, the drug industry is similarly sustained by high prices that the unlucky few who need novel drugs can't afford. As long as we fail to recognize that the Biotech Social Contract relies on everyone having proper insurance, we'll pursue the wrong solutions towards affordability.

We have entrusted our government and insurance companies to distribute the costs of healthcare across our population and across time so that people unfortunate enough to be sick don't suddenly find themselves choosing between the branded drugs they need and their rent, food, or daycare. Insurance practices in America conform to laws passed by our elected representatives. So if the politicians we elect to Congress allow insurance companies to turn away people based on pre-existing conditions or to charge high copays, or if they pursue price controls that cut investment towards better treatments, then we have harmed ourselves and future generations.

## Where Do We Go From Here?

If we truly hope to expand access and remove the financial burden of getting sick from the backs of Americans, then let's upgrade our insurance system to one that actually provides proper insurance to everyone, rather than blaming the innovators for the prices of their newest drugs. Spending should be spread more evenly, instead of insurance companies hitting patients with toxic out-of-pocket costs when they are sick and most vulnerable. Imagine if, after being mugged, the victim had to make a copay to have the police show up.

The solution is to limit annual out-of-pocket costs for all patients and make sure that limit is low enough that patients are not discouraged from following through on what their doctors recommend for them.[49] Neither generic drugs nor branded drugs without generic alternatives should have copayments—of any size—because there is no ethical alternative to nudge the patient towards. In those cases, the patient is just following a doctor's advice, which is what a patient is supposed to do—and what society should want them to do.

Cutting out-of-pocket costs would lead to improved adherence to treatment, better health outcomes, and lower long-term healthcare spending. Physicians will be able to rely on clinical data and medical guidelines to prescribe treatments properly, increasingly with the help of algorithms embedded in electronic medical records that, to ensure that doctors are following medical guidelines, payers can influence systematically, instead of haphazardly, as they do now with copayments.[50]

Diabetics are more likely to stop taking their treatments earlier in the year when they are still paying out of their deductibles than later in the year, after they have hit their out-of-pocket maximums. They are more likely to continue to stay on treatment if they have steady jobs and can afford their copayments than if they have lost their jobs and are looking for new ones. Yet neither of these factors should interfere with a diabetic patient staying on treatment. Longer term, if a patient goes blind, starts experiencing painful neuropathies, or loses a limb, this becomes a personal tragedy and a loss to society—the patient suffers, risks losing independence, and will need emergency treatments and long-term care paid for by insurance.

But if cost-sharing discourages proper treatment and actually ends up costing insurers more money in the long run, then why do they do still burden patients with out-of-pocket costs? After all, aren't these insurance plans rationally run businesses (and in the case of government plans like Medicare, isn't it run by people motivated to do the right thing especially when it saves money)?

The problem is how most plans are set up in the first place. For example, the people responsible for managing drug spending only think about whether spending money on one drug will reduce spending on other drugs. They don't think about whether spending on one drug will save the system money on surgeries, ER visits, and other healthcare services, which fall into someone else's budget. And since Medicare takes over paying for everyone's healthcare when they turn 65, a private insurance company won't actually see savings from curing a hepatitis C patient when he is 57 years old with a drug that will prevent him from needing a costly liver transplant when he's 68. Instead, that extra cost is borne by the patient and Medicare years later.

There is therefore an argument for integrating all health insurance into one budget so that drugs and surgeries are considered together and over the lifetime of a person, from birth into old age. This bleeds over into a discussion of a single-payer system. Whether this benefit of a single-payer system out-weighs the risks of entrusting a single bureaucracy with patient care is beyond the scope of this book.* The key point I'm making is simply that, because of fragmented accounting (drugs vs surgery, young vs old), insurance plans don't necessarily act rationally from a big picture standpoint.

---

* A single-payer system would capture both the total costs and the total savings of new treatments, running cost-effectiveness models that latitudinally span the entire population as well as longitudinally extend out to patients' whole lives. Further integrating how much more individuals could produce if they stayed healthy and attributing some value to just being alive, happy, and contributing to one's family and community, one could construct a grand unified model of the value that a drug brings to society. Extend that model over the course of a hundred or more years, during which any one drug is on-brand for only 10–15 years but then is a cheap generic the rest of the time, and it would be evident that most new drugs are cost-effective and valuable in the long-run, sometimes more than paying for themselves from all the savings on high-cost services. Consider the example in the opening chapter of the bone-strengthening drug that reduces the need for hip replacement surgery. And yet, we are far from such an idealized insurance model (one that would eagerly incentivize more genericizable innovation by paying for it) not only because our healthcare system is fragmented and the incentives of the various plans misaligned with society's true goal of investing for its long-term benefit, but also because neither the American government nor any government for any large country has demonstrated the bureaucratic competence to be entrusted with the complexity and accountability needed to pull off the kind of central planning required of a single-payer system (even China is encouraging a competitive healthcare insurance market). Basically, for a country the size of America, a single-payer system is likely only appealing in theory, like so many theories, but would be a tragedy of human incompetence in practice. Leaving all insurance plans as fragmented as they are but passing legislation that requires that everyone be insured and eliminates or sets low caps on out-of-pocket costs so all patients can afford what their physicians appropriately prescribe would solve the problem more simply.

## Misalignment and Myopia

A larger truth is that payers have an incentive to let the overall cost of healthcare rise. For example, by law (per the ACA), most insurance companies must spend 80-85% of their revenues on patient care, the so-called Medical Loss Ratio (MLR),[51] which includes hospital services and drugs, leaving 15-20% for the insurance companies to spend on their own operations, with anything left over as profit for their shareholders. If their profits are linked to the size of the pie, then they will want that pie to grow. For appearances, they will want to be seen trying to contain costs, but they don't actually win in the long run by cutting costs. In theory, multiple payers bidding to manage a government plan or administer one for a private company will try to demonstrate that they can provide great care at a low cost to the client. However, with all the consolidation in the insurance business, most purchasers only have two or three plans in their region to choose from, and some have just one. When there are so few choices, insurers can tacitly collude to keep costs high: Without saying so (which would make it actual, illegal collusion), one can convey through inaction that, "I won't offer your customers a discount to switch to my plan if you don't offer my customers a discount to switch to your plan."

Payers set their budgets annually, having to guess as to their costs over the next year so as to set their premiums at just the right level. They want to make sure that they are competitive with what other plans charge but are still left with the 15-20% margin to cover their own operating costs (and, in the case of for-profit plans, have some profit left over). Sometimes they are caught off guard by the launch of a drug for which they failed to anticipate the price and demand, as happened when Gilead launched its breakthrough hepatitis C drugs, Sovaldi and Harvoni, in 2014. It was in fact predicted well in advance (and some did) that a pill with near perfect cure rates wouldn't be cheap and would inspire many more patients to seek treatment,[52] but insurers failed to budget accordingly and tried to stop many patients from being cured until the following year's budget cycle.[53]

What payers really want is predictability of expenses so they can adjust their future revenues to future expenses. Were they to do a better job of anticipating what's coming through the R&D pipelines of biopharmaceutical companies, they might budget more effectively and spare patients the kinds of rationing tactics payers employed in the case of hepatitis C drugs. Many of those restrictions were later lifted, either by court order (because it's illegal for Medicare and Medicaid to deny access to care on the basis of cost) or simply because drug prices fell due to competition.

Furthermore, private payers often cite the mobility of their customers (patients typically switch plans every few years) as a reason why it's not worth paying for a treatment today that will result in savings down the road. This is clearly parochial thinking; if all payers agreed to pay for a preventative treatment, they would all benefit as they got each other's patients over the course of many rounds of musical chairs.

As our flawed healthcare insurance system struggles with its own contradictions, it will continue to present itself as society's hero—trying ever so valiantly to contain costs—while vilifying everyone from physicians to drug companies and even patients. But an informed observer will note that these same plans prosper in the long run from the same rising healthcare costs they decry and are not making decisions based on what would actually benefit society in the long run.

Ultimately, the fact that drugs are inaccessible and unaffordable to some patients is due to insurers choosing to engage in aggressive cost-sharing. This practice is making sick patients pay more for drugs their physicians prescribe and set patients up to fail to follow their physicians' recommended course of treatment. Patients deputized by cost-sharing into second guessing their doctor's orders are understandably frustrated and looking for someone to blame. Having paid for what they thought was insurance, they expect—and deserve—better than to be so conned. These patients' suffering and angst rightfully attracts media attention. What media should illuminate is the true nature and value of America's Biotech Social Contract and the heartlessness of its flawed insurance system.

# 5

## HONORING BOTH SIDES OF THE BIOTECH SOCIAL CONTRACT

**Patients would be far better served if the public would constructively** redirect its outrage to the lack of universal insurance in America and the heartless practice of imposing high out-of-pocket costs on the sick and vulnerable. Insurance companies and government policies behind our current system of inadequate insurance coverage and high copays are at the root of why some patients go without the care they need.

The central element of the Biotech Social Contract, as I see it, has little to do with what price is "fair" for a branded drug. That's an unwinnable debate and a search for unquantifiable value. Instead we should ask whether or not a drug will eventually go generic, offering society reassurance that there is an end in sight to the high cost of any new drug.

Industry needs to do more to fully honor its end of the contract. When a drug's patents expire, the company selling the branded drug should be legally compelled to help generic drug manufacturers make generics, both by supplying them with samples of branded product to compare their own versions to and transferring the know-how for ensuring that those generic copies are as identical as possible to the original. Patients should trust the quality of generics and, if we were to acknowledge the inventorship of generics and celebrate genericization, for example with a Public Domain Day for Drugs, then the company losing branded exclusivity would have some stake in ensuring that their legacy is not tarnished with low-quality generics.*

Companies have been pursuing and will continue to pursue every legal means at their disposal to prevent the uptake of generics, particularly in the case of biosimilars, which are more complex and offer more opportunity for legal and technical gamesmanship.[54] The generics industry and the Federal Trade Commission estimate that America is losing out on almost $10 billion of savings each year due to such stall tactics, which is a problem and makes for many galling headlines, but it's also less than 3% of total drug spend.[55]

Arguably, the industry as a whole can afford to swear off such excessive cleverness, which would lessen its public relations challenges. Assuming it won't, regulators should pursue avenues to accelerate genericization in ways that won't impact innovation (I offer some ideas in Chapter 13).†

## Investing in the Climb

Populist demands to cut drug prices may dangerously tempt some voters and politicians to follow through with such policies, but the innovative edge of the biopharmaceutical industry is powered by the willingness of the US market to reward groundbreaking research. Even European biopharmaceutical companies would likely not bother investing in the development of many kinds of new drugs if they couldn't count on selling them at high enough prices in the US. Hitting the biopharmaceutical industry with price controls in reaction to understandable but misdirected outrage would only rob ourselves and our children of the compounded growth of our giant mountain of generic drugs.

---

* Though maybe the best solution to ensuring the quality of generics is to shift some of the budget and accountability for quality control to the central distributors and pharmacies through which most generics flow.

† It's easy to say "should" and for every "should" that I believe is actionable, I'll propose how to do it. In this case, I aim to convey that ending stall tactics is preferable but not essential. So while I say we "should" end stall tactics, my argument still stands even if we can't or don't. At less than 4% of all drug revenues, tactics that stall the market entry of generics are a tolerable inefficiency in a process that is working reasonably well. The real problem, also small but growing with no corrective measures in sight, are drugs that can't go generic at all (discussed in Chapter 8).

Also, if we conflate investing in new drugs that we will someday "pay off" with simply spending money on expensive healthcare services (which never go generic), then we may make the wrong budget cuts and thereby only worsen our long-term costs and outcomes.

Consider a home mortgage. A borrower spends 15-30 years paying off a mortgage, typically while younger and employed. Those mortgage payments can be substantial, but once the owner makes the final payment, she can celebrate by burning the mortgage contract, living in the house rent-free, and eventually passing it down to her children and grandchildren. In this way, past generations paid off their branded drugs and gifted us the generics we have today. We can do the same for our children (and even throw a patent-burning party once branded drugs are similarly paid off).

What also becomes evident using this framework is that the costs of doctors, surgeries, and treatments such as dialysis for kidney disease are like rent and will remain high forever—we can only hope to prevent the need for these expensive services with inexpensive drugs.[56] A heart bypass and a cardiac surgeon may never go generic, but cholesterol lowering statins, which prevent hospital admissions and even surgeries, will be cheap indefinitely.

One might object to the mortgage analogy by pointing out that we don't use some generic drugs forever. Some drugs are phased out as newer, better ones come to market. That may seem like paying a mortgage for a home that you'll abandon to go live in another home on which you'll pay a new mortgage. Just as that's not how home ownership works,* neither is it how we make medical progress. A better analogy is that a family pays off the mortgage on its first home, a shack really, and each generation pays for additions and upgrades by taking on new loans that it then also pays off. After several generations, the improved family home may not even resemble the original structure or retain a single one of its beams, and yet it was made possible and paid for by a series of mortgages covering the cost of incremental improvements.

Had prior generations been content to rent the same old shack, today the family might discover that they couldn't possibly afford to upgrade it to a proper, well-built family home. This approach scales to entire communities. It's by being willing to build incrementally on what we've already accomplished that villages eventually become cities. Similarly, all the generic drugs we have today are only possible because society was willing to incentivize and invest in the development of drugs that provided the scientific foundation for modern treatments.

All technological progress works this way. It doesn't matter whether the drug that represents the first step towards someday curing a disease is part of the comprehensive treatment we'll have in 50 years, just as it doesn't matter whether the latest iPhone has any of the same components as the original iPhone. Had we not incentivized the first steps, we would not have climbed the scale of progress to get to the ultimate goal. It is that climb, each step a permanent advance, that paying for branded drugs incentivizes and makes possible. If we hold out for the ultimate product, refusing to pay for any cancer drug short of a cure, the research to get there would never get done, and we'll stay just where we are forever.

We can collectively afford to fund this climb. When politicians say that we can make do with fewer new treatments to fund other priorities, they're

---

* You can sell the first house and use the money to buy the second, so the equity one earns from paying off a mortgage is preserved.

pitching a false premise.[57] When skeptics argue that it's either new drugs or investment in schools and hiring more teachers, they're presenting false choices.[58] It's true that not all progress is of equal importance. If we stopped investing in better smartphones and faster Internet speeds, the state of current technology would serve America well for the coming generations. But if we don't invest in biomedical innovation, our children will suffer from the same illnesses that plague us today.

Yet when we talk about making room for all the other investments we should be making, including education and clean energy, let's first cut the inordinate amount of bureaucracy, a lot of it in healthcare itself, that wastes society's resources (see Chapter 10). Arbitrarily pitting these other priorities against biotechnology and new drug development is as unnecessary as it is unproductive.

When President Kennedy proposed that Americans send a man to the moon, he asked the country to boldly commit to a goal that would require substantial funding, partnerships between government and corporations, and immense intellectual capital. He explained that, "in a very real sense, it will not be one man going to the moon—if we make this judgment affirmatively, it will be an entire nation. For all of us must work to put him there."[59] Individual scientists and research teams will be the ones to discover the next generation of cures and treatments, but their successes will be the product of a collective societal effort. Just as the Apollo program produced breakthroughs in engineering, computing, and our understanding of spaceflight, let us recognize that the high cost of today's new drugs fuels and inspires the continued discovery of tomorrow's medical advances, providing high-value, affordable generics that will benefit us all for the rest of time.

# PART 2

# HOW TO KEEP DRUG PRICES IN CHECK

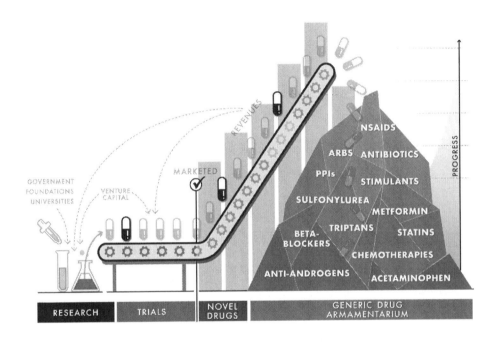

# 6

# WHY WAIT FOR GENERICS? EMBRACING FAST-FOLLOWERS

In 1994, the biotechnology company Genzyme launched Cerezyme,* an enzyme replacement therapy to treat Gaucher disease, a rare genetic disorder that causes a specific lipid to build up in the body. The buildup can create problems for the spleen and liver, weaken bones, and limit the production of blood cells, causing anemia and other conditions that are difficult to manage. In many cases, this necessitated major surgery, most commonly, the removal of the enlarged spleen.

Prior to the release of Cerezyme, doctors had been using its predecessor, Ceredase, to treat Gaucher disease. Ceredase was incredibly effective, making it possible for people with Gaucher disease to lead fuller lives and reducing the need for spleen removal surgery, but Genzyme produced it using human placental tissue—a lot of it. It took 50,000 placentas to create a year's worth of the Ceredase for one patient. In addition, this production technique carried the risk of viruses being transmitted from placenta donors to patients.

By 1994, Genzyme had figured out how to make the drug more purely in cells using recombinant DNA technology, and over the next few years,

---

* Now a subsidiary of the French pharmaceutical company Sanofi.

all Ceredase patients were switched over to the new drug, Cerezyme.[60] At an average dose, the annual cost of Cerezyme in 2005 was roughly $200,000 per year.[61]

For 19 years, Cerezyme was the only treatment available for this rare disease. That's a long monopoly, which isn't common, but Cerezyme is a biologic drug, one of the first the industry ever launched, which makes it much harder to copy than drugs composed simply of chemicals (in Chapter 8, we'll discuss what's been done to more efficiently genericize biologics). Other companies saw an opportunity to compete for a slice of this market and worked on their own enzymes. With a proven treatment already on the market, it wasn't easy to convince patients to enroll in a clinical trial of a new, unproven drug, but a few companies forged ahead. Finally, in 2010, the company Shire was able to bring a competing product to market and undercut Genzyme's price slightly.* In 2012, Pfizer launched its own version at a steeper discount. Patients could almost always count on Cerezyme to be covered by insurance and Genzyme was generous in helping those who had gaps in coverage, so the new competition didn't necessarily lower prices for patients themselves, but the launch of these Cerezyme-followers (forerunners to what today we might call biosimilars—more on this in Chapter 8) ensured drug supply against problems with any one manufacturer and also lowered the price society (insurance) paid.

In this case, Genzyme was able to enjoy a long monopoly since theirs was the only drug of a given class or type. This is known as an "in-class monopoly," and it used to be fairly typical in the biopharmaceutical industry. For twelve years, Roche's drug Rituxan was the only "anti-CD20" antibody on the market (meaning that it could bind to a protein called CD20 on B-cells, destroying them), treating diseases such as leukemia and, more recently, multiple sclerosis. For five years, Novartis dominated the treatment of chronic myelogenous leukemia (CML) with the drug Gleevec, the first BCR-ABL kinase inhibitor on the market. For three years, Merck was the only company to sell a DPP4 inhibitor, Januvia, to treat type 2 diabetes in the US.

---

* Genzyme's 2009 manufacturing problem (contamination at their production facility) created a Cerezyme shortage that abetted Shire's progress, driving patients into Shire's clinical study and motivating regulators (the FDA) to approve a new product to mitigate the risk of future shortages.

As the industry has become more productive with more companies competing with one another to solve the same problems, long in-class monopolies have become less common. Now, when a company launches a novel "first-in-class" drug, others are often not far behind with their "fast-follower" drugs (by comparison, the Cerezyme-like drugs Shire and Pfizer launched were very slow followers). Fast-follower drugs are sometimes similar enough that a physician might feel that a given patient might be adequately treated with any one of them. And yet, these drugs are different enough that each is covered by its own patents, and pharmacies can't take the initiative to just substitute one for the other, at least not without calling the doctor to send in a new prescription.

Fast-follower drugs are often maligned in the press and by the public as non-innovative. Detractors call them "me-too" drugs that are not worth their prices, and suggest that they contribute to the growth in drug spending. The first drug in a class could be manufactured redundantly at two or three different sites, as some are, to ensure against supply disruption and will eventually become inexpensive by going generic. So why waste time, creativity, and money on developing a second or third drug in the same class?

## Competition Gives Payers Leverage and Patients Options

Because drugs in the same class can seem similar, some people think that only the first drug in a class represents innovation, and the others are just copycats. Critics say that these me-too drugs don't deserve a high price because the companies that made them didn't seem to take as much risk to develop them as the first-to-market company.[62] If the first drug to market generates $2 billion/year in sales and the second drug $1 billion, critics appear to consider the sales of that second drug unearned and excessive. Yet, if not for the second drug, those patients would presumably either be taking the first drug (and so its sales would be $3 billion/year) or possibly they wouldn't be getting any treatment (e.g., if they couldn't tolerate the first drug due to some side effect), which would be unfortunate. So society and its patients are not disadvantaged by the existence of the second drug.

Competition within any given class of drug benefits society in two major ways.

Firstly, for patients, having multiple options means a greater chance for safe, effective treatment. For some patients, all drugs in a class may be interchangeable in terms of efficacy and side effects. But other patients might respond much better to one drug versus another of the same class. Different compounds in a particular class may be approved at different dosages or dosing schedules (i.e., how frequently they are taken). The differences between therapies in the same drug class may manifest as different side effects or efficacy profiles or interact differently with other drugs a person may be taking (known as *drug-drug interactions*).

For example, some patients have genetic differences that cause their liver enzymes to degrade some types of chemicals faster than would the liver enzymes of most other patients. A patient who is a fast degrader might break down one drug quickly, deriving less benefit from it. A me-too drug that is resistant to that patient's particular enzymes might work better. These differences have been observed for pain medications, anti-depressants, antibiotics, and many other drug classes. With several options, a physician has a better chance of finding a drug within a treatment class that works for a particular patient.

Secondly, having fast-followers in a class (I'll use this term interchangeably with "me-too") allows payers to play drugs off one another, offering preferential formulary status and market share in exchange for price concessions. It's simple economics: More sellers means price competition. Of course, it doesn't always appear to work that way. Fast-followers sometimes launch at a higher list price than the first-in-class drug, prompting a matching price increase on the first drug in the class. But even when list prices appear to go up, payers usually are able to extract greater rebates from all the manufacturers than they could when there was just one drug (see Chapter 7 for why insurance companies encourage higher list prices). So, generally speaking, net prices go down compared to where they would have been had the first drug enjoyed a monopoly.

For example, the first two drugs designed to inhibit the protein PCSK9 and treat high cholesterol were approved within weeks of one another, allowing payers to play them off each other to keep their prices in check. The first-in-class migraine drug targeting CGRP had two competitors in the same class within its first year on the market. Similar scenarios are playing out in most drug classes, from SGLT2 inhibitors for diabetes to CAR-T treatments for cancer. Though long in-class monopolies are becoming less common, they are still common, and there is room for more fast-followers.

## Why Aren't There More Fast-Followers (Me-Toos), and Why Aren't They Embraced?

Despite the benefits of me-too drugs, a lot of biopharmaceutical R&D dollars are being directed to developing first-in-class drugs, often for rare diseases—drugs that are more likely to earn the FDA's coveted "break-through" designation. That's where the regulatory incentives lie and where payer hurdles are often lower. Furthermore, many in the industry, sensitive to being labeled "non-innovative," fail to see the nuanced benefits of fast-followers, preferring the advantages of being first. Politicians talk about price controls not being intended to discourage innovation but to reduce what they see as the unnecessary development of me-toos, failing to realize that it was the launch of several me-toos that drove the price of hepatitis C cures down quickly. And payers don't consistently encourage me-too development, using them only to extract discounts from the market leader but not actually rewarding the me-toos with any significant market share (i.e., using them as a stalking horse).

For example, as mentioned in Chapter 4, Gilead was first to market with a once-daily pill called Harvoni that could cure hepatitis C and was followed by AbbVie's twice-daily Viekira Pak. But while AbbVie was willing to compete aggressively on price, payers were happy to just extract large rebates from Gilead and relegate AbbVie to less than a fifth of the market. Because the hepatitis C market was very large, with total annual sales in the US briefly growing to a peak of almost $20 billion/year, that fraction was still a sizable reward in absolute terms for AbbVie. But that is not an encouraging example for other companies considering how to challenge a first-in-class drug with their fast-followers in smaller markets. Getting 15% of a $2 billion/year market might not justify investing hundreds of millions of dollars to develop a slightly differentiated fast-follower, but a third of the pie might.

Regulators want to see more options for each drug class in the pharmacopeia.* At a conference in late 2015, the director of the FDA's Office of New Drugs John Jenkins lamented the lack of me-too drugs in the industry pipeline and among FDA's approved drugs list that year, declaring that me-too therapies for chronic diseases were often "me-better" and can be a boon for public health.[63] In early 2018, among the regulatory reforms suggested by the President's Council of Economic Advisors was an expedited approval pathway for me-too drugs.

Former FDA Commissioner Scott Gottlieb made a similar case with an emphasis on biologic drugs, saying that payers need to reward those who make biosimilars (akin to generics but of biologic drugs—more on that in Chapter 8) with market share, even if it means painfully kicking their addiction to the rebates payers extract from market leaders (who typically pay less generous rebates as they lose market share).[64] The alternative is longer in-class monopolies and slower genericization of biologic drugs, throwing the Biotech Social Contract off kilter.

Furthermore, some drug classes, such as CAR-T cell therapies and gene therapies, are not genericizable by any approaches conceivable today (I propose "contractual genericization" as a solution in Chapter 8). In these cases, me-toos represent the only foreseeable commoditization strategy.

## Combining Drugs Can Lead to Better Solutions and Lower Prices

Another major benefit of me-too drugs becomes evident when drugs from different classes are used in combination to create more effective therapeutic regimens. For example, HIV has long been treated with a "triple

---

* *Pharmacopeia* is a medical term for all the drugs physicians can choose from when considering how best to treat a patient. Throughout this book, I instead refer to it as a "mountain" or "armamentarium."

cocktail" of three kinds of drugs (two polymerase inhibitors and one integrase inhibitor), and hepatitis C is now easily cured with combinations of two or three types of antivirals.

Think of this like a plumber putting a wrench and a pair of pliers together to solve a difficult problem that would be impossible to solve with either tool alone. Imagine if there were only one wrench and only one pair of pliers. If one company owned both, it would have a monopoly and could set a high price for its combination therapy. If a "wrench" drug were owned by one company and the "pliers" drug by another, they might not be motivated to think about how to combine their drugs into a single pill or therapeutic regimen in the first place. Each certainly would want to charge a high price for its own drug since each could be considered necessary. But if there were multiple wrenches and multiple pliers on the market, with multiple companies each owning a set, this would create opportunities for multiple solutions and greater price competition among them.

When biopharmaceutical companies compete at the level of solutions by combining or sequencing multiple drugs to offer patients better outcomes, me-too drugs turn into necessary building blocks of solution sets that will compete for market share. When Gilead first launched its hepatitis C polymerase inhibitor Sovaldi, which remains the only hepatitis C polymerase inhibitor on the market, it charged $84,000 for a 12-week course of treatment. Sovaldi couldn't cure any patients on its own and needed to be used with at least one other type of hepatitis C drug. In 2015, Bristol-Myers Squibb released daclatasvir, a hepatitis C NS5A inhibitor meant to be taken with Sovaldi. The combination achieved a high cure rate, but with daclatasvir priced at $63,000, the total cost of the combination was $147,000 for a 12-week course of treatment. But Gilead had its own NS5A inhibitor, which might be considered redundant if you think in terms of classes of drugs and not the big picture. Gilead released Harvoni, a pill combining Sovaldi and its own NS5A inhibitor, and priced it at around the same level as Sovaldi alone. This made it impossible for BMS to compete, not to mention the fact that Harvoni was a single script with a single copay for the patient and one tablet per day instead of two. BMS, knowing that this would be Gilead's strategy, had tried to develop a hepatitis C polymerase inhibitor of its own, but those efforts failed, dooming its long-term prospects of competing in the hepatitis C market. Therefore, BMS' NS5A, although first-in-class, suffered from BMS not having a me-too polymerase inhibitor. Fortunately for society, AbbVie and later Merck were able to piece together their own sets from various me-toos and came to market to compete with Gilead, bringing down the price of curing hepatitis C.

Drugs do not actually need to be co-formulated into a single pill to be used together; they can simply be co-administered at the same time or during the same course of treatment. If they are owned by the same company, their prices can be functionally linked via co-contracting with payers (e.g., Drug A and B each costs $10,000/month, but together the price is $15,000/month).

These pricing and convenience advantages of combinations are also why every oncology company is developing an anti-PD(L)1 antibody (the FDA has approved five, and there are upwards of 20 more in development). This is the one drug class everyone knows is going to be part of a solution set for many cancers. As soon as there is a hint that a new type of drug class could work in combination with it, companies rush to get their own versions in that class, fearing that they will be stuck with nothing if their solution set ends up missing a key ingredient (why BMS lost in the hepatitis C market). That fear is logical and warranted and is driving the creation and acquisition of many drugs within a single class.

## Society's Leverage: Lowering Costs Ethically

The proliferation of similar drugs within the same class and having several classes of drugs that treat the same problem shifts the balance of power to society. Of course biopharmaceutical companies have at their disposal several perfectly legal tactics for competing for market share and preserving their prices, and they should be expected to use all of them. But society has at its disposal a number of tactics for containing drug costs that its agents (insurance plans) do not always employ. Unstated and yet still integral to the Biotech Social Contract is the tenet that the payer should play similar drugs off one another to get the best deal on behalf of society—without simply resorting to copays or other forms of cost-sharing to dissuade patients from seeking treatment.

On the whole, payers would seem to be effective negotiators.* Between government mandated rebates for Medicare and Medicaid and those private insurers negotiate for themselves and on behalf of government plans, payors got $135 billion in rebates and price concessions (28%) off the $479 billion of total drug costs on a list price basis in 2018,† reducing spending to $344 billion in 2018.[65] But we also know that insurance companies don't always negotiate as hard as they could. Based on their *net* prices, branded prescription drugs represent only 7.4% of total healthcare spend, so some payers can't be bothered to devote the time and resources to digging into price negotiations for me-toos except for the most expensive classes of treatment (e.g., hepatitis C, diabetes). Sometimes insurers are stuck between the rock of paying more for a drug and the hard place of being vilified in the media for denying access to treatments. Most disconcertingly, society's agents have found a way to align their own profit motives with higher drug prices. Pharmacy benefit managers (PBMs) can increase their profits by favoring high-cost drugs, from which they extract money-back rebates instead of recommending lower-cost drugs, even generics, without a rebate. (More on this in Chapter 7.)

Society (via government policies and contracts with PBMs and private insurance companies) should encourage the development of me-too products, especially for non-genericizable complex biologics classes, by rewarding some market share to each new entrant. If they do not, companies will have nothing to show for putting the third or fourth new, yet weakly differentiated drug in a class on the market, and they won't bother doing so in the future.

---

* And while one often hears that Medicare is forbidden by law from negotiating drug prices, the reality is that Medicare simply outsources those negotiations to insurance companies, which do a pretty effective job on the government's behalf, just without any government people literally at the negotiating table.

† While this figure mostly represents rebates to PBMs and government mandated rebates, about 10% of this total is from copayment assistance the companies offer directly to patients. To the extent that private insurance companies know that companies will help some patients pay their copayments, it seems to be a kind of tacitly negotiated price concession.

Directing market share to a me-too requires nudging physicians who prefer to use one drug in a class to use others after the first has hit its quota. As it would be unethical to force a physician to prescribe a drug that's substantively worse than an alternative, this is only possible in cases where a patient could be prescribed either one. Payers already do this to some extent by lifting reimbursement restrictions such as step edits and prior authorizations in exchange for greater rebates, so mechanisms exists to do so thoughtfully with the goal of keeping the most number of drugs in each class in play. By rotating which drug in a class is preferred at any one time, payers can influence the market share of new patients that each gets, allowing those who start taking a drug to keep taking it for as long as it works.

Payers could use copays for non-preferred drugs in a class to nudge patients to a preferred drug without violating the Biotech Social Contract as long as (a) the preferred drug in the class is good enough (i.e., not substantively worse than the others), (b) the preferred drug has no copay, and, importantly, (c) if the patient doesn't benefit from the preferred drug or suffers from its side effects, payers should waive the copay for whatever drug in the class the patient needs to switch to. As long as the recommended "copay-free" sequence is a medically sound option, then differences in patients' ability to pay would not disadvantage anyone. If a me-too drug is not good enough, then it would be unethical to force patients to take it just because they can't afford the copay for other drugs. But what exactly does "good enough" mean?

Before we assume that one can instigate price competition among several similar drugs, the key questions are (a) How meaningful are the differences among all the drugs in the same therapeutic class? and (b) How medically ethical is it to overlook those differences to exploit the similarities? If one drug is cheaper than others in its class but has a higher rate of a non-serious side effect, such as a mild rash, it doesn't seem unconscionable to ask a patient to try that drug first. If they do experience a rash, then the physician can switch them to one of the more expensive alternatives that doesn't cause rash. The company with the rash-causing drug will have to offer a price discount to an insurance company to require that patients try it before authorizing payment of one of the other rash-less drugs in that class. Or the inferior drug might merely be a bit less convenient than the best one, as we saw in the case of hepatitis C drugs when AbbVie, marketing a twice-daily pill, offered discounts to win market share from Gilead's once-daily pill.

So good-enough drugs can be leveraged against better drugs to save society money. The challenge is defining what is "good-enough" and what is so good that it's "unconscionable to deny." For example, let's say fast-follower Drug B is effective in all patients at slowing a certain cancer, and the first-in-class Drug A is effective in only half of patients, but we can't tell ahead of time which half. In this case, it would be difficult for a physician or insurance company to require that patients try the unreliable Drug A first, offering Drug B only to the half of patients whose disease got worse since, in this case, worse means that their cancer has progressed, and they are now more likely to die. Drug B would be considered "unconscionable to deny" to all patients and Drug A could not be considered "good enough."

There would certainly be a good argument for trying to develop a diagnostic test to predict which patients would benefit from Drug A and which won't, since that would give insurance companies leverage in their price negotiations. They could offer cheaper Drug A to those 50% of patients who the test says would benefit from it. But absent such a test, in a just world, Drug A would lose all market share regardless of any discounts its manufacturer might offer. Drug A would simply be supplanted by the better Drug B, which would now enjoy a monopoly (until going generic). And while Drug B might be in the same class as Drug A, an improvement so large that it makes Drug B "unconscionable to deny" represents enough progress that it's not even appropriate to call Drug B a me-too. It might be more appropriate to call it a "next-generation" drug in that class.

Still, the public sometimes confuses drugs that seem to be in the same class as being me-toos of one another and interchangeable. For example, it's common for people to talk about insulins as being a many decades-old class, yet insulins have progressed through multiple generations of improvements such that the advanced insulins marketed today are meaningfully better than those from the 1950s (more on that in Chapter 13). So while old insulins are cheaper and used in many countries around the world, when people talk about the insulins in America, they are unknowingly referring to more advanced, notably safer products that are unaffordable for some patients because our insurance system has made them so.

## Racing for Cures

While not all drugs in the same class are similar enough to one another to serve as leverage for payers in pricing negotiations, many are and create competitive tension. The companies that enjoy the profits of success remain motivated to innovate not only by the fact that their leading drugs, in the long run, will go generic, but also by the threat of fast-follower companies stealing market share in the nearer term with good enough me-toos.

We now operate in a world in which drug companies must continue to expeditiously innovate and combine products to maintain their competitive edge and pricing power. Such competition benefits society by lowering prices below what drugs would cost if they enjoyed in-class monopolies, and it also drives the entire innovation ecosystem. Larger companies often must acquire the technologies they don't have, which cycles some of their profits down to smaller companies and universities, providing them with the fuel and incentive to come up with the next, must-have breakthroughs.

In Lewis Carroll's *Through the Looking-Glass, and What Alice Found There*, the Red Queen explains that, in her world, one has to run just as fast as one can just to stay in the same place, and to get ahead, one must run faster than that.[66] Such are the rules of the biopharmaceutical industry, except that companies are racing one another to invent and acquire more and better chess pieces with which to best vanquish diseases.

GOVERNMENT
FOUNDATIONS
UNIVERSITIES

VENTURE
CAPITAL

MARKETED

REVENUES

PBM

PROGRESS

| RESEARCH | TRIALS | NOVEL DRUGS | GENERIC DRUG ARMAMENTARIUM |

# 7

## FALSE HEROES: PHARMACY BENEFIT MANAGERS AND THE PATIENTS THEY PREY ON

It's hard to know when actual prices for a particular drug really do go up, because there is so little transparency in pricing. A lot of the public discourse on pricing is based on "list prices," which no one—neither patients nor payers—actually pays. As is the case with cars and anything on Amazon, everything is always on some kind of sale or subject to discounts of one type or another. In the world of pharmaceuticals, these discounts are called "rebates" and often take the form of payments from the drug company back to the insurer. The particulars of a rebate that a drug company offers to an insurer—its magnitude and how it varies according to market share—are kept confidential, essentially based on the age-old sales tactic of "Because you're special, I'll give you a special price, but don't tell the other guy."

Pharmacy Benefit Managers, or PBMs, are the companies who negotiate with drug companies on behalf of payers (and some PBMs are actually owned by insurance companies, so one can think of them as just agents of payers), and—importantly—retain a portion of the rebates that pass through them. In effect, PBMs profit from the very high list prices they purport to heroically negotiate down. A biopharmaceutical company offering a lower list price without a rebate would threaten the PBM business model, so PBMs discourage this tactic by not rewarding it. Instead, they encourage drug companies to keep their publicly known list prices high and give an ever bigger confidential rebate to the PBM, from which the PBMs siphon off their own rent before passing on the lower net price to the payer while boasting, "Behold what I have negotiated for you!"

Let's take a closer look at the numbers to see how all this works (or doesn't).

In 2018, although list prices for branded drugs increased by 5.5%, net prices (what drug companies actually get after discounts and rebates) were essentially flat compared to the year before, having come in nominally 0.3% higher, though really lower when adjusted for inflation.[67] So increased prices of some drugs were more than offset by the savings from other drugs going generic. Indeed, total spending (what the US is paying, in total, for drugs) is increasing, by about 4.4% in 2018 from the prior year, but it's because more patients are being treated. That should be good news. That's what progress looks like!

Of course, none of that matters if you are a patient who can't afford what your physician prescribes—and there are all too many people out there who can identify with this. A major part of the solution requires lowering or eliminating out-of-pocket costs, as discussed in Chapter 4, but it's worth exploring just how much waste there is in the middle zone between drug companies and patients due to payers' and PBMs' tactics.

In 2018, US drug spending based on list prices was $479 billion, yet net drug price spending was $344 billion, approximately 28% lower.[68] That means that, even if we stuck to "cost-sharing" but simply linked what patients pay to net prices that PBMs negotiate instead of list prices, patient costs would be reduced by 28%, saving around $17 billion of the $61 billion in out-of-pocket costs Americans paid in 2018.* Insurance companies and

---

* Consider that saving patients 28% by lowering drug prices by 28% would render the entire biopharmaceutical industry a non-profit and shutter innovation. So pegging patients' out-of-pocket expenses to net prices instead of list prices is a much more surgical solution, which payers would compensate for with a tiny increase in premiums, less than 1%, though could also absorb by slashing their own bureaucracy.

Medicare count on that $17 billion extra from patients to pad their own budgets, allowing them to charge slightly lower premiums/taxes, a perverse kind of insurance policy since it means that the sick subsidize the healthy.

Realistically, being able to negotiate secret rebates is a useful tactic for playing drug companies off one another, as PBMs have done with Gilead, AbbVie, and Merck to drive down the cost of hepatitis C cures in recent years. However, right now, some patients are increasingly bearing an unfair burden, and most Americans are being misled about the true costs of important medicines.[69] To understand why and how, let's begin with a quick rebate primer.

## Rebates and How They Impact Patients

Imagine if an agent offered to help you buy a car and promised that you would only need to pay her 20% of whatever she saved you. You buy a car that is listed at $40,000 by the dealership, but you only end up having to pay $30,000, after your agent negotiates on your behalf. Your agent has saved you $10,000 and retains $2,000 as her fee, so really the car cost you $32,000, and you saved $8,000. That's still good.

Now, imagine that a car dealership decides to cut out the middleman and list those same cars at $30,000, the same amount the dealership would have received after giving discounts to agents. That would be cheaper than going through an agent since you wouldn't have to pay the $2,000 fee. The agent won't direct buyers to that dealership because their prices leave no room for the dealership to offer any discounts, which means the agent won't earn her commission. If anything, agents will encourage dealerships to raise their list prices, either directly or tacitly. If the agent can pressure the dealership to raise the list price of that car to $50,000, the agent will be able to negotiate it down by 40% to $30,000, earn a $4,000 commission, and come out looking like a hero to the buyer, though the car would now functionally cost $34,000!

This is what's going on in the drug industry, and it is a big reason why list prices are increasing. The question, of course, is why don't biopharmaceutical companies bypass the PBMs and sell their products directly to insurance companies? Yes, any company that did so would be ostracized by the agent community, but why should that matter?

The unfortunate truth is that as PBMs have grown, they have amassed wide influence. They have entrenched themselves as middlemen with massive bargaining power, which stems from how concentrated the PBM market has become. The top three PBMs, Express Scripts, CVS/Caremark, and United's OptumRx, represent 80% of the PBM market and serve insurance plans covering half of the US population.

So, what's the big deal? PBMs keep a piece of the rebate, but at the end of the day, they are saving patients money, and that's what matters...right? And that's the problem: saving patients money matters, but this system doesn't actually do that. Though rebates save money for society as a whole, currently rebates actually *increase* the true share of costs patients shoulder.

As discussed, a portion of the rebates negotiated by and passed through PBMs is kept by the PBMs. Some of those rebates are passed on to the insurer, particularly for drugs covered by Medicare, less so when drugs are covered by private payers. But—critically—none of this makes its way back to patients, who are still subjected to cost-sharing through deductibles and copays based on the list prices of drugs.

For example, a patient with a 20% copay on a drug with a $10,000-per-year list price must pay $2,000. After rebates, that drug might cost the PBM, say, $6,000. So, in actuality, the patient is paying $2,000 for a drug that cost $6,000—so the patient's copay, in effect, is 33%, not 20%.[70]

It gets worse if the patient hasn't yet met his deductible. If this patient has a $10,000 deductible that he hasn't met, he might have to pay the full list price for the drug, in this case, $10,000, while his insurance company pockets the $4,000 rebate from the biopharmaceutical company! (Recall the car repair analogy in Chapter 4.) Payers defend this practice by claiming that rebates help to defray the cost of insurance for everyone, meaning that, perversely, sick patients are subsidizing insurance for the healthy. *That's not how insurance is supposed to work!*

As the public learns more about PBM tactics, they are justly appalled and outraged. And it doesn't stop with retaining a portion of drug rebates.

PBM contracts with their clients are filled with all kinds of hidden pockets of profit, according to one leaked contract.[71]

In March 2018, the insurer United Health caused a stir in the world of health insurance by enacting what would seem to be a banal and obvious new policy: Beginning in 2019, United would begin passing rebates through to some patients.[72] The details remain opaque—and whether consumers have derived any real savings remains to be seen—but this is an overdue gesture designed to assuage Americans' anger over their growing out-of-pocket expenses. United's program will cover plans affecting only seven million Americans, but hopefully more plans will follow.

Unfortunately, if insurance companies appear to be giving with one hand, they're likely taking away with the other. In 2018, a new so-called benefit called a "copay accumulator" began appearing in health plans across the country. As mentioned in Chapter 4, copay accumulators are designed to negate the efforts of drug companies to help patients pay out-of-pocket costs for drugs, particularly the costs of specialty medicines that can reach tens of thousands of dollars per year per patient. The goal is to ensure that no matter what anyone does to help a patient afford their medications, insurance won't kick in until the patient has suffered financial strain.[73]

Almost anyone would agree that this system is heartless and needs to be reformed. Drug manufacturers' assistance programs are steps on the path to making drugs affordable to those who need them, but they are not a fix in and of themselves. No matter what rebates or coupons biopharmaceutical companies offer, it won't make any difference if PBMs and insurance companies remain bent on making healthcare feel unaffordable to patients, on nudging them into foregoing care, and on extracting what they can from vulnerable patients to lower the cost for healthy people, who have no idea of the costs they will face should they develop a chronic disease and need care.

## Bad Press and Higher Costs

Drug companies get bad press when they are seen raising their list prices, even when their non-public net prices are actually flat or down. PBMs offer preferential coverage status (e.g., a lower copay than a competitor's drug) and therefore more market share to companies that are both willing to charge a higher list price, swallowing the bitter pill of bad press, and accept a lower net price that insurance companies want, so that these PBM middlemen can feed off the rebate in between. If a drug company were to just offer a low list price, it would save the insurance companies and society that ultimately pays the bills just as much money and save itself the bad press, but then the PBMs couldn't profit from rebates. Unfortunately, because patients' out-of-pocket costs are linked to list prices, they suffer the consequences of PBMs' business model.

## Do PBMs Have a Role—Any Role—to Play?

Whether or not insurers should continue to rely on PBMs to manage drug price negotiations is a point of ongoing debate.[74] One could argue that the bloated administrative costs of PBMs' complex scheming and the profits they generate represent a layer of rent that society can do without.

By my crude estimate, if what PBMs skim off the top by these controversial means were redirected to patients, it would shave over a third from their out-of-pocket spending on drugs.* As an added bonus, doing away with PBMs would help close the gap between list prices that Americans see (and are outraged by) and the net prices that more accurately reflect the cost of drugs to society.

---

* Extrapolating to the whole PBM market from the financial statements of Express Scripts, a PBM with 28% market share in 2017, and assuming that even as much as 75% of PBM gross profits are derived from rebates which are then spent on unnecessarily complex administration and profits (which would mean that 25% of gross profits covers the cost of necessary administration), then PBM profits and excess operating costs that one conceivably could try to eliminate add up to ~$23 billion, which is 6.7% of the estimated $344 billion of total net US drug spend in 2018 per IQVIA. The fraction of just retail drugs that PBMs are responsible for, which are around 71% of all drug spending, would be closer to 10%.

IQVIA Institute for Human Data Science, *Medicine Use and Spending in the U.S*; Express Scripts 2017 10-k SEC filing: Timothy Wentworth, "US Securities and Exchange Commission, Form 10-K: Express Scripts Holding Company" (annual report, Washington D.C., 2017), https://www.sec.gov/Archives/edgar/data/1532063/000153206318000004/esrx-12312017x10k.htm; "Select Emerging PBMs Gain Market Share," *Health Strategies* (blog), Feb. 23, 2017.

Still, someone has to do the work of managing formularies and negotiating drug prices, just as someone has to do the work of organizing health insurance overall. That said, there are precedents for eliminating PBMs from the process. Today, not all insurers sub-contract with PBMs, choosing instead to create their own formularies and negotiate directly with drug companies.

If PBMs do continue to play the role of drug rebate negotiators, they should compete based on their overall level of effectiveness and efficiency, without the perverse incentive to encourage higher drug prices in order to negotiate steeper rebates. If, as a recently proposed federal bill directs,[75] PBMs were required to pass the entire rebate to their insurance-company customers, many of these perverse incentives would go away—as would a portion of the PBM industry's profits (so it will not come as a surprise that the PBMs lobby hard against this kind of reform). So be it. Ultimately, the PBMs that do a more effective job of negotiating rebates will have more competitive overall fees and win more business for themselves from insurance companies—and that's how it should work.

## The Cost of Bureaucracy

Any close look at PBMs reveals a complex shell game of rebates, copays, accumulators, and other mechanisms payers use to pad their profits. But it raises another question: How much does it cost to design, implement, and administrate such a complex system? You may have already come across statistics to that effect, such as "Administrative costs are 8 percent of health care spending in the US and 3 percent on average among wealthy countries."[76]

In March 2018, *The Economist* analyzed what they called the "excess profits" (those above the 10% return on capital that they deemed reasonable) of the two hundred largest healthcare companies, ranging from pharmaceutical companies to pharmacies to payers.[77] They concluded that excess profits only represented about 2% of total healthcare spending (or 4% of what they estimated the US overspent relative to other countries) and that even if these excess profits were eliminated, it would not represent a tremendous savings. In addition—and despite what much of the public believes—*The Economist* found that pharmaceutical companies were not the worst offenders in this regard. Looking back a couple of decades, the study pointed out that while average drug prices (net of rebates) had risen by about 5% annually, their development costs have also climbed steeply, cutting their return on capital in half since the late 90s and nearly eliminating excess returns. Meanwhile, the profits of the middlemen, including PBMs, insurers, wholesalers, and pharmacies, have, over the past 15 years, climbed from 20% to 41%, and that they represent two-thirds of the healthcare industry's excess profits.

This is not to suggest that the public should direct its ire to whichever stakeholder in the healthcare industry commands the highest profits. What matters is the value that each is offering for what they are charging. My argument is that drug companies are ultimately building a generic drug mountain that will serve mankind for the rest of time at a low cost, while the countless middlemen who extract high rents from society, including from desperate patients, warrant greater scrutiny and reform.

As with children's stories, where there is a hero, there is necessarily a villain, and therefore rising list prices give the public the sense that it is the drug companies engaged in callous extortion despite payers' best efforts. But in reality, it is America's flawed and fragmented health insurance system that perversely incentivizes middlemen to embrace higher drug prices in exchange for their secret discounts and unfairly foists healthcare costs onto patients under the guise of having "skin in the game."

# 8

# WHEN A DRUG WON'T GO GENERIC: PROPOSING CONTRACTUAL GENERICIZATION

The Biotech Social Contract calls on the drug development industry to make drugs that will go generic without undue delay, thereby adding to that mountain of generic drugs. But if drugs don't, won't, or can't go generic, they pose a significant threat to the contract and the sustainability of the industry. Some drugs, such as gene therapies and CAR-T cell therapies, are truly uncopyable—someone can claim they have made a copy, but the FDA won't trust the copies to be close enough to the original to allow its use in place of the original. As a consequence, no exact copies will come to market to compete on price with the original in the way generics do.

This situation creates two problems: (a) the prices for these drugs might never drop, and (b) the companies selling them have less incentive to innovate and create new drugs to replace revenues that would normally be lost to generic competition. Drugs that don't go generic exist outside of the Biotech Social Contract—and in violation of it.

## Why Biologics Are Difficult—or Even Impossible— to Copy

First things first: As you read this chapter, you'll notice that most of the conversation revolves around biologic drugs, not traditional "small-molecule" chemical drugs. The reason is that once a small molecule drug goes generic and its chemical formula is accessible to all, formulating and manufacturing a generic version of it is a relatively straightforward process—kind of like mixing a cocktail using a recipe and mass-produced, consistent ingredients. Zestril and Lipitor are examples of traditional, small-molecule, chemical drugs that gave way to generics quickly and easily (lisinopril and atorvastatin, respectively).

Biologics are a whole other matter. These protein-based, large-molecule medicines are produced in living cells using a fermentation process akin to wine making and are like wines in that one batch is never exactly the same as another. It is extremely difficult (if not impossible) to produce generic versions of biologics that are as close to identical in composition as generic versions are of small molecule drugs. In the past, that made it difficult to get generic versions of biologics approved, which meant that many biologics couldn't go generic and the prices stayed high.

## Biosimilars—A Step in the Right Direction

To address the problem of biologics being hard to genericize, as part of the ACA Congress enabled the FDA to come up with a way of recognizing when two biologics are close enough to be called similar, even if it is impossible to prove they are the same. There are fewer companies that specialize in making these "biosimilar" biologics than companies that can make generic small molecules (just as there are fewer vineyards than bartenders), and it generally costs more to manufacture biologics. Therefore, when a branded biologic "goes biosimilar," the price might not erode as steeply as it would in the case of generics. Only a handful of biosimilars have launched on the US market to date, though several others approved by the FDA are held up only by legal challenges or settlements, so it's just a matter of time before they come to market and start bringing prices down.[78]

The European biosimilar market offers cause for optimism. Over twenty biosimilars in several drug classes, including those that treat anemia, auto-immune disorders, cancer, and arthritis, have entered the European market and several more await approval by the EMA, the EU's FDA equivalent.[79] Indeed, Europe offers a strong model for approving biosimilars in order to produce greater competition and price erosion in the biologics market.*

Fascinatingly, while biosimilar launches have triggered price drops, there is little correlation between a biosimilar's market share and the over-all price reduction in the total market.[80] This means that a biosimilar need only gain a small foothold to push down the prices of branded biologics, even if the brand maintains a substantial share of the market. The entrance of a single biosimilar can reduce overall prices because it shifts the balance of negotiating power to payers, who then extract a big enough discount from the original branded biologic to keep it on their formularies. As I mentioned in Chapter 6 about me-too drugs, it's important that payers reward biosimilars with market share and not just use them to extract discounts from the market leader. Towards this end, the FDA recently promised to increase biosimilar competition and suggested that the Centers for Medicare and Medicaid Services (CMS) could incentivize biosimilar growth by switching CMS's payment model for many biologics away from Medicare Part B, which is somewhat less price sensitive,† to be more like Medicare Part D, which negotiates rebates more aggressively.[81]

With greater competition, prices should drop to be only modestly higher than the cost of production, which is typically 5 15% of the branded drug price. This means that, with enough competition, biologic drug prices might drop by as much as 70-90%.[82] Compared to small molecule drugs, the biosimilar approval process is slower and more complex, which means

---

* Although Europe relies less on generics than the US, as mentioned in Chapter 3, it's blazing a trail in the adoption of biosimilars.

† Drugs reimbursed under Medicare Part B tend to be those that have to be administered by physicians, often infused in their offices. Medicare requires that physicians or hospitals purchase these drugs themselves and then reimburses them at a fixed percentage more than the cost, with the small premium (typically 4.5% or 6%) meant to compensate the doctor or hospital for the hassle of having to buy and store the drug. But that small premium can perversely encourage physicians to use more expensive drugs since 6% of a $5,000 drug ($300) is a lot more than 6% of a $500 drug ($30). So a biosimilar coming in at a lower price than a branded biologic drug would be less profitable for a physician. Clearly that reverse incentive has to change.

that it may take longer for enough competitors to reach the market to drive down prices to that extent. For example, a price drop that took less than 12 months for the cholesterol-lowering statin Lipitor might take several years for the protein-based TNF-alpha inhibitor Humira, but all signs point to biosimilars, like generics, offering society great value.[83]

However, existing biosimilar legislation only applies to simpler types of biologics, such as enzymes and antibodies. There is still no regulatory path by which the FDA can recognize biosimilars of complex biologics like cell therapies, for reasons I'll explain below. However, that doesn't mean that society can't get out of paying branded prices for these complex biologics in the long run.

## Drugs That Don't Go Generic: Sizing the Problem

The good news is that there aren't many drugs that don't, won't, or can't go generic, and society is spending comparatively little on them at the moment. Let's look at some numbers, using spending from the two biggest government plans as a reference point.

According to CMS, only 121 drugs account for about 68%, or almost $101 billion, of the approximately $148 billion that the government spent on prescription drugs in 2018.[84] Based on how difficult it is to manufacture these 121 drugs,* some being easier to copy than others, more than half (55%) of this sum is spent on branded drugs that are readily genericizable and therefore can be expected to eventually drop considerably in price once their patents expire.

Another 11% consists of spending on branded drugs that are administered in ways that make genericizing them challenging. For instance, the bronchodilator Advair Diskus, a specialized device that allows a patient to inhale a combination of two drugs, is only just starting to see some generic competition. In order for a generic version of this type of drug to be approved by the FDA, the maker must provide evidence that the delivery device—in

---

* This analysis is my own and required comparing figures gleaned from CMS's website based on 2017 data and IQVIA's 2018 data on total drug expenditures. Classifying which drugs are genericizable is not difficult for anyone in the drug industry who can recognize which drugs are simple chemicals, which are simple chemicals formulated in complex devices, which are simple biologics, and which are complex biologics. I list these in order of how hard they are to manufacture, from easier to hardest, which corresponds to how hard they are to genericize or biosimilarize.

addition to the drug itself—will work just as reliably as the branded drug's device. But even these should eventually succumb to generic competition.

Another 30% of this spending is on comparatively simple biologic drugs that should face biosimilar competition. Many, like Remicade, Neupogen, and Avastin, already have approved biosimilars on the market, which has already led to price erosion or eventually will.[85]

Based on these data, we can conclude that 96% of the US government's branded drug spending is on drugs that will drop in price as generics or biosimilars come to market. That means only 4%, approximately $6 billion, is spent on drugs that, based upon today's knowledge and technology, cannot go generic (I'll address this 4% below in more detail). That's a small percentage, which seems good, but these drugs represent rents that will stack over time. Like a small plug of hair in the sink, this spending will grow and grow, threatening to clog the entire system sometime in the future.

There are two solutions to this small but growing problem, one of which is already in play, which I'll call "indirect genericization," and the other we need to bring about through an act of Congress, which I'll call "contractual genericization."

## A Workaround: Indirect Genericization

Of that 4% we spend on drugs that probably can't go generic, I approximate that half is spent on complex biologics that, while hard to biosimilarize,*

---

* These numbers are my own approximations based on my analysis of Medicare spending, which I have not published. I'm likely off in my calculations, maybe by 3x but probably not 10x, but it's not important that the numbers be precise. The point is that we are currently spending very little of our drug budget on drugs that can't go generic. Whether that's 2% or 6% doesn't matter—we shouldn't allow spending on such drugs to grow and therefore need novel regulations to simulate genericization of these drugs when their patents expire (i.e. contractual genericization). If I'm wrong about the magnitude of the problem and the real spending on such ungenericizable drugs really is 20%, then it's all the more urgent that we introduce contractual genericization. If I'm wrong the other way and spending is less than 2% on such drugs, it just means that the Biotech Social Contract is being violated to a much smaller degree than I fear, but we should still prevent the problem from growing by introducing contractual genericization. Some might think that we needn't act now since the problem is currently insignificant. However, I think that if we wait until many companies are addicted to the cash flow streams of many ungenericizable drugs whose patents have long expired, then passing legislation that mandated simulated genericization will be a lot harder, as those companies will be fighting to preserve their unhealthy business models. The drug industry has long been in the business of charging mortgages for their products, not rent. We must make sure that this remains the case before the industry shifts to an unhealthy rent model.

might actually be disrupted by other, simpler branded drugs that are themselves genericizable. For example, in hepatitis C, the standard treatment used to be a biologic treatment that required injecting pegylated interferons.[86] Many patients experienced difficulties tolerating peg-interferon-based treatment, and it only cured 40% of patients after as much as a year of injections. But then came new small molecule drugs, taken orally, that increased cure rates to nearly 100%, while cutting the treatment time to as little as eight weeks. These drugs all but retired peg-interferon-based treatments. Someday, all of these drugs will likely face increased competition from their own generics—all of which obviates the need to genericize peg-interferon.

Another interesting case study is that of IVIg, which is a mixture of antibodies collected from the blood of healthy donors for infusion into patients with a variety of immune-related problems. Companies that specialize in extracting proteins from blood sell their own branded versions of IVIg that physicians recognize as being largely interchangeable. Therefore, when a hospital needs to purchase IVIg, it can shop around, but due to a relative scarcity of donated blood, IVIg supplies are almost always tight, and the prices remain high. Several biotechnology companies are working to develop biologic drugs that could replace IVIg but are manufactured more conventionally (i.e., not purified from blood). Such an IVIg replacement would be expensive at first, like any branded drug, but it would reduce what we spend on IVIg, and it would address the supply problem. Eventually, the patents would expire, biosimilars would come to market, and prices would drop.

One more example. NovoSeven is a last-resort blood-clotting factor used to treat patients with hemophilia, a condition in which a patient's blood doesn't clot normally, turning a small cut into a life-threatening emergency. Hemophilia occurs when a person is born missing one of two clotting factors: Hemophilia A occurs when patients are missing Factor VIII and Hemophilia B occurs when patients are missing Factor IX.* Normally, patients with Hemophilia A and B are both treated with regular infusions of the clotting factor they are missing. But sometimes patients develop antibodies that neutralize the benefits of the clotting factors, essentially rejecting the therapy and putting them back into the danger

---

* These proteins are formally named using Roman numerals and are pronounced "Factor 8" and "Factor 9."

zone.[*] If they get a scratch, suffer internal bleeding from an accident, or need surgery, then daily infusions of NovoSeven can save their lives by helping their blood clot. NovoSeven is very expensive to manufacture and has to be used in high amounts, so it carries a high price. While too early to be sure, the odds look good that NovoSeven will be indirectly genericized by better drugs coming down the pike, drugs that are simpler to make and more convenient to administer to patients.

It's even possible that, in the near future, hemophilia will be cured or nearly cured with gene therapies that are too complex to genericize but impossible for other types of drugs to beat (hard to beat a single infusion that gives you your life back). Such non-genericizable, non-disruptable therapies represent the final 2% of drug spending and require a new strategy to protect the Biotech Social Contract.[†]

## Truly Ungenericizable: The Challenge of Gene Therapies

Complex biologics, such as gene therapies, pose a challenge to the contract.[‡]

Here's why. Let's say that Company A developed a gene therapy, and 15 years later, its patents have expired. Along comes Company B wanting

---

[*] If a patient's immune system reacts to an infusion of Factor 8 or 9 as if it were a vaccine and then attacks the drug the next time it's infused, then it can neutralize the effects of the drug, leaving the person essentially untreated.

[†] Such gene therapies can actually be disrupted by side-stepping of the genetic disorder using IVF and genetic testing to allow couples who know they are carriers to select an unaffected embryo when having children. Some families that already know they carry hemophilia mutations already do this to spare the next generation the burdens of this disease, but to be broadly effective, side-stepping would require broader education about the utility of preconception genetic testing as well as widespread insurance coverage of IVF, at least for purposes of side-stepping genetic disorders. Genetic side-stepping is best described by Lee Cooper.
Lee Cooper, "To Fight High-Priced Drugs, Sidestep the Disease," *Medium*, Dec. 27, 2018, https://medium.com/@leecoo4/to-fight-high-priced-drugs-sidestep-the-disease-b40e4a689c58.

[‡] A gene therapy is an extremely complex type of drug that inserts novel genetic material into the cells of a patient whose own DNA is missing a functional copy of an important gene. For example, children with Spinal Muscular Atrophy are missing a functional copy of the SMN1 gene, which is needed for normal function of neurons. Children with this disorder can be rescued by an infusing of a gene therapy that consists of a virus modified to insert a normal copy of SMN1 into their neurons. Some gene therapies involve taking a patient's bone marrow stem cells out, exposing them to a virus carrying a copy of the gene they are missing, and infusing the genetically engineered cells back into the patients. When this procedure is done to help patients suffering from sickle cell anemia due to a mutation in their gene encoding hemoglobin that distorts their red blood cells (into a sickle shape), the modified bone marrow cells make healthy red blood cells. When this procedure is done to help babies born without immune systems due to another genetic mutation (e.g., Bubble Boy Syndrome), the new stem cells save their lives by restoring their immune systems.

to make a biosimilar of that gene therapy. Company B copies the manufacturing process of the original gene therapy, generates data showing that it works similarly in animal studies, and even manages to produce some clinical data from human trials. Now it's time to submit their data to the FDA in order to have their drug approved as a biosimilar. Instead, Company B is met with a blank stare. We don't yet have analytical tools that can determine, reliably, whether or not two gene therapies really are the same. Without these analytics, the FDA has no legal basis for granting it approval as a biosimilar. It would be like someone showing you two alien creatures and claiming they are twins. While they might look the same to your eyes, you wouldn't even know where to begin in trying to confirm whether they are twins or not—especially knowing, as we do, that even identical human twins aren't truly identical.[87]

Unfortunately for Company B, the FDA would have an ethical duty not to approve their drug as interchangeable with the original. Company B could always submit its gene therapy to the FDA as a novel drug, but that would require larger clinical trials and cost a lot of money, far more than it costs to develop a generic or biosimilar drug. If approved, Company B will have developed a "me-too" branded drug, which isn't a bad thing (see Chapter 6), but it's not an easy path, financially—not nearly as easy as, say, bringing a generic small-molecule to market.

Ultimately, the result is that this strategy isn't enticing enough to encourage many companies to compete with Company A's gene therapy—certainly not enough competitors to drive its price down by 70%, 80%, or 90% as we might expect when a drug really goes generic.

Any me-too/biosimilar gene therapy would also face significant hurdles even before it got to the FDA. For instance, consider a gene therapy for a genetic condition that can be diagnosed at birth and that works best when administered in the first few months of life. Maybe this gene therapy need only be given once to help a child live a normal or near-normal life. Now imagine that a competitor has developed its own version and needs to show how well it works in a human clinical trial.

With a miracle drug already on the market, it is hard to imagine any parent being willing to enroll their child in the clinical trial. Why take a chance on an alternate treatment, no matter how similar it seems based on animal tests, when a proven, approved treatment is available?* Even slight differences could cause the biosimilar gene therapy to be worse, which is why the FDA requires trials like this in the first place. In this situation, it might be years before the patient begins to show symptoms or signs that the biosimilar was inferior, and by that time, the optimal window for treating the condition would have closed. What parent or doctor would take that risk?

In such a scenario, the first company to bring a gene therapy to market would have an undisruptable "natural" monopoly.† Currently, there aren't many gene therapy programs like this in clinical development. Those that are on the market are extremely expensive (Novartis' gene therapy Zolgensma, which treats children with spinal muscular atrophy, costs $2 million per patient). Even at such prices, these therapies will likely stay below 10% of total drug spend for decades to come because there are so few patients with relevant diseases, but as time passes and gene therapies become more common, these "natural" monopolies will undermine the Biotech Social Contract. The solution is a regulatory one: simulate genericization after a drug's patent has expired. But before we get into how that might work, let's look at some numbers.

There are thousands of rare genetic disorders, many of which could potentially be addressed through gene therapy. In theory, solving one such

---

* In a randomized controlled trial (sometimes called an RCT), a patient starts the trial by being randomly assigned to get either the Experimental Drug arm or the Control Treatment arm of the trial (arm here means "group"). Sometimes the Control Treatment is just placebo. But for a biosimilar trial, the Control Treatment is the original drug that the biosimilar must show similarity to. Usually, neither the physician nor the patient know what they got until the end of the trial—they are said to be "blinded"—and since both the people doing the experiment and the patients who are being experimented on are blinded, the trial is said to be "double blinded." A trial might enroll dozens or thousands of patients, depending on what data the FDA needs to see to decide whether to the approve the experimental drug. For the comparison of the data in the two arms to be valid, the patients enrolled in each of the arms should be similar to one another, which is why all the patients who qualify for the clinical trial are randomly assigned to the Experimental or Control arms of the trials. If one enrolled males into the Experimental arm and females into the Control arm, you would never know if the differences observed between the two arms (let's say the Experimental arm did better than the Control) were due to gender differences between the patients in the arms (e.g., maybe males have milder disease symptoms) or because the Experimental treatment was actually better.

† At least until we find ways to get ahead of treatment entirely by side-stepping the disease in the first place.

disease might generate $350 million/year in the US for a biopharmaceutical company.* Therefore, treating even 10% of the 6,000 genetic disorders listed in the genetics OMIM database could eventually drive societal spending above $200 billion/year. For context, that's about 60% of what we are currently spending on all prescription drugs in the US each year. If the benefits of future therapies are anything like the gene therapies in development today, they would not feel at all discretionary to the patients and families devastated by these disorders. Clearly, until we come up with a scientifically and ethically sound way to let gene therapy biosimilars come to market, we need an alternative way to achieve the same end.

## Contractual Genericization: Applying a Standard Solution to Natural Monopolies

If a drug can neither go generic nor be replaced with a better technology, it might remain a monopoly forever. The company that developed it would have the ability to charge a high price indefinitely, which violates the Biotech Social Contract, though that's not the fault of the company. In any industry, a company will charge what the market will bear until competition or a change in supply or demand forces it to lower the price.

Given the scientific limits that prevent us from making biosimilars of complex biologics like gene therapies, how can we make them conform to

---

* Most biotechnology companies hope that their innovation will lead to a so-called blockbuster drug, which corresponds to at least $1 billion in global annual revenues. In the case of rare orphan disorders, the US conventionally represents 30–40% of global sales (roughly $350 million for such a blockbuster). Therefore, to calculate a price for the drug in the US, one could divide roughly $350 million by the number of patients that would likely be treated in the US each year. So if one would expect to treat 1,000 patients each year with a drug in the US, one might set a price of $350,000/patient/year. If there are only 500 eligible patients in the US, then one might charge $700,000/patient/year. Some companies might aim to generate a higher return and would charge more per patient. Companies rarely aim lower. You can probably think of examples of drugs that cost more per patient and generate more in revenues, but those are the ones that make the headlines and there are many others that cost less and make less. Whether we average at $350 million/year/drug for this thought experiment or any other large number, the point is that there are so many genetic disorders that the costs for gene therapies could stack to a truly large number in perpetuity. And investors don't need to be paid in perpetuity to be motivated to fund the development of a drug—they only value the first 10-15 years of profits—and so simulated genericization after a drug's patent expires would save society a lot of money in the long run without reducing the incentive to fund the development of these products in the first place.

the Biotech Social Contract and become inexpensive after their patents expire? The answer is actually simple. It's the same answer that America has long had for natural monopolies: Regulate them with price controls. You might be surprised that I'm suggesting that Congress impose price controls on drugs, but what I'm advocating for is very different from the price controls that tend to get bandied about by academics and politicians. To be precise, I am suggesting that we employ price controls for drugs that appear to be immune to genericization *after their patents have expired*—not while they are still patent-protected and not if they are genericizable.

I'm suggesting that Congress enact a law that says that a company that owns a monopoly in a class of drug that shows itself to be ungenericizable must, after its patents have expired or some specified length of time, lower its price to be close to the cost of production, as if it had gone generic. In this case, price erosion will not have occurred through the process of natural competition in a free market, but through regulation, which is why I call this "contractual genericization."

If that sounds like overreach, consider how the biodefense industry is regulated. The government negotiates contracts with certain companies that manufacture vaccines and therapies for pandemic flu, smallpox, and other biodefense-related diseases. These vaccines, while unnecessary under normal circumstances, might suddenly become necessary, so it is imperative that our country has a reliable supply of them. The government helps fund the research and offers a guarantee that, as long as the products are approved by the FDA, the government will purchase a certain number of doses every year at a pre-negotiated price.

Unlike biodefense products like pandemic vaccines, which are produced with the hope that they will never be needed, there is a ready market for most of the drugs that biopharmaceutical companies develop. As long as society is willing to pay for branded drugs, companies won't need government subsidies or purchase guarantees to motivate them to invest in making these drugs (antibiotics being a special exception—see sidebar). But when these drugs can't go generic, society gets a raw deal by having to pay branded prices long after a drug's patents have expired.

So after a drug's patents expire and if there aren't already generics or biosimilars on the market to compete down that drug's price, I propose that the US, either through a government agency or a contractor, enter into an agreement with the manufacturer to continue to produce it as a "contract generic." Such an agreement would guarantee purchase of a certain amount of drug at a price that is slightly more than the cost of production.* That guarantee would motivate the company to continue making the drug. In essence, once the patent exclusivity period is over, the production facilities of non-genericizable drugs would be regulated like public utilities—which makes sense, because their products, off-patent drugs, essentially are a public resource (i.e., the mortgage has been paid off).

Since the intent here is that the branded period last for the typical 10-15 years that initial core drug patents typically cover, a key concern is that companies will keep coming up with product upgrades to patent in order to delay genericization, as is common today. With ordinarily genericizable drugs, generics manufacturers challenge these secondary patents in court, getting leverage in their negotiations for when they can finally enter the market and start competing on price. But when a drug just can't be genericized conventionally, there won't be anyone to challenge the secondary patents. Therefore, to the extent that a company makes legitimately useful post-launch upgrades to its product, such as improving the manufacturing process or composition to make the product purer, safer, easier

---

* This same agency or contractor would need to audit each company to ensure that production costs are calculated properly or else companies might find ways of creatively inflating the production costs of a drug, for example assigning people's compensation fully to the drug's production costs even when some of them are splitting their time between making that drug and making others. Ultimately, as an enforcement measure to protect against accounting games, it makes sense that the manufacturing of a contract generic drug be hived off in a separate entity, which regulators could require the original manufacturer to divest to another company to be run competently and leanly. That way, if the original company were to run into financial difficulty due to other failed investments, it would not be able to inflate the operating costs of the contract generic manufacturing unit. Should it try to do so, the US Government agency that oversees contractual generics could put the manufacturing facility up for bid and require its sale to the winner. It might even turn out that there would emerge specialized contract manufacturers that would bid for the right to manage contract generic manufacturing. The manufacturing sites would stay, but management might change periodically as such companies competed to shave down the costs of administering the manufacturing sites. To the extent that the original manufacturer wanted to protect manufacturing trade secrets from falling into competitors' hands, it would be motivated to manage its contract generics efficiently to keep their costs low so that regulators would not see an opportunity to save society money by forcing divestment of a contract generic production to another manufacturer.

to produce, or better tolerated, those upgrades should be rewarded with short regulatory delays of genericization of the kind I propose in Chapter 13. I also include a detailed roadmap of how we can implement contractual genericization at the end of Chapter 13.

## The Special Case of Antibiotics, Generic Too Soon

Antibiotics are like pandemic vaccines in that we want to know they are there well before we need them. Companies have brought novel antibiotics to market because they were told that patients are dying of multi-drug resistant bacteria and that hospitals badly need them to save lives. But when they finally got those antibiotics approved, they discovered that there were only a few patients who really needed them and so their sales were marginal. Those few patients had indeed been a cause for concern and drove headlines about drug resistant strains potentially killing thousands. Physicians and hospital administrators really were panicked that these strains would spread throughout their facilities and kill vulnerable patients recovering from surgery. They feared the worst if they didn't get new drugs with which to combat these strains. But when companies delivered the goods, the worst didn't materialize. Hospitals were able to use old drugs very effectively to manage the vast majority of their patients, using the new, expensive branded antibiotics very sparingly.

Companies lost money on their investments, but the doctors' fears eventually came true. Drug-resistant strains spread, and physicians were glad to have the new antibiotics. By then, the new drugs were old and generic or close to going generic, becoming inexpensive just in time to help treat the growing number of patients who needed them. As the next generation of resistant bacterial strains emerged, physicians and hospitals would again issue an urgent call for new antibiotics. But investors are now understandably hesitant to fund the expensive development of new antibiotics because they know there's no real market for them yet.[88] In response to their hesitation, the US,[89] British,[90] and other governments have realized that they need to offer some sort of payment guarantee, just as they did with the biodefense vaccine contract. One could argue that antibiotics represent a rare case of patent periods not being long enough to allow companies to recoup their investment, but going forward, a guaranteed payment model, not unlike the one used for biodefense products, is the more reliable way to encourage future antibiotic development.

---

## The Downsides of Contractual Genericization

Critics of this proposal might say that price-control regulations will slow innovation. Public utilities, for example, don't have an incentive to innovate. To keep costs low, public utilities keep salaries down, don't give out significant bonuses as rewards for risk-taking, and don't have substantial budgets for R&D. They offer steady, low returns for investors, steady jobs, and need to just not screw up. Unless public utilities get a mandate and additional funding—for example, from a rate hike—they try to keep doing what works forever.

To those critics, I would say, "Exactly!" This model and set of expectations are exactly what we, as a society, need from the majority of the generic drug industry. Just keep making generic drugs steadily and reliably. Quality control, for sure, but no innovation needed!

However, when it comes to complex biologics and the companies developing them, it is critical that we preserve the current incentives to innovate. That's why contractual genericization only kicks in after a drug's patents have expired. The first 10-15 years on the market give the companies the opportunity to collect their rewards for successfully inventing and commercializing new drugs. Very few drugs enjoy high prices beyond the first 15 years on the market, so there is little reason to think innovation would be stymied by using a contractual generic to cap profits beyond that horizon.

Other critics might point out that this approach to genericizing a drug would indefinitely lock in only a single manufacturer of the drug, often at a single facility. Should catastrophe strike the facility, society might experience shortages and patients would suffer.

As a safeguard against such unforeseen events, the company that makes the original drug could be mandated to transfer its manufacturing know-how to a second company and even a third company. In this way, society is guaranteed both manufacturing redundancy and price competition. This approach presumes that the FDA would recognize that the drugs produced at different facilities are the same, but that is not an outrageous presumption. The FDA routinely allows companies that make biologics to scale up their manufacturing by moving to larger facilities.

This is not to say that manufacturing transfers of this nature are foolproof. Take the famous case involving Genzyme, a company we've talked about before. Genzyme originally launched the enzyme Myozyme for the treatment of infants with Pompe disease, then decided to expand the drug's use for the treatment of older children. It needed to produce much more drug, but the FDA considered the differences between the original small-scale Myozyme (made in a 160-liter container) and the new larger scale (2,000 liters) product to be too significant to call them the same drug. This forced Genzyme to treat the batches from the new manufacturing process as a new drug, which it called Lumizyme, and that meant running a new clinical trial to get Lumizyme formally approved as a separate drug for older patients with Pompe.

So if society were to rely on compulsory transfer of manufacturing to achieve manufacturing redundancy and price competition, the solution could be hindered or upended if the FDA deemed the products non-interchangeable. In the case of Lumizyme, the limited supply of Myozyme meant that older children had no choice but to enroll in a trial of Lumizyme. But if there had been enough Myozyme available to treat both infants and older children, why would anyone enroll in a clinical trial of a copy that the FDA didn't consider equivalent, even one produced with the assistance of the original manufacturer?

The Myozyme/Lumizyme case is a rare one, but it is more likely to occur with complex biologics like gene therapies. Therefore, contractual genericization of an otherwise ungenericizable drug would appear to be a more reliable way of fulfilling the social contract than compulsory licensing of manufacturing know-how to competitors. Hedging against supply shortages could also be achieved by other means, such as building up a large reserve of frozen doses, when freezing is an option.

In any case, even a company subject to contractual genericization could be mandated, as part of their contract, to work with the FDA to open up a second and even third qualified site and allowed to charge enough to cover the costs of all that redundant manufacturing so that patients would be assured of supply.

As we'll discuss in the next chapter, contractual genericization could also help contain costs in cases where the market for a generic drug shrinks to be too small to sustain the critical mass of manufacturers that keeps prices down through competition (i.e., natural oligopolies). For biologics in general, it's also possible that this approach would work better than relying on biosimilars, which some fear will not bring prices down very much like generics do.[91] The point is that innovators count on a finite period of high profits as the incentive and fuel for their work, and what society cares about is seeing those innovations eventually become inexpensive. So to both parties, whether prices drop after the mortgage period due to competition or contractual genericization is of secondary importance as long as they drop.

## Another Workaround: Prevention

In the long run, prevention might obviate the need for expensive treatments altogether. For example, the need for CAR-T cell therapies might decrease if cancers were detected earlier when they might be more easily cured with surgery, radiation, and other conventional therapies.[92] And gene therapies developed for rare genetic disorders potentially might be disrupted by more widespread preconception and prenatal genetic testing that enables families to side-step these disorders.[93] In fact, insurance companies would find it cost-effective to pay for genetic testing for everyone and IVF for the few percent of couples at risk of passing a genetic disorder to their children than to skimp on these technologies and end up paying more than 10-fold more for gene therapies for affected children, especially when many gene therapies simply can't be perfect cures (some of the prenatal damage from genetic mutations is irreversible after birth).

Yet, even after the advent of widespread screening, one would still expect that some non-genericizable gene therapies would remain necessary indefinitely since not all genetic disorders are hereditary or detectable and not all cancers will be caught early enough to cure with more conventional therapies. Though they are unlikely to grow to be a large fraction of total drug spend anytime soon, it is worth considering a mechanism such as contractual genericization to ensure that even these therapies abide by the Biotech Social Contract.

---

## A Fair Trade

The US government's Congressional Budget Office is charged with running economic models that predict the impact on the federal budget of every proposed change in the law. The CBO is staffed by brilliant, data-driven people. They have put out reports on the impact of expanding insurance coverage to more Americans, for example showing the extent to which increased spending on insurance would be offset by savings from patients getting preventative care. Whenever proposals to modify what portion of costs patients should have to pay are put forth, the CBO models whether that will lead to increased utilization of drugs by patients and whether those cost increases will be offset by fewer surgeries and other expensive healthcare services.

I don't know the details of the CBO's mathematical models. It's possible that the CBO sees that a growing number of drugs are non-genericizable and models their long-term impact on the federal budget. I doubt it because the concept of non-genericizability is not widely discussed yet (I hope to change that). So if they don't, they should.

Here's a trade I would like to see with the CBO model. Let's introduce contractual genericization to bring down the federal government's and society's spending on non-genericizable drugs. Let's see to what extent that offsets any increases in the federal budget due to the elimination (or, at least, fair and reasonable capping) of out-of-pocket costs. That's the kind of bargain that the Biotech Social Contract upholds, and it's time that we bring all drugs and all patients into alignment with it.

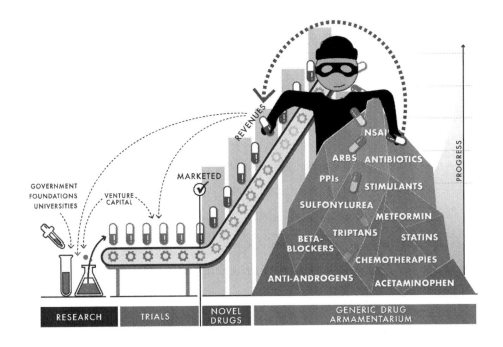

RESEARCH | TRIALS | NOVEL DRUGS | GENERIC DRUG ARMAMENTARIUM

# 9

# PREVENTING PRICE-JACKING OF OFF-PATENT DRUGS

By now, it should be clear that in order for the Biotech Social Contract to work, drugs that go generic must stay inexpensive for the rest of time. Unfortunately, regulatory loopholes and quirks in certain commercial markets have allowed bad actors in the industry to egregiously raise prices on old, off-patent drugs. You may have heard or read about such cases, which have drawn media attention and public ire in recent years—as well they should.

As we did with non-genericizable drugs in Chapter 8, let's take a closer look at the size of the problem, why it happens, and what can be done about it.

First, a bit of context. Despite what you might assume from mainstream headlines, price-jacking of sole-source,[*] off-patent drugs has a relatively small impact on total drug spend. Old, sole-source drugs tend to address very small markets and typically are priced modestly, which is often why they are manufactured by just one company and, though the patents are expired, others have no interest in competing. By my estimate, known examples of such drugs being price-jacked add up to less than 1% of

---

[*] Made by one company.

what the US spends on prescription drugs each year. This is not to say that the practice isn't abhorrent. But, generally speaking, companies like this are the exception, not the rule.

What makes price-jacking of old drugs wrong is not that it makes these drugs unaffordable to patients—that's still due to our broken insurance system—but that these companies are taking advantage of all of society. Their goal is to siphon off money that they think society won't notice, which means they don't want to draw attention to themselves by causing any patient that needs their drug to go without. Such companies had typically provided copay assistance and supplied free drugs to patients when their insurance wouldn't pay or if they didn't have insurance.[94] Still, the media found patients who were disadvantaged and rightfully raised hell. In a world in which patients have insurance with capped or no copays, they probably wouldn't even notice that a drug's price had been dramatically increased. Such insurance reform is important to allow patients to afford any drugs they need, but it would make it easier for such companies to parasitize society's collective wallet without being noticed—unless we close the loopholes that let price-jacking happen.

But before we attempt to fix the problem it is important that we understand the facts.

## Price-jacking: A Case Study

More than sixty years ago, the drug *pyrimethamine* was developed to treat a variety of pathogens, including the parasite that causes malaria. In 1953, the drug was released by what is now the British big pharma GlaxoSmith-Kline under the brand name Daraprim. Over the years, malaria became resistant to the drug, and its uses have narrowed—but not completely.

The drug remains an effective treatment for toxoplasmosis, a disease caused by a fairly common parasite that is often picked up from cats. In fact, as much as half of the world's population and up to 23% of Americans carry the parasite, though most carriers never experience any observable symptoms and do not require treatment.[95] However, young children who contract the parasite and carriers who are immunocompromised (i.e., those with weak immune systems) are more likely to develop acute toxoplasmosis, which can lead to encephalitis and organ damage.[96] Pregnant women who contract the parasite can suffer a congenital infection that may cause devastating pre- and post-natal complications, including miscarriage, stillbirth, microcephaly, epilepsy, and deafness.[97] In India, Africa, Indonesia, and South America, the need is great, with millions of people requiring treatment every year. As a result, there are multiple suppliers of the drug outside of the US, and the competition between the suppliers keeps the costs down, which is how it is supposed to work in the market for a generic drug.

Cases of toxoplasmosis are much rarer in the US, but the risk of harm is such that pyrimethamine remains an important component of our armamentarium.[98] None of the generics manufacturers that compete in the large global pyrimethamine market bothered to get FDA approval to sell their product in the US because the market here was so small. Fortunately for the American patients who needed the drug, GSK continued to supply the US market for decades, not bothering to raise the price, even as the rate of toxoplasmosis in the US declined and its market shrank. Even into the 21st century, Daraprim cost just $1/pill for a 20-60 pill treatment. With only 8,000-12,000 prescriptions written per year, this amounted to revenues of less than $1 million per year for GSK. It had been a larger product for GSK in the past when there were more patients, but it became insignificant, lost amidst the hundreds of other pharmaceuticals GSK sold with total annual revenues climbing into the tens of billions of dollars.[99]

Selling Daraprim in the US might even have been a money losing proposition for GSK. The company could presumably have raised the price to keep it profitable. But sometimes large companies opt to off-load off-patent products with limited markets to smaller companies rather than risk negative publicity that comes with a large price increase.

Companies are generally more willing to endure negative publicity for smaller price increases for expensive branded drugs that address larger markets since these have a more significant impact on their bottom lines. Increasing the price of a $1 billion/year drug by 5% boosts revenues by $50 million/year. Increasing the price of Daraprim by 500% would have looked egregious yet would only have boosted revenue by $5 million.

Daraprim just wasn't worth the trouble for GSK, which in 2010 sold the rights to distribute Daraprim in the US to a small generic drug company called CorePharma. The sale price was not disclosed but it was probably modest. CorePharma now controlled the only source of Daraprim for the US market and immediately raised the price of the drug to $13.50/pill, quickly boosting revenue from the drug, though—interestingly—attracting almost no media scrutiny.[100] That proved far more profitable for CorePharma than making a generic and competing with GSK. Although it's entirely possible that had CorePharma made a generic and competed with GSK on price, GSK would have just dropped out rather than continue to lose money, leaving CorePharma as the sole supplier. So at $1/pill, all roads led to Daraprim being a sole-source drug in the US.

As long as Daraprim was in the hands of GSK, its price would likely have stayed low. GSK had more to lose from bad press than anything it could gain from one such small product, and no shareholders or executives who would discernibly benefit by maximizing Daraprim profits. But once the drug ended up in the hands of a much smaller company, the rewards of raising its price became more pronounced.

With the market shrinking, some price increase might have been necessary to keep it worth manufacturing for any company. Maybe a 13.5-fold increase was more than was needed to make the product worthwhile for CorePharma, but, as we'll see, it hardly represented the limits of a true price-gouging strategy.

In 2014, Impax, a larger generics company, acquired CorePharma. At the time, Daraprim revenues were a mere $9 million per year. Still too modest of a market to attract competing companies, even though the chemical isn't difficult to manufacture, and the FDA approval process for a generic would have taken only about a year.[101] One year later, Impax sold Daraprim's rights to a newly formed, small company called Turing Pharmaceuticals for $55 million, a price that would seem difficult to justify, given the size of the market—and instead an indicator that Turing was planning to jack up the drug's price, just as CorePharma had done. As you might expect (or probably already know from media coverage and public outrage that ensued), Turing immediately raised Daraprim's price. What was astounding was that they did so by over 55-fold to $750/pill.[102]

Had Turing stopped there, Daraprim's suddenly surging revenues would have attracted other companies to launch pyrimethamine generics, and within a year or two, competition would have driven the price back down. Turing would have enjoyed a year or two of high revenues, amounting to a windfall of several hundred million dollars, while taking a hit to its reputation in the industry and strong, but fleeting, backlash from the media and the public. It would have been unlikely that sustained coverage and outrage and Congressional hearings would have followed.

But Turing didn't stop there. It had cleverly exploited an FDA safety regulation to block generic competitors from coming to market, taking advantage of a particular mode of distribution normally reserved for highly personalized treatments, like cell therapies, and drugs with especially dangerous side effects.

## A Red-tape Monopoly Strategy Irks the FDA

Jazz Pharmaceuticals sells the drug Xyrem for narcolepsy, a disorder in which people lose muscle tone and can fall asleep instantly during the day. Xyrem is chemically nearly identical to the illicit sedative GHB (also known as "the date-rape drug" and discussed more in Chapter 15) and therefore must be distributed carefully under an FDA-mandated drug safety program (for example, making sure patients aren't taking other sedatives). Jazz's patented distribution methodology relies on a single pharmacy which prevents generic companies accessing Xyrem for bioequivalence studies, a necessary step to get their own versions approved. This is essentially the strategy that Turing later employed when it got control of Daraprim. Furthermore, competitors wouldn't be able to come to market since Jazz could refuse to coordinate distribution of their generics through its one pharmacy.

When the FDA reviewed and approved Jazz's safety program in February 2015 (before Turing made headlines), its commentary revealed that it did not think it critical to limit distribution to one pharmacy and suspected Jazz's real purpose for favoring this approach was just to block generics.[103]

Two years later (after Turing made headlines), the FDA waived the requirement that Xyrem generics be distributed through Jazz's pharmacy, and later that year approved the first Xyrem generic, made by Hikma.[104] However, Jazz sued Hikma, claiming it infringed its patents, and the two companies settled, agreeing that Hikma could launch its generic in 2023, sooner than would have been the case had they had to wait for Jazz's patents to expire but still 21 years after Xyrem had first been approved.* Jazz's strategy represents an exploitation of the patent system to secure a long monopoly extension for what amounts to a straightforward upgrade of a drug's distribution system. An incremental extension of regulatory exclusivity (see Chapter 13) would have sufficed. The Biotech Social Contract calls for industry to develop drugs that will go generic without undue delay. I think that the Xyrem case is an example of an undue delay.

---

Despite the facts that Daraprim had been on the market for decades and its side effects were well known and considered modest, Turing claimed that the side effects warranted management through a Risk Evaluation and Mitigation Strategies (REMS) program. Under this pretext, Turing sold Daraprim exclusively via a "specialty" pharmacy, which tracks each bottle to make sure it's shipped only to patients confirmed to have the appropriate medical condition, tightly controlling distribution of the product.

So how did using a specialty pharmacy block potential competitors from entering the market? The answer lies in the generic manufacturing process. When a generic company wants to make its own version of a branded drug, it has to purchase some quantity of that branded drug from a pharmacy, to use as a reference point in its bioequivalence studies. As many as 5,000 doses may be required.[105] But Daraprim could only be obtained from Turing's specialty pharmacy and only by patients, which meant that potential competitors would not be able to do the bioequivalence studies required by the FDA.

Turing had found a loophole, and it resulted in a monopoly accompanied by a huge price increase for a drug whose patent had long since

---

* "Orange Book: Approved Drug Products with Therapeutic Equivalence Evaluations," *UFDA*, accessed Nov. 1, 2019, https://www.accessdata.fda.gov/scripts/cder/ob/patent_info.cfm?Product_No=001&Appl_No=021196&Appl_type=N.

expired. To be clear, Daraprim was not and is not a generic drug; it is still the original branded version. But it had been off-patent for years and was for a long time sold at a low price, so it effectively might as well have been generic before it was price-jacked. Society would be right to feel that it had paid off the Daraprim mortgage and now had a right to enjoy the benefits of the drug forever at a low cost. If the prices of novel branded drugs are mortgage payments, what Turing did was the equivalent of stealing the title to your house and offering to sell it back to you.

If you're wondering why these kinds of cases are as rare as I suggest, consider atorvastatin, the statin sold by Pfizer as Lipitor. Once the most lucrative drug in the world, atorvastatin is still used by millions of patients in the US, so the market for it can sustain many generic manufacturers that all compete with one another on price for market share. Should a company like Turing acquire the rights to sell one of those generics and jack up its price, it simply wouldn't be used. It would lose out to all the other manufacturers. Turings only happen in the absence of competition.

The Turing story does not yet have an entirely satisfying ending. Later renamed Vyera and then Phoenixus, the company continues to sell Daraprim with a list price of around $780/pill, although patients typically pay a small fraction of this cost.[106] Medicaid plans pay much less because of legally mandated rebates, and Medicare Part D and private insurance plans also get rebates.[107] Still, the company was reportedly on track to generate around $60 million in sales in 2019, mostly from Daraprim, so it continues to reap the rewards of price-jacking.[108] And there are still no generics on the market.

But like a vaccine that leaves our immune system stronger, Turing exposed loopholes that Congress and regulators are now working to close.

## Stopping the Next Turing

Turing was not the first company to employ tactics intended to delay the launch of generics, but in the wake of the Daraprim scandal, Congress and the FDA are trying to close this loophole by requiring companies to provide drugs to would-be generic competitors in sufficient amounts to allow for proper equivalency studies.[109]

Even with some loopholes closed, there is still ample opportunity for unscrupulous companies to price-jack sole-source, off-patent drugs. In 2016, there were nearly 100 such drugs in the US market, according to FDA statistics, and some of these have the makings for the next Daraprim (though many don't because they are not uniquely essential).[110] Post-Turing refinements to the law might prevent a company from dissuading or blocking potential competitors from entering the market, but there is nothing on the books that would prevent a company from acquiring the rights to one of these drugs, jacking the price up, and reaping a few years of inflated profits until competitors enter the market and bring the price back down. Currently, we depend on such erratic and inefficient competition to regulate markets over the long haul. The cost of that inefficiency comes at the expense of patients at worst and payers at best (and therefore society as a whole), and it risks supply disruptions, as we've seen with some products when prices drop too low.[111]

For a solution, we can revisit the idea presented in the previous chapter, whereby the US government would mandate that manufacturers whose products do not undergo natural genericization (either because their markets are too small to be attractive to generic companies or because their product is too complex to genericize) must agree to sell their drugs at a low but profitable price under purchase guarantees—as is done now for biodefense products and is being proposed to incentivize companies to make antibiotics. The price of the drug would be set at a fixed premium to the cost of production, approximating what it would be selling for if it were faced with normal generic competition.

Returning to the Turing case study, if GSK could have counted on a purchase guarantee for Daraprim from the US government (or more likely a drug wholesaler under contract with the US government), GSK might have continued to sell the drug for a low price, even if higher than $1/pill. Patients and society might have been better off if we had encouraged GSK to just raise the price of Daraprim to $6/pill if that would have made it worthwhile to keep producing the drug, obviating the entire CorePharma and Turing fiasco. So contractual genericization doesn't always mean lowering a drug's price, but it does mean ensuring that the price reliably stays lower than what it might be with little or no competition.

Another proposed solution to sole-source price-jacking includes allowing generics from other countries to be imported as soon as the price of a sole-source generic goes up in the US.[112] In the case of Daraprim, generics have been made and sold cheaply in India and other countries for years. It's hard to imagine Turing going to all the trouble of acquiring and jacking up the price of Daraprim in the US if it knew that much cheaper imports would have been made available immediately thereafter. This approach would, in essence, merge the US toxoplasmosis treatment market and the global market, which carries an added benefit: It would eliminate the risk of a sudden shortage should something catastrophic happen to the sole manufacturer for the US market (which could have a severe impact on patients who contract the parasite). In order to entice international generic suppliers to enter the tiny US market for this drug, the FDA or another government agency might have to provide assistance with documentation or waive application fees, but all of that might nevertheless end up being cheaper than incentivizing US companies to develop generic competitors to sole-source products, as Congress has proposed.[113]

If this solution seems enticing, it comes with its own caveat. The FDA is responsible for monitoring the quality of generic drugs made for the US market and has its work cut out for it. Contaminated products and pills with incorrect concentrations of drug still get through to the US, and these are ones that have actually gone through FDA review.[114] Therefore, if America turns to overseas generics manufacturers for savings any time an FDA-approved sole-source generic is price-jacked, patients may pay a high price in terms of drug quality unless those alternative suppliers are put through a rigorous review. Unfortunately, those reviews take time and would leave us without a rapid response to a case of price-jacking.

So I would argue that the simplest solution to regulate natural monopolies is to bid out the US market for rarely used, old drugs to high quality suppliers and pick two (to avoid supply disruptions) who will do it for the lowest price, even if it's higher than the price we pay now. Alternatively, we could award the supply contract to a single manufacturer (e.g., GSK would hopefully have put in a reasonable bid to make Daraprim at a higher but still reasonable price) who either commits to stockpiling enough product to buffer against a manufacturing disruption or else manufactures the drug at two separate sites.

## What Is, and Isn't, Price-jacking

The backlash against Turing and other companies that had price-jacked old drugs, including Valeant, was certainly warranted, but it also had a chilling effect throughout the drug development industry as executives wondered whether an angered public would mistake every high-priced drug for Turing-like profiteering. As an investor, I could see that many management teams were taking public opinion into account when considering future pricing strategies. Similarly, many investors pulled back from biotech after the Turing story hit headlines, making it harder for even those companies that were developing new drugs for new diseases to raise money to fund their programs.[115]

Public outrage—even when justified, as in the case of Turing—is a blunt instrument that can have unintended consequences on innovation. It's important, therefore, that we close loopholes that permit bad acts such as Turing's from giving the public cause to be upset while also making a distinction between what Turing did and other situations where an old drug's price has been increased, but where the effect has been positive.

For example, the drug epinephrine has been available for decades to treat life threatening anaphylaxis but to make it faster to administer (since seconds count when a child's throat is swelling) it was put into an autoinjector pen known as EpiPen. That improvement came with a price increase, which some might perceive as price-jacking an old drug (see Chapter 12).

Even without upgrades to the drug, a price increase doesn't necessarily signal profiteering.

As diseases are treated with better drugs, the market for older ones shrinks, just as improved treatments for HIV protected patients' immune systems, reducing their risk of becoming infected with toxoplasmosis, and shrank the market for Daraprim. When a company sells less drug but still has to cover the fixed costs of continuing to make it, the cost per patient necessarily has to go up.

Something like this may be occurring with lomustine, an old chemotherapy for glioblastoma. Lomustine is now rarely used because safer and more convenient drugs have become available. Even after a recent sharp 15-fold price increase, it still only sells around $1-2 million per year, which makes for little profit but big headlines and, in this case, even resulted in Congressional scrutiny.[116] Maybe a smaller increase would have been enough to justify the effort of continuing to make it, but some increase was certainly necessary as its market shrank.

Even large price increases of an old drug might be a natural consequence of a disease's gradual eradication. Today, HIV-infected patients have to take expensive cocktails of antivirals to stay healthy, costing payers around $25,000/year/patient.[117] When they go generic, their prices will likely drop by over 90%, because there are over a million patients in the US, enough to entice many generics manufacturers to compete. Even at $500/year/patient, a generics manufacturer that wins 5% of the market would generate over $25 million/year in the US.

But let's say that someday, after the antivirals are generic, a company develops an effective HIV vaccine that drops the rate of new patients becoming infected and, as those already infected die of old age, the number of HIV-infected people gradually falls. At some point, the market would shrink so much that it would be difficult to maintain the drug supply without at least modestly raising prices. If there were to be five suppliers, each spending $1 million to maintain their production capabilities and competing with one another to treat the remaining 1,000 patients, then the average cost per patient would need to be $5,000/year just to cover the suppliers' operating costs. That would require a 10-fold price increase from $500/year. As we got down to 250 patients, signaling a near eradication of HIV from the United States, these companies would have to raise their prices to $25,000/year just to break even, the same as today's branded prices. Such increases might be perceived as price-jacking, but it's hardly profiteering when there's no profit being made.

As with Daraprim and lomustine, a reasonable solution could be to bid out an HIV drug supply contract and allow one or two winning high-quality suppliers (those who come in with low prices) to serve the US market. If other companies figure out how to make the drugs for even less and can therefore charge even less, then they can bid for the contract when it is put out for re-bids every few years. Competitive bidding is a common practice in the public and private sectors and can be employed to meet society's need for a steady, inexpensive supply of rarely used generic drugs.[118]

## Compounding Pharmacies Are Not a Solution

Shortly after Turing price-jacked Daraprim, a group of enterprising high school students synthesized the drug and offered to sell it for cheap. As admirable as their effort and noble as the sentiment behind it might be, this can't be our long-term solution to price-jacking. Society wants its old drugs to be inexpensive, but it also wants them to be manufactured reliably by professionals. And it wants drugs and manufacturing practices to meet certain standards, namely Good Manufacturing Practice (GMP), which is what ensures that therapies work as advertised, won't be contaminated, and will provide the right dose consistently.

A more credible challenge to Turing emerged in the form of a compounding pharmacy, Imprimis, that offered to make and sell the drug for GSK's 2010 price of $1/pill. Most pharmacies just dispense drugs that are made elsewhere by drug companies. But there are thousands of compounding pharmacies across the US, hold-overs from an earlier pre-FDA era, that are still legally allowed to purchase the raw materials necessary to make and sell a drug to individual patients. They are only allowed to do this as long as they compound the ingredients into forms and doses that are not already available in FDA-approved, GMP-manufactured forms. For example, if a drug has been FDA-approved for adults but is sold as a pill that is too large for children, a doctor can still legally and appropriately prescribe it off-label to a child (see Chapter 15), ordering a compounding pharmacy to make the drug into smaller pills or package it as a powder to be mixed into applesauce.

Compounding pharmacies basically make homemade versions of drugs, which introduces risks of dosage errors and contamination, in some cases with devastating consequences. In 2012, 76 people died of meningitis after receiving steroid injections that had been contaminated with fungus during preparation at the New England Compounding Center facilities. This prompted Congress to pass the Drug Quality and Security Act the following year, which ostensibly gave the FDA a stronger mandate and more leeway to stop compounding pharmacies from making drugs that are already available as GMP-manufactured, FDA-approved pharmaceuticals.[119] However, the industry remains weakly regulated and has a disturbingly high error rate.*

So it was initially surprising to hear that one PBM, Express Scripts, would reimburse for prescriptions of Daraprim filled cheaply by Imprimis. The FDA initially took notice, but Imprimis avoided being shut down by exploiting a small loophole. Daraprim must be taken together with another drug called leucovorin to work, so Imprimis mixes the two drugs together into one pill. It's not a significant difference, arguably a bit more convenient for patients, but it makes the Imprimis product different from FDA-approved Daraprim. In theory, were Daraprim meant to be taken on its own and were Imprimis just compounding pills of pyrimethamine that were the same as Daraprim, Imprimis would be violating the law, the FDA would have to shut it down, and Express Scripts would have had no choice but to reimburse Daraprim at the prices Turing was charging. While a loophole cut in society's favor in this case, we should not count on compounding pharmacies to systematically offer cheaper alternatives to old price-jacked drugs, nor should we need them to.

For that, we must close the loopholes that permit price-jacking in the first place, and it is within our power to do so.

---

* From some of what's reported, I think I would trust earnest high school students more than some compounding pharmacies.

Marissa Martinelli, "John Oliver Explains How Certain Pharmacies Get Away with Fraud and Worse," *Slate*, Sept. 30, 2019, https://slate.com/culture/2019/09/last-week-tonight-john-oliver-compounding-pharmacies.html.

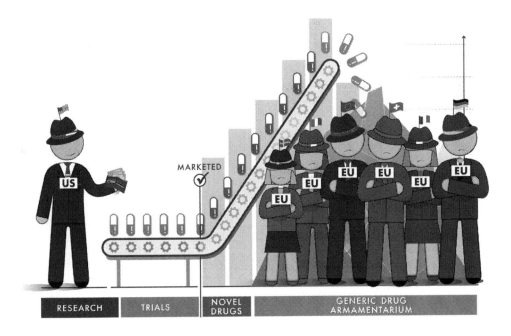

RESEARCH     TRIALS     NOVEL DRUGS     GENERIC DRUG ARMAMENTARIUM

MARKETED

# 10

## WHY DRUGS ARE CHEAPER IN OTHER COUNTRIES— AND WHY THAT'S STILL GOOD FOR US

**Many countries played a role in the development of Harvoni, the first** single-tablet cure for hepatitis C. In the lead up to its release, Gilead Sciences ran over 100 studies all across the world.* To support its application for FDA and EMA (European) approval, Gilead enrolled more than 1,500 US and Western European patients with the type of hepatitis C most common in Western countries. That makes sense since those are the major markets in which Gilead would later sell billions of dollars of Harvoni. But Gilead also ran trials in other countries—including 47 that enrolled patients in Australia, 43 in Central America, 37 in Canada, 38 in Africa, 40 in China, 13 in India, nine in Russia, and nine in the Middle East.† Why did Gilead take such an international approach? Hepatitis C is an international disease, one that hits developing countries especially hard.

---

* Clinicaltrials.gov; a few of these trials were actually run by Pharmasset, a small biotech company that Gilead acquired which had discovered sofosbuvir, a critical component of Harvoni.

† https://clinicaltrials.gov/ct2/results/map?term=sofosbuvir&map= ; some of these represent overlapping trials run in multiple countries at the same time.

"Map: Sofosbuvir," Clinical Trials.gov, US National Library of Medicine, accessed Nov. 1, 2019.

In fact, the majority of those infected by hepatitis C worldwide live in 91 developing countries—at the time of Harvoni's launch in 2015, that meant tens of millions of people.[120] However, most of those countries cannot afford to pay much for novel drugs. Was Gilead being altruistic or was a global clinical trial strategy aligned with Gilead's profit motive? As it happens, enrolling patients in even poorer countries allowed Gilead to prove that Harvoni cured types of hepatitis C that are rare in the US but more common elsewhere, which later also allowed patients in the US with those rarer types of hepatitis C to be treated.

When it was first approved in 2015, Harvoni launched with a list price of $94,500 in the US. Soon after, Gilead launched Harvoni in France at closer to $50,000, and less than that elsewhere in Europe. In many developing countries around the world, the price was approximately $600-900,* in part because Gilead allowed seven India-based generics companies to produce a generic for the 91 developing countries hit hardest by hepatitis C.

Although it might seem that Gilead was being altruistic by almost giving away the drug, Gilead was also being realistic. These countries are poor and could never manage to pay much more than that given that they are home to tens of millions of patients infected with hepatitis C. Gilead makes a relatively small amount of money on the deal and many more patients get treated at prices those countries could afford. Besides, the plan had always been to profit from the US, and to a lesser extent, Europe and Japan, which remain the world's major markets for nearly all branded drugs. So the whole rest of the world benefitted from the fact that Gilead had a profit-motive to cure the minority of hepatitis C–infected patients who live in the few major pharmaceutical markets.

Since 2014, more than five million of people around the world have been cured of hepatitis C, thanks to Harvoni and other similarly effective drugs. This includes about one million in the US.[121] No one can deny the effectiveness of Harvoni or overestimate the difference it has made to

---

* In India, Sovaldi generics hit the market at $10/pill, but competition drove the price down to roughly $4/pill, which is $224-336/course of treatment, >99% less than in the US.

Ketaki Gokhale, "The Same Pill that Costs $1,000 in the US Sells for $4 in India," *Chicago Tribune*, Jan. 4, 2016, https://www.chicagotribune.com/business/ct-drug-price-sofosbuvir-sovaldi-india-us-20160104-story.html.

millions of patients and families. But some people took note of the price discrepancies across markets and Gilead's revenue numbers (more than $59 billion in worldwide revenues from Hepatitis C drugs from 2014-18, 34% of which came from outside of the US) and weren't happy.[122] In the US, there were calls for price reductions. Some countries, including Spain, asked courts for permission to break Gilead's patents so that they could manufacture generics and get access to Harvoni at a lower price.[123]

Large price discrepancies across markets are not uncommon, and, to some, they are evidence that pharmaceutical companies charge gratuitously high prices in the US, that they are price-gouging, and that they could charge less and still earn a profit. Even those willing to concede that price discrepancies between wealthy nations and developing countries are justified might question why prices are so much higher in the US than in comparatively wealthy countries. These are good questions, and the simplest answer is this: For-profit companies, regardless of industry, attempt to maximize their profits based on all the rules they have to play by.

But before we get into the rules drug companies have to play by, let's look at the big picture.

## Why Do Branded Drugs Cost More in the US?

A drug that costs $20 to manufacture might sell for $1,000 in the US and $50 in Mexico. Given the cost to make the drug, it's profitable for the manufacturer either way, and Mexico is not as wealthy a nation as the US. But let's reframe the question: While one might justify charging so little for the drug in Mexico, what justification can there be for charging a lower price, say $700, in Germany, a country that is comparably wealthy to the US?

List prices are often higher in the US than Japan or Western Europe, and so are out-of-pocket costs for drugs, though none of that would matter to patients if our insurance system worked like it is supposed to (see Chapter 4). But America pays more—quite a bit more—at the societal level, as well. The US market accounts for roughly one third to one half of the drug industry's revenues and more than half of its profits.[124] So, why does America bear the majority of the cost burden, and is that fair?

The fact that America spends more than other countries on drugs seems to fit with the theme of America spending more on healthcare overall. America spends 17.8% of its GDP on healthcare as a whole, much more than the 9% average of comparably wealthy European nations.[125] That's not because Americans necessarily "consume" more care than citizens elsewhere. Rather, the main driver is that prices—for drugs, yes, but also for healthcare services and the professionals that provide them (doctors, nurses, specialists)—are much higher in the US.[126]

There are many reasons for this. For example, the US system suffers from inefficiency. America wastes more on paperwork and bureaucracy, which contributes to the high overall cost of healthcare. According to research published in the Journal of the American Medical Association (JAMA) in March 2018, 8% of America's healthcare budget is spent on administrative costs for our healthcare system.[127] That is far higher than the 1-3% spent by comparably wealthy nations for administration, which includes things like coding insurance claims, billing, and handling pre-authorizations. Streamlining that one source of waste could offset half of what America spends on branded drugs.

## Real Waste

A broader study of waste published more recently in JAMA looked at other opportunities for improvement and concluded that our system wastes $760-935 billion, or 20-25% of $3.8 trillion in total healthcare spending (and more than twice what we spend on all drugs) on fraud, failure of coordination, administrative complexity, unnecessary procedures, etc. Of that remarkable number, they attribute about $20 billion to inappropriate drug pricing.[128] $20 billion is not a small number in an absolute sense, but if they are right, that's only 5.8% of all drug spending in the US. It would be worth fixing (for example, contractual genericization would cut spending on drugs that should have gone generic), but a 5.8% discount on all drugs won't solve affordability for patients—only insurance reform can do that. Meanwhile, the authors point to hundreds of billions of dollars of other waste that could be cut to free up resources to pay for those reforms. The authors propose that America could save up to $93 billion by improving "care delivery," which includes helping to prevent diabetes and obesity, reducing smoking, detecting cancers earlier with screening programs, and generally making sure that patients don't fall through the cracks in the system and fail to be properly treated. Compare that to the $61 billion patients spend out-of-pocket on all drugs. It's clear that America can make drugs affordable to patients without raising healthcare costs if it just cut a portion of truly wasteful healthcare spending. And if it isn't up to the task, then it hardly seems ethical or wise to solve the problem at the expense of biomedical innovation.

---

Another reason America spends more in general is that educating healthcare professionals costs much more in the US, which results in higher salaries, which, in turn, results in higher prices for the services they provide.

But do these reasons also explain why America spends more on drugs? I don't think so. Healthcare services such as surgery, which are necessarily provided locally (so-called medical tourism, where people travel abroad to receive medical care to save money, is rare and impractical on a large scale) are affected by land costs, education costs, and the cost of living. But drugs are manufactured products with typically one, low price of production regardless of where they are ultimately used.

A more credible explanation, at least in part, for why the US spends more on drugs than other countries is that Americans get earlier access to innovative medicines.[129] Sometimes, that's the result of the approvals process being slower in other places. Other times, it's because a country has tougher reimbursement policies, which makes the market less lucrative, which, in turn, makes bringing the drug to that market less of a priority for companies. In these cases, governments being tough on drug prices saves money but delays the arrival of new, expensive medicines. For a patient that could benefit from a new drug, that hardly seems like a worthwhile tradeoff. By that rationale, the world can save a ton of money—all we have to do is put off funding medical innovation indefinitely.

Companies may even sell their drugs overseas at very low prices to protect their US market share. Because Genzyme had chosen to make its first-in-class Cerezyme available to every patient with Gaucher's disease it could find in every country, even if that meant giving it away for free, Shire and Pfizer had a hard time finding untreated patients to enroll in trials of their competing enzyme replacement therapies. As a result, Genzyme enjoyed a longer monopoly than its patents alone would have made possible.

Drug companies have their business strategies, but they also consist of people, many of whom who are inspired to do what they do because they want to help patients and ease suffering. I've found that often to be the case with people drawn to a career in healthcare, including some I've met who work for insurance companies. And it's hard for good people to ignore the pleas for help from patients who can't access a treatment that could help them because their government thinks it's too expensive. Which hints at the main reason why drugs are more expensive in America.

America pays more for drugs because it remains unwilling to outright deny patients access to treatment on the basis of their ability to pay, which makes the American market a reliable source of funding for the drug industry. I hope that doesn't change, because that empathy drives medical progress and, as long as drugs continue to go generic, that progress will be cost-effective.

By threatening to deny their patients access to new drugs, other wealthy countries, such as France and Germany, often win price concessions (but sometimes don't and may follow through on their threats) precisely because the industry exists first and foremost to serve the large, price-insensitive US market.[130] If the US played by Europe's rules, there would be so much uncertainty as to whether a successfully developed drug would be paid for or how much a company would be allowed to charge that investors would have a much harder time justifying the risk of supporting new drug development.

Thankfully, that is not the case—at least not yet. Drug companies know that almost any drug that improves on the standard of care stands a good chance of generating high-enough sales in the US to have made the effort and risk worthwhile. America's unyielding willingness to pay for better medicines rather than deny them to patients has made the US the guarantor of the drug industry's continued viability.

Without wielding a credible threat of denial, the US cannot truly negotiate with drug companies that have uniquely effective drugs (when there are me-too drugs and generics to play off one another, American payers should and do negotiate). In addition, drug companies see America as their primary profit center, so every price concession risks setting a dangerous precedent that could undermine the future profitability of other drugs that company might sell. Investors and executives concerned by the viability of the drug industry as a whole watch for signs that payers in America might actually start exhibiting a willingness to deny on the basis of cost.

By contrast, the drug development industry sees Europe as a fragmented secondary market that is more willing to deny its residents the latest medical advances.[131] It is a source of supplemental profits where companies find a price in each country that maximizes profit and minimizes what economists call "deadweight." Simply put, some profit is better than no profit. If anything causes companies to hesitate to price a drug low in a given country, it is the concern that the drug will be imported and sold in wealthier countries, but this practice is generally kept in check by international law and each country's fear that it would be cut off from further supply.

When negotiating with relatively wealthy countries, companies are also mindful of not giving discounts so large as to feel grossly unfair to the US payers and the US public. Given the current outrage and sense that the US is being treated unfairly, it seems companies were right to have been concerned by differential pricing and may have let the gap widen too much.

Should the US payers change their stance and be willing to deny treatments based upon cost, they'd have more leverage in price negotiations for all the drugs that have already been developed, but the impact on innovation would be significant. Investment in new medicines would pause, which really means many ongoing programs would be defunded and shut down, until investors could understand how payers would set prices. So US payers would have to be transparent about how they calculate "fair" prices so that investors and drug developers could plan ahead. If investors and companies had to assume much lower prices when making financial models, funding would logically dry up for many programs in early development today, particularly for rarer diseases and certainly for a lot of personalized medicines, which help comparatively few patients. This would be terrible news for patients and families suffering from these diseases and a short-sighted approach for society as a whole. While these drugs would indeed be expensive in the short term, as generics they are cost-effective for society in the long term, per the Biotech Social Contract.

## No Deal in New Zealand

Every negotiation involves balancing interests: drug companies want to help patients (both out of compassion and to keep them from falling into the arms of competitors), drug companies want to earn a profit (which itself is necessary to keep inventing drugs), and payers want to save money. Drug companies sometimes have a monopoly on a unique treatment (i.e., no me-toos or generics) and some countries have a single-payer system that also wields leverage, yet in almost all cases they can agree on a price so that patients don't go without.

In 2013, the government of New Zealand balked at the >$600,000-per-year cost of Alexion's drug Soliris, an antibody for the treatment of the rare blood disease Paroxysmal Nocturnal Hematuria (PNH) even as it acknowledged that the drug likely saved lives. It stated that even if the drug were priced at UK or Canada levels, it would still be too expensive to cover in New Zealand, and implied that it would need a 95% discount to consider the drug cost-effective. On principle, Alexion refused to sell Soliris to New Zealand at that low price or to provide free drugs to its patients, who numbered fewer than two dozen and had to make do with blood transfusions. Patients and their advocates lobbied the government to reconsider, making the argument that "the public should be able to decide whether to spend more on 'life saving' medicine or to put interest on student loans, or to raise taxes, or to stop wasting money on the military or movie productions."[132] But the government did not relent.

As a consequence, New Zealand became a preferred clinical trial site for early testing of competing PNH treatment. In this way, its righteousness was a boon to companies that otherwise would have had to coax PNH patients off of Soliris to prove that their own drugs could work as well or possibly better. Once companies had at least some evidence that their drugs worked on Kiwi patients, it was easier to convince patients in other countries to discontinue Soliris and enroll in trials of these experimental agents. New Zealand may be assuming that prices will come down once there is more than one PNH drug on the market. But if it merely turns out that one of those new and better drugs displaces Soliris as the standard of care and is priced as highly, New Zealand will have to confront the reality of either paying that high price or truly forcing their patients to go without, at least until the treatment goes generic.

## Single-payer Leverage

Some have proposed that prices are higher in the US because other countries have single-payer systems that negotiate on behalf of their entire populations, whereas the US system is fragmented, with each insurance company or pharmacy benefit manager (PBM) negotiating on behalf of fewer patients.[133] They might point out that Germany pays slightly less on average for drugs than the US, and the UK pays about half as much (though, again, such studies are always confounded by the secrecy surrounding rebates in each country).[134] If such a person is tempted to ascribe these price differentials to the advantages of a single-payer system, keep in mind that the US PBM Express Scripts negotiates on behalf of over 100 million Americans[135]—more than the population of every European country except Russia, and greater than Canada and Australia combined. If, after negotiating rebates, Express Scripts pays more for a drug than the UK, France, or Sweden, it's not because they don't have the leverage derived from the size of the customer base. True leverage stems from being willing to walk away, and, fortunately for 100 million Americans, Express Scripts knows it can't deny patients access to important treatments (though again, they do extract price concessions in the form of rebates when they can play me-too drugs against one another).

## Compulsory Licensing

Poor countries have another way to get access to new medicines more cheaply than in the US: simply ignore a company's patents and authorize generics manufacturers to make copies of the drug. This is known as compulsory licensing, and it is permissible under international law when a court rules that there is a legitimate need for the drug and deems the company's price negotiations to have been unreasonable. HIV antiviral drugs are the most famous examples, and several countries have secured compulsory licenses to patents for these medications. If a country is not capable of making a compulsory-licensed drug itself, it might get another country with generic manufacturing capabilities to engage in compulsory licensing on its behalf, as Rwanda did when it got Canada to make HIV medications cheaply, but only for Rwandan patients.[136]

However, the motives behind compulsory licensing are not always as they seem. Thailand was keen to employ compulsory licensing to grant its for-profit, government-approved pharmaceutical company the right to make HIV drugs, even though it could have purchased higher-quality drugs more cheaply from Indian generics manufacturers. It was just a ploy to support its own domestic pharmaceutical industry. Eventually, thousands of Thai patients taking their government's substandard drugs developed resistance, making their viral infection harder to control.[137] Thailand went further, seeking compulsory licenses on a range of drugs for cardiovascular disease and cancer, but partly reversed course under US trade pressure. More recently, a Russian court granted a compulsory license to a Russian drug company to patents for Celgene's Revlimid and Pfizer's Sutent, two cancer drugs.[138] But these cases are not common.

Compulsory licensing is rare for three reasons. First, it isn't right to drive a hard bargain and force a poor country to invoke compulsory licensing. It's simply wrong to withhold essential medicines from people who truly can't afford them, so companies tend to find ways of making needed drugs available in poor countries inexpensively, obviating compulsory licensing.

On a more practical level, companies don't have a financial incentive to play hardball on prices with very poor countries. Wealthy countries don't compare their prices to those in developing nations and can explain away steep discounts there as philanthropy.

The third reason is that countries that invoke compulsory licensing risk damaging trade relations, if they do so regularly or in unwarranted circumstances. It's not entirely surprising that Russia allowed one of its own companies to trod on the intellectual property rights of two American companies at a time when relations between America and Russia have cooled. If Russia wanted a concession from the US, it might offer to reverse course on compulsory licensing of American drugs, as Canada once did in the early 1990s, while negotiating for its place in the North American Free Trade Agreement, after decades of making generics of novel drugs in violation of America drug patents.

In any case, compulsory licensing, or the threat of it, only keeps drugs inexpensive when the therapy in question can be produced cheaply and easily, as is the case for most small molecule drugs. Countries that wield compulsory licensing as a tacit threat will increasingly find themselves in a bind as novel drugs become more complex. Drug-device combinations, biologics, and cell and gene therapies are difficult and expensive to manufacture. Unless their goal explicitly is philanthropic,* companies would sooner not sell a drug to a country than sell it below the cost of production, which for complex drugs can be quite high. Countries used to getting drugs at a steep discount will either prove willing to deny patients access to these therapies, which is possible, or we will discover that there are breakthroughs so compelling that even they really are willing to pay more than they previously did or thought they would.

## Are US Prices Unfairly Higher?

Lower prices in other countries do not necessarily mean unfairly lower prices. In many countries, branded drugs are priced comparably to the US market when we adjust for wages and purchasing power. For example, in 2016, the price of Harvoni in the US was about $73,000; in Portugal, the adjusted price was about $71,000 and in Poland, $119,000.[139] Of course, given all the secret rebates and discounts negotiated by governments and

---

* It's entirely possible that companies will try to be generous, partly out of kindness and partly to shut competitors out of being able to recruit untreated patients into clinical trials of similar drugs. But affording the cost of making those donated doses will mean that companies have to charge more in wealthy countries.

private payers, it is difficult to say whether these prices truly reflect what was paid (see Chapters 4 and 7).

And even when drugs are cheaper in other countries, it doesn't necessarily mean that they are more affordable than they are in America. Affordability is also a function of how much money a customer has, not cost alone. A recent study found that while FDA-approved cancer drugs are more expensive in the US, they are also more affordable in the US.[140] A drug priced at two months' salary for an average American might cost more than a year's salary in India. To be fair, studies like this don't always take into account insurance coverage, cost-sharing, or rebates, so the results are often based upon list prices, not actual cost.

In Europe, many countries set their prices based on what other countries pay, a practice known as "reference pricing" (discussed in more detail below), though it doesn't work as one might expect, and it has no relationship to the notion of global fairness. A study of list prices and affordability for drugs for rare diseases across a dozen countries showed that, while the nominal list prices were indeed consistent, these drugs were far less affordable in poorer countries (Greece, Hungary, Poland) than in wealthier ones (Germany, Sweden, France), once wages, purchasing power parity, and other wealth-normalizing methods are taken into account.[141]

So, is this the intention of pharmaceutical companies? It wouldn't make much sense for a company to make their products unaffordable—there's no profit in that. What happens is that each country negotiates for secret rebates/ discounts from the reference price for a drug, which allows a company to make at least some money and that country to treat at least some patients. The point is that achieving consistent and affordable pricing based upon a single reference price across many countries is more theory than reality.

Come negotiation time, European payers rarely look at US prices, which wouldn't help them win lower rates from drug manufacturers, while in the US, payers are known to grumble about lower European prices. Yet, drug importation remains illegal, so just knowing that prices are lower elsewhere doesn't offer concrete leverage. Grumbling eventually can turn into something more substantive. Therefore, companies set US prices to maximize profits with US payers and European prices to maximize European profits, doing their best (unsuccessfully, it seems) to avoid massive discrepancies that might cause friction with US payers or the public.

## The Favors Other Countries Do for America

In a February 2018 report, the President's Council of Economic Advisors lamented the "free-riding actions of many small countries," which reduce companies' worldwide profits and place a heavier burden on the US patient. The report suggested trade policies that could help reduce this burden but did not provide specifics.[142] This and other studies seem to indicate that some countries could afford to pay more than they do for drugs and that if that were reconciled, drug companies would be able to reduce how much they charge for their products in America without sacrificing profit.[143]

But before we get into who can pay what, we need to consider what would happen if American drug companies simply couldn't sell drugs in other countries. As noted earlier, the US accounts for roughly one third to one half of drug company revenues and more than half of its profits.[144] If companies could only sell in the US, they'd have to charge about twice as much to generate the same return on investment. So though other countries may pay less than Americans might think is fair, they are still subsidizing the operations of a drug industry that makes treatments Americans want.

Another way other countries help keep America's drug costs down has to do with clinical trials. Gilead was able to show that Harvoni worked in the types of hepatitis C that are rare yet still a problem in the US because they could find patients infected with these strains of the virus more quickly in other countries. It would have taken much longer to recruit enough of these patients in the US to prove to the FDA that the drug worked on these particular strains. In addition, working with scientists, physicians, and manufacturers in other countries helps keep costs down since labor costs are lower in many of them.

Americans value the benefits that drugs offer. They demand more innovation and don't want to be ripped off. So if the world were just America, one might surmise that Americans would still demand that drug companies work on cures for cancer and Alzheimer's and infectious diseases

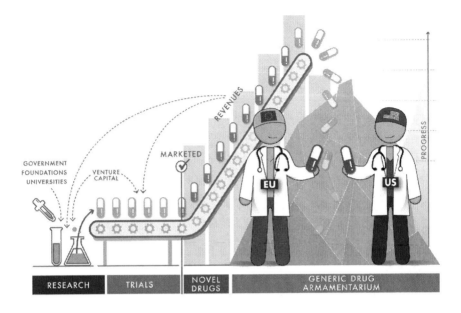

and that insurance companies find some way of covering these expensive drugs. In reality, all the other countries comprising the Rest of the World (RoW) participate in the drug development process, contributing a large fraction of patients to global clinical trials and half of the profits necessary to meet drug companies' current return on investment targets, ultimately allowing America to enjoy lower drug prices than if it were the only country on earth.

But let's say a country helps an American company develop a drug but then refuses to buy it because the price is more than they are willing to pay. Patients participating in clinical trials would have undertaken great risk, but they would not benefit once those trials were finished. Indeed, that's as unethical as it sounds.

For example, HIV medications are far more easily tested in Africa where the rate of infection is higher, and then the drugs are sold at a large profit in the US but distributed very cheaply in Africa. Compulsory licensing was conceived with the recognition that to do otherwise would be unethical.[145]

So if companies aren't willing to sell drugs to countries at prices they are willing to pay, then they should stop relying on patients there for clinical trials, which would result in drug development taking longer and costing more, to the detriment of patients everywhere, including America.

Americans have such a strong drive to both innovate and treat patients that I think the drug industry would continue to exist in some form if it only served the American market. But without other countries subsidizing drug development in all the ways I just mentioned, America would contend with higher drug prices.

Now consider the inverse scenario. What if there were no America? Without the American market, the modern biopharmaceutical industry would likely shrink dramatically or essentially cease to exist. It wouldn't be able to generate a sufficient return on investment if it were developing products for countries that are willing to deny treatments to patients based on cost. Perhaps other wealthy nations would discover that they are willing to pay more for drugs than they do now if the alternative is watching their citizens suffer and die prematurely of diseases that biotechnology could address. Hopefully this exact experiment will never be run, but there are other ways we might discover whether other countries are willing to pay more than they do now, namely reference pricing.

## Reference Pricing: A Hypothetical

*This section was developed with contributions from Anthony Bower.*

What if America simply forced the issue of "fair" pricing by introducing regulations stating that it won't pay more than other comparably wealthy countries? Such international reference pricing has been repeatedly proposed by politicians and academics as a solution to high drug prices in the US. Let's look at how it might play out.

Firstly, depending on how it was implemented, reference pricing might only impact list prices, making it entirely ineffective at lowering the cost that payers incur. Companies could set a high international reference price, and then simply offer secret rebates in each country to arrive at the prices they charge now.*

---

* This is already occurring in the UK, with its euphemistic private "patient access schemes" that provide discounts to the UK National Health Service that cannot be price-referenced on the European continent by countries that want to reference the prices the UK pays.

## Complicating Global Partnerships

Often, different companies market a drug in different countries, such as when a US biotech company licenses European rights to its drug to a foreign company in exchange for sharing in the work and cost of its development. US law requiring reference pricing would only apply to the company commercializing the drug in the US, leaving the partner with foreign rights free to set the price in Europe to maximize its own profits. If the reference pricing law were applied without making exceptions for such international partnerships, then odds are that the US would enjoy European prices for many partnered drugs, but the benefits would be short-lived because companies would stop splitting commercialization rights in this way (no US company would give away its ability to control price), which would create friction for innovation and commercialization while doing nothing to reduce US drug prices.

But let's assume that the US government took secret rebates into account by forcing companies to report what they charge in each country and setting net prices in the US based on international net prices. In theory, if a country won price concessions from the company, those savings would flow through to the US.

But, in practice, it's likely to come out differently. The US, being the biggest and most price-insensitive market, will end up exporting higher US prices to Europe. The economics are quite clear on this point, and company pricing departments are well aware of the global dynamics and highly incentivized to stay ahead of the game. Therefore, those who think that referencing US prices to those in Europe will lower prices substantially in the US would be disappointed. The endgame would actually end up being even worse for America. The US Congressional Budget Office has said as much.[146]

## Reference Pricing Already Exists in America

Some critics of reference pricing would be wrong to say that the general approach is unprecedented or would be highly unusual for the US. It is going on now in virtually all drug markets, *including* the US with its Medicaid "best price" regulation and even Medicare with its "average sale price" reimbursement model.[147] When Medicaid, which provides health insurance for the very poor, decrees that it will take a discount off the best price in the US private sector, it's getting the benefit of the low price negotiated by the best negotiator in the private sector and then taking a further discount.

Let's say US policy requires a company to sell a drug in the US at the German price. And for simplicity's sake, let's assume that the company controls the global commercialization of the drug and that it is launching the drug in both markets at about the same time. Any price concession the company grants to Germany will, in theory, flow through to the US. So the company sets a single price that will maximize the sum of the profits from the two markets. Because the US is price-insensitive and is the largest market in the world, that price will be high, calibrated to extract value from the US. In Germany this will result in access to the drug being restricted to only the sickest patients. The decision is regrettable from the company's perspective but is especially clear because there are four times as many potential patients in the US. Still, even if Germany were the same size as the US, as long as the US is fundamentally unwilling to deny access based on price, the optimal pricing strategy in certain circumstances might be to just charge a very high price in the US and forget about the German market entirely.

## Piling on: Reference Pricing with Penalties and Outright Price Controls

Some drug price control proposals call for both international reference pricing and penalties for companies that raise their prices in the US.[148] That would appear to deter companies that export their US price to Europe from recouping lost profits abroad by raising their price in the US. So it's possible that this particular combination of policies would result in either US prices of existing products staying the same or maybe even going down to be closer to Europe's levels depending on how much of their profits they were getting from Europe. However, such a policy would not stop companies from setting a single, very high price on new drugs, which is what I describe in the US-Germany example. Some policies have therefore also proposed that the US government would simply negotiate the price of all new drugs. That would entail the company offering a price, the US government offering a price, and if they couldn't agree, then a third party would pick a price. Ultimately, this is simply a price control. It would introduce so much uncertainty into the industry's ability to generate a return from its successes that current and future R&D would wither.[149]

The Germans are worse off in this scenario, but Americans are not better off and could end up paying more. If Germans decide to deny some patients treatment with the drug because they find the price too high, which they do, the drug company will make less money in Germany and therefore charge a higher price in less price-sensitive markets such as the US.[150] At this new higher price, Germany might treat even fewer patients, requiring companies to again raise their prices to make up the difference.

In the end, maybe no one would get treated with the drug in Germany, though the company would reassure American payers that they are paying the same price as what is charged in Germany. In that case, referencing results in higher costs for US patients and zero access for German patients. And absurd as it may seem, pricing parity could assuage those drug pricing critics focused on "fair" pricing around the world, blinding them to what they could be doing to keep absolute costs in the US as low as possible by other means.

If other countries now stop buying branded drugs because they consider the price too high, we trigger the exact America-only scenario we already discussed. To preserve their profitability, drug companies would then raise prices in the US to make up for 1) lost international profits, 2) higher development costs from having to move their clinical testing entirely to the US, and 3) longer drug development timelines. If a drug company hit a limit on how high it could price its existing drugs (e.g., a company might sell only drugs that have several me-too competitors and be unable to raise prices), then it would collapse, cutting its workforce until it could survive on whatever revenues it still had coming in.

But we also have to speculate that the countries to which America pegs its drug prices, if they couldn't then afford the higher American prices exported to them, might feel justified to turn to compulsory licensing, especially the less wealthy ones in Europe with nationalist governments. The end result for the drug industry would be lost profits, protracted disputes in various courts to prevent compulsory licensing, and a lot of bad press made worse by having to raise their prices in the US.

## America's Generosity Must Hold

Millions of patients around the world in developing countries enjoy medicines for everything from HIV to heart failure because wealthy nations like the US, indeed the US most of all, paid higher prices for those medicines while they were still branded. While the subsidy that the US pays to help make new medicines available affordably in poor countries can be embraced as philanthropy, Americans can be forgiven for struggling to understand why they should be subsidizing the treatment of patients in other wealthy nations that could be but aren't making a proportional contribution to the Biotech Social Contract.

So the question is what America should do about this perceived unfairness.

If, in our indignation at paying more than others, we adopt other countries' practice of denying access altogether on the basis of price, there will only be losers: The biotechnology industry, much of which is based in the US, would likely collapse, and the growth of society's highly cost-effective generic drug armamentarium would soon slow or cease entirely to the detriment of current patients and future generations.*

Should America insist that companies deny other countries access if they aren't willing to pay the same price or higher prices than they do now?

Some countries might be inspired to pay more (either by paying higher prices or treating more of their eligible patients in cases where they now restrict access), which might take trade diplomacy (as the US did with Canada when negotiating NAFTA).[151] But merely dictating higher prices to other countries could reduce their participation in the Biotech Social Contract and make industry even more dependent on generating profits in the US, raising drug prices for Americans.

It's worth weighing all of what works in the status quo, both the obvious and subtle, against the unintended consequences of radically changing how we handle branded drug pricing to make sure that we don't accidentally give up more than we stand to gain.

Just as many countries buy into global efforts to curb pollution or stop overfishing, we need to make the case for the global long-term benefits of paying for branded drugs to help patients today as an investment towards generic drugs that will cost-effectively serve the world for the rest of time. In the meantime, America has to decide what it wants for itself and whether it is willing to support the Biotech Social Contract, regardless of what other countries decide to do.

---

* We'll be paying for hip replacement surgeries forever while the bone building drug that could obviate the need for those surgeries would remain a hypothetical.

# 11

## IN TOTAL: DRUG PRICES ARE CLOSE TO WHERE THEY NEED TO BE

One might think that companies already maximize their prices in the US, but that's clearly not true. If America really is unwilling to deny essential drugs based on cost, then those prices could easily be higher. One way to tell whether prices are too high is to look for evidence of grossly inflated salaries or profits.

Taking a problem to an extreme often reveals its working parts. A company charging $10 billion/patient/year for a very effective drug to treat 1,000 patients with a very rare condition would make $10 trillion/year. If this company were built like a typical biotech company serving such a small number of patients, it might have 100 employees and $100 million/year in expenses (e.g., salaries of employees, but also rent, cost of manufacturing the drug, accounting and legal expenses), which are insignificant compared to the revenues. So after paying 21% in corporate tax, the company would have a 79% profit margin, which would stand out.

Alternatively, to keep its profits down, the company could pay its 100 employees each billions of dollars each year, which would also not go unnoticed. Or it could pay average wages but employ tens of millions of people, which would also stand out as particularly wasteful, having so many people working for the benefit of so few.

And if you cut the price of that company's drug by 90% or even 99%, the company would either still be wildly profitable with a profit margin over 78%, or the workers would still be wildly overpaid, or there would still be far more workers than would seem reasonable. Such absurdity is how you would recognize that a drug is dramatically overpriced.

But when you look at the drug development industry in the US, the numbers are not consistent with drugs being wildly overpriced, despite how the drug industry is portrayed by the media. The drug industry generated $344 billion in sales in the US and about $1.15 trillion worldwide in 2018. It has profit margins that range from 10-20%, which is less than banks and software, and around the same as the oil and gas industry.[152] Roughly 3% of the US workforce (4.7 million people) is directly and indirectly employed in the drug industry (roughly 15 million globally) and earn an estimated average salary between $60,000-80,000. This is slightly above the US median income of $58,500/year—although not unreasonably higher considering all the scientists and others with advanced training that work in drug development.[153] Executive compensation gets a lot of attention, but there are so few executives that even if they all got paid $1 million year (and most are paid much less),* they would account for a small fraction of the industry's expenses.

Consider that it would take only a 20% drop in drug prices worldwide or a 30% cut in the US price alone to wipe out most profits and executive compensation, both cash and stock (since stock values are tied to profits). Without funding from investors (who would not want to invest their capital in an unprofitable industry) and unable to recruit workers from other industries that pay better, the drug industry would shrink and make fewer new medicines. Yet to a patient without insurance, a 20% or 30% discount on a $20,000/year drug doesn't make it affordable—that's what we need

---

* I'm only counting cash compensation. The headlines one sees about executives making millions of dollars are due to situations where an executive's stock or stock options have gone up in value. However, since in the case of this thought experiment we are considering what happens if we cut drug prices and wipe out industry profits, then the value of all stock goes to zero and all stock compensation is worthless, leaving only cash compensation to consider.

insurance reform for. So if the industry is to continue to employ the people it does and attract investors to fund innovation, it will have to maintain its current revenues and profits.

As this book goes to print, Congress is debating a proposal to impose a combination of price controls and international reference pricing. Lawmakers want to reduce America's spending on branded drugs by $100 billion/year for ten years, $1 trillion in total, which represents a 37% reduction in branded drug revenues.[154] The Congressional Budget Office (CBO) notes that the industry launches approximately 30 new drugs per year, a projected 300 novel drugs over a decade. Yet somehow the CBO calculates that a 37% cut in American branded drug spending would only reduce the number of new drugs created by 8-15 over 10 years.[155] How could they think the impact is so modest?

One answer is that the CBO believes that reference pricing would raise prices in Europe, so maybe the CBO assumes Europe will pay more for drugs. This puts too much faith in the healthcare systems of countries that have already proven themselves willing to deny patients access to treatments. Another answer is that the CBO assumes that drugs already pretty far along in development will still prove worthwhile for companies to bring to market. That's probably correct. Price controls would have the greatest chilling effect on the earliest stages of innovation. Pension funds, university endowments, and other investors would likely pull their money from venture capital funds that invest in biotechnology, because those funds would no longer offer good enough returns. Those funds would then no longer be able to seed the industry with as many novel projects. After five years, it would become more apparent that, for certain types of challenging diseases or therapies that are expensive to develop, there are fewer clinical-stage drug candidates. After that, the real reduction in new drug approvals would become clear.

By asking the CBO to look out one decade, as is conventional when considering the impact of new legislation but inappropriate for the long timelines involved in drug development, Congress is being short-sighted and the public is being misled. If the CBO were to calculate the reduction to new drug approvals in the second decade after the introduction of such price controls, it would become apparent just how much American patients would stand to lose.

## Price Check

Why don't companies just raise drug prices 10-fold if America is price-insensitive? Because the executives and board members who run these companies actually feel the social pressure to justify their prices. They can justify profits that are above average, but not record-setting. Similarly, they can justify employing a finite number of employees and paying them salaries that are generally above-average, but not record-setting. Given these limitations, total revenues of the drug industry can only be so high at this time. Competition is a second factor: There are many drug classes that have multiple similar drugs that insurers can play off one another, as happened with hepatitis C drugs to cause their prices to come down dramatically. And finally, whenever a company finds a great, one-of-a-kind drug that is highly in-demand and can command a high price, the on-patent life of that drug is finite, so any inflated profit this company makes is temporary.

Profitable drug companies lose revenue and profit every time one of their branded drugs goes generic, which allows us to see how they respond to these situations. Some of them lay off people and shrink down to a size that allows them to remain profitable from their now-reduced revenues. Others have developed new drugs that they can launch to replace the lost revenue. If a company hasn't developed any new drugs, they will often use the cash they have accumulated from selling their old drugs to buy companies that are developing new drugs, which rewards those companies' innovators and investors. Drug companies can also make up for lost revenue by raising the prices of their other drugs, which only works for so long because those drugs, in most cases, also eventually go generic.* So as long as drugs go generic, the only way for drug companies to survive for the long

---

* As I discussed in Chapter 8, ungenericizable drugs can turn a dynamic company that should be hungry to discover new drugs into one that can sit back on its laurels, just enjoying the profits of one product. Introducing contractual genericization would bring these products back into alignment with the Biotech Social Contract and ensure that all companies stay hungry for the next medical breakthrough.

run is to continue to launch new drugs at prices that allow the industry to stay profitable.

Any one company might look like it's doing exceptionally well at any given time, but they don't stay on top forever and investors own a portfolio of drug companies. So the companies doing well compensate for the ones that are struggling. Any discussion of price controls therefore cannot assume that the industry will be fine if only the standout drugs get clipped. It's those drugs that make the whole portfolio work, just like a restaurant that charges a lot for a few items can't be accused of price gouging if the profits of the business as a whole are reasonable—those items might be what are sustaining the business. So we have to look at the whole enterprise. An analysis of the drug industry overall shows that there is little room for price cuts either globally or in the US, certainly not enough to make drugs affordable for patients without insurance or the many who can't afford their out-of-pocket costs. The solution patients need is insurance reform.

At the societal level, drugs going generic is the drug price control we have long had and the only one we need to ensure that society continues to get value from what it pays for drugs.

# PART 3

# BEYOND CONVENTIONAL THINKING

RESEARCH     TRIALS     NOVEL DRUGS     GENERIC DRUG ARMAMENTARIUM

MARKETED

REVENUES

PROGRESS

# 12

# DIRECT-TO-CONSUMER ADVERTISING: HATED, MISUNDERSTOOD, ESSENTIAL

In mid-2019, television viewers in the United States stopped seeing a familiar sight during commercial breaks: A middle-aged man, sitting at a picnic table by the beach massaging his foot.[156] He grimaces as his feet— "feet that made waves in high school"—are wracked with the "shooting, burning pins and needles" of diabetic nerve pain. Cut to the bare feet of a surfer, a dad kicking a ball, and the boot-clad feet of a carpenter building a home. "So I talked to my doctor, and he prescribed Lyrica," says the man, a refrain that has been repurposed across decades of pharmaceutical advertisements. These commercials have fueled countless satires and sparked a fierce, ongoing debate about the role of marketing and advertising in the use and price of drugs. As is often the case in the healthcare industry, a closer look reveals some surprising truths and misconceptions.

# Paternalism and the First Wave of DTC Drug Advertising

In the past, patients were expected to place complete trust in their doctors. Doctors, with their training and superior knowledge about available treatments, were to be obeyed without question and were even permitted to make decisions on patients' behalf without obtaining informed consent. If the doctor deemed it best, it was not unusual for him to keep a patient in the dark about their own condition—for instance, a doctor might inform a patient's family of an incurable cancer diagnosis, but not actually tell the patient. This approach to medicine, often referred to as "paternalism," made it possible for doctors to process more patients in less time. To our modern sensibilities, it might feel more analogous to the way a veterinarian treats sheep.

In the days of paternalistic medicine, pharmaceutical companies promoted FDA-approved drugs directly and exclusively to physicians.[157] Direct-to-consumer advertising (DTC) did not emerge until the 1980s,* prompting an outcry from physicians and watchdog groups alike.

Those practicing paternalistic medicine felt their authority challenged by patients asking too many questions and demanding treatments that a doctor considered inappropriate. They argued that DTC ads left patients misinformed and clamoring for medicines they did not need. To be fair, in these early days, some companies took advantage of the lack of advertising regulations to play fast and loose with the facts or seize on the fears of the worried well.

This backlash resulted in the FDA issuing a swift moratorium on DTC pharmaceutical ads in 1983. Two years later, strict rules and regulations were put in place to make sure information was as clear and complete as possible. Since the airtime required to put all that information into a radio or TV ad was expensive, DTC drug ads were mainly relegated to print advertising. The modern era of DTC advertising didn't arrive until 1997, when the FDA allowed television and radio ads to mention a drug's most

---

* Patients have never been consumers in the traditional sense. They aren't engaging in discretionary spending on their medicines; rather, they are counting on physicians to prescribe what they need for problems they feel powerless to solve.

important risks and then direct patients to other sources for additional information (as opposed to requiring ads to numbingly rattle off all the details included in print ads). Per those regulations, all pharmaceutical DTC ads that make medical claims:

1. cannot be false or misleading;

2. must present a balance of risks and benefits;

3. must state facts that are material to the advertised uses; and

4. must include every risk from the product's approved labeling (if in print) or several sources where a patient might find information about all the risks.[158]

That's a lot of information—approaching what a physician would learn if they read the scientific literature—and it is often dry and inaccessible, because it is restricted to scientifically proven medical claims. Vague wording and imagery can result in skewed, overly rosy messaging, which results in a gray area policed, appropriately, by watchdog groups and the FDA.

With the emergence of the Internet, patients became more informed— even if not always *better* informed—about their health. They came to their doctors with printouts of what they saw online, which didn't always agree with what their doctors had told them, and sometimes the Internet was right.

In medicine, as in everything, the opposite of knowledge is not ignorance but the illusion of knowledge—thinking you know when you actually don't. This confidence can lead to physicians not staying up to date with recent medical discoveries and inadvertently steering patients away from the best treatment options. And that's why paternalistic medicine is on its way out, and why doctors who still practice it are considered dinosaurs.[159]

Physicians have increasingly come to accept their limitations with humility and embrace shared decision-making, which empowers patients to stay informed and involved in defining their own treatment plans. Today, what little paternalism is condoned (e.g., restraining a post-surgical patient who rips out their IV in a panic) is considered a last resort after attempting to inform and collaborate with patients and their caregivers.[160]

In this changing environment, DTC drug advertising was sometimes embraced as a way for patients to become more informed and to engender discussions about new treatments. Even physicians (45%, according to a study published in 2006) began to see the merits of DTC advertising.[161]

After all, physicians today are more overworked than ever, facing ever greater demands on their time and attention. The knowledge they must master and the tools they must know how to use are continually changing and expanding. They know more than physicians did fifty years ago, but not on a relative basis—there is simply more to know now—and what they don't know is increasingly evident. Their every decision is scrutinized and second-guessed by patients and their family members, other physicians, insurance companies, and lawyers, and their mistakes are all the more public in the Internet-era.

It isn't reasonable to expect physicians to read and internalize every piece of literature about every new drug that hits the market.[162] While many physicians will hear out pharmaceutical sales reps to stay informed of the latest advances, some institutions and physicians discourage or even ban sales reps from meeting with doctors.[163] So having a patient mention symptoms or treatments they've learned about through a television commercial or magazine ad can spark a discussion that might not otherwise have happened and lead to a better treatment decision.

## The Arguments Against DTC Advertising

Of course, a lot of doctors and other people remain staunchly opposed to DTC drug advertising, many of whom cite reasons ultimately rooted in paternalism, wishing patients would stop getting their information from anyone but their doctors.[164]

A well-cited article written in 1999 by two physicians captures the anti-DTC view:[165]

> *[The DTC advertising of a drug] unreasonably increases consumer expectations, forces doctors to spend time disabusing patients of*

*misinformation, diminishes the doctor-patient relationship because a doctor refuses to prescribe an advertised drug, or results in poor practice if the doctor capitulates and prescribes an inappropriate agent.*

They go on to suggest that DTC advertising somehow compels doctors to prescribe what they know are wrong treatments for patients:

*If [doctors] believe that patients want and expect drugs then doctors will prescribe them even when they know they are not indicated, even when patients don't specifically ask for them, and even when an individual patient never expected the drug but the doctor thinks he or she did.*

Some physicians cite demands on their time as a reason for doing away with DTC advertising. They argue that they simply don't have time in their schedules to deal with patients who come into their offices with treatment ideas they got from television commercials. Similarly, a 2006 study revealed that some doctors disapproved of medical information on the Internet for related reasons.[166] While I don't agree with their proposed solution, it's impossible not to acknowledge that doctors are short on time.

In healthcare, there is a strong push by hospitals and practices for "productivity," which means doctors are expected to max out the number of patients they see in a day. At the same time, the administrative burden on doctors has been climbing. For every ten minutes they spend with a patient, they spend twenty staring at a screen, entering more and more details as demanded by payers. Doctors call it "pajama time" since much of it is done while lying in bed at night, and most report spending up to two hours every night doing this work.[167] This is especially problematic for family physicians, who are often the first line of care and are expected to have some level of expertise in every area of medicine. They are pushed to be ultra-productive in their time with patients, and their time away from patients is filled with administrative work—not, for example, with reading the latest journal articles to learn of new treatment options. Strained for time, I can appreciate why some doctors wish that patients would ease up with all their Internet- and DTC-driven questions and demands.

As recently as 2015, the American Medical Association (AMA) called for a ban on DTC ads, claiming that they drive up demand for expensive drugs when lower-cost alternatives are available and that the cost of ads contributes to rising drug prices.[168] Others have argued that DTC ads can boost off-label use of some treatments.[169]

Some of these arguments have more merit than others. Critics are right to complain when companies misrepresent their products by claiming more efficacy than has been proven or omitting important side effects. That's what the FDA and Department of Justice (DOJ) are there to police—and they do so regularly.[170]

When it comes to conditions like irritable bowel syndrome, food allergies, and depression, diagnosis can be inexact, so DTC advertising may well contribute to over-diagnosis and over-treatment.[171]

As with anything else, potential risks must be weighed against potential benefits in order to arrive at a reasonable conclusion. When it comes to DTC advertising, the FDA, the very agency that shut it down the first time around, has conducted many such benefit-risk analyses over the years. They have repeatedly found that, when done in accordance with regulations, DTC drug advertising confers a net benefit by making patients better equipped to advocate for their care.[172] Let's look at the major benefits and some counter-arguments to the risks to see what might have led the FDA to arrive at that conclusion.

## The Benefit-Risk of Informing Patients

As you may have noticed, a number of arguments against DTC drug advertising assumes that the biopharmaceutical industry is singularly focused on increasing profits, which they achieve by influencing vulnerable and unwitting patients to take advantage of well-meaning but powerless physicians. Those are pretty shaky assumptions.

First of all, as anyone who has ever seen a drug commercial knows, DTC advertising urges patients to "Ask your doctor if [drug name] is right for you." These ads are meant to spark conversation and inform patients, not to encourage patients to bully their doctors and demand specific prescriptions. Physicians and nurses are trained to say "no" to inappropriate requests, even when patients are adamant.

The US legal system considers a doctor to be a "learned intermediary," and that part of her role is to protect even the most insistent patient from harm.[173] An informed physician should always have the fortitude to say no and will have a range of strategies for doing so. No, you don't need that drug. No, there's an alternative that's cheaper and probably safer, because we understand it better. No, let's try to treat this without drugs first. No, I'd rather order a test that confirms you have that condition before prescribing this. No amount of pestering or biased information can force a physician to write a prescription against her own better training and judgment.

At no point in the educational process are doctors and nurses trained to violate the Hippocratic Oath and cave to a patient's demands for inappropriate treatment.[174] The vast majority of healthcare professionals understand this and practice with judgment and care. Are there exceptions? Based on what physicians themselves have said, it seems there are, but that is hardly grounds for reducing patients' access to information that meets FDA standards. Granted, saying no isn't always easy, especially when physicians are increasingly being held accountable with patient satisfaction surveys and online reviews. But it is part of the job—and the oath—they took.

A study published in 2005 elegantly demonstrates the benefit-risk tradeoff of patients asking for treatment based on DTC advertising.[175] In the experiment, actors were trained to pose as patients with different types of mood disorders. Some reported symptoms consistent with major depression that, based on medical guidelines, merited treatment with an anti-depressant. Others reported symptoms consistent with an "adjustment disorder" that didn't merit a drug prescription. The actors were instructed to either request that the doctor prescribe a specific branded drug, Paxil; ask for medication in general without mentioning a specific drug by name; or not request treatment, leaving it up to the physician to initiate a treatment discussion.

Those who were in the major depression group but didn't request medication were treated in accordance with standard of care only 56% of the time (which doesn't necessarily mean that they got anti-depressants; some were appropriately referred for counseling). Those who did ask for treatment, either generally or for Paxil specifically, were treated in accordance with standard of care 90% of the time. In other words, patients who asked for proper care were more likely to get proper care. Only a minority (27%) of the major depression group who requested Paxil by name were actually prescribed Paxil. Another 26% got a different drug, including generic drugs, and others were referred for counseling. The results suggest that even when patients ask for drugs they saw in an advertisement, doctors can make their own decisions about proper treatment.

Equally important, actors in the adjustment disorder group that did not ask for treatment were offered a drug only 10% of the time. So, 90% of physicians acted appropriately and only 10% misdiagnosed the condition. However, 39% of actors in the adjustment disorder group who made a general request for medication received a script for an anti-depressant, and 55% of those who asked for Paxil specifically got a prescription for Paxil. Yes, those doctors were over-treating. While some may have misdiagnosed the condition, many more simply failed to say "no."

In this study, many doctors practiced medicine properly regardless of what the patients asked for. Many did not. Pressed for time as many doctors are, maybe it can be expedient to give patients what they want even when it isn't what they need. But that's not proper medicine and it shouldn't be blamed on DTC advertising. Trying to make patients less informed and less inquisitive smacks of old-fashioned paternalism and negatively impacts those actually suffering from treatable conditions who wouldn't get treatment if they didn't know to seek or ask for it. The data show that patients who don't speak up risk not getting the treatment they need.

What people on both sides of the DTC advertising debate can agree on is that physicians need more productive time with patients. There are lots of ways to help achieve those ends. For example, people need more training on how to be effective patients (e.g., how to effectively share their own stories with doctors,[176] how to find credible medical websites, and how to read drug labels).[177] Doctors need better electronic health records that reduce the need for redundant data entry. We should train and hire more primary care physicians and allow nurses to handle more routine care so that doctors have the time to put their advanced training to good use.

Physicians report that one of their greatest challenges is getting patients to stick with a prescribed treatment. An estimated 50% of patients regularly undermine their own care by forgetting to take doses of their medication.[178] It's worth noting that DTC advertisements help in that regard, reminding patients who have been prescribed a medication to take it as directed.[179]

## DTC Advertising: Driving Costs Up...or Down?

Let's consider AMA's claim that the drug industry charges higher prices for drugs in order to pay for DTC advertising. In 2017, DTC spending amounted to $6.1 billion, less than 3% of total branded US drug revenues.[180] So, even if AMA's claim were true and DTC spending were completely eliminated, the overall savings for patients would be minimal—and that's assuming that DTC costs are passed directly to patients in the form of higher drug prices, which is not necessarily true.

In fact, DTC advertising most likely *lowers* the cost of a drug on a per-patient basis. Here's why.

A biopharmaceutical company invests in a drug's development believing that it will generate a future return that is based on the price of the drug, the number of patients with the relevant disease, and the fraction of those patients who will be diagnosed and actually prescribed that drug (i.e., the penetration of the drug into its target market). DTC advertisements increase the number of patients diagnosed with a given disorder as well as the number of diagnosed patients who are then treated with the advertised drug, boosting overall revenues and profits.[*] However, that doesn't mean costs go up on a per patient basis.[181]

As with any product, the costs of developing and bringing a drug to market are spread across the entire customer base. Without DTC advertising, drug companies would have to presume lower penetration, which would mean fewer patients treated, and, hence, a higher cost per patient.

---

[*] If this weren't true, pharmaceutical companies wouldn't spend money on these kinds of ads year after year.

In today's environment, where patients' out-of-pocket costs are influenced by drug prices, that means DTC advertising lowers out-of-pocket costs for patients who need treatment.

DTC advertising can also indirectly lower costs for patients and all of society. Advertisements for branded statin drugs (back when statins were still branded) drove more patients to seek treatment for high cholesterol, and yet physicians were able to treat many of them with non-advertised generic statins, inexpensively preventing heart attacks and strokes associated with high cholesterol and driving further savings in medical expenses.[182]

Critics who think that DTC advertising is purely profit-motivated and only pretends to have educational aims are missing the point. DTC advertising is indeed profit-driven. If it weren't, companies wouldn't be able to justify the expense. But that doesn't mean that it doesn't have informational value that can lead to better patient outcomes. That's not just the biopharmaceutical industry's opinion; it's the FDA's, too. What's the point of a new invention if people don't know it exists and don't benefit from it?

## Why Not Promote Disease Awareness Instead of Drugs?

Many countries around the world take a very different approach to DTC drug advertising. Some even go so far as to outlaw all advertisements, even those that only describe the symptoms of a treatable disorder and urge sufferers to talk to their doctors. Other countries, such as Canada, compromise by permitting limited ads that mention either a drug or a disease, but not both. Only the US and New Zealand explicitly permit companies to mention both a drug and the disease it treats in the same ad.

Promoting disease awareness, even without mentioning a particular treatment, is itself beneficial. Raising awareness can help destigmatize a disease and encourage sufferers to seek medical care. For instance, throughout the 1980s, an HIV/AIDS diagnosis was met with fear and prejudice, prompting many to avoid being tested or seeking treatment. When the basketball legend Magic Johnson announced in 1991 that he was HIV positive, his courage made it okay for millions of people to talk about their experience with the disease.[183] Later, in public service announcements, he urged people to get tested and many did.

Advertisements meant to increase disease awareness can achieve many of the same benefits as the traditional "ask your doctor about this brand" DTC approach. Both types of ads inform potential patients about conditions they might not have known about, both point out symptoms, and both can result in patients initiating useful conversations with their physicians. Awareness-oriented DTC advertisements are less controversial with physicians, since they are less likely to send patients into their offices with specific drugs in mind. So, is this the ideal way to go? As usual, we should engage in some benefit-risk analyses first. Let's look at an example.

The disease-awareness approach makes the most sense for the biopharmaceutical company producing the drug that is the logical best choice for any patient with a particular diagnosis. Gilead funded a hepatitis C awareness campaign encouraging people to get tested for the virus but often didn't mention the name of any drug (they didn't need to since most physicians already considered Gilead's drugs to be the best).[184]

Sometimes patients don't even realize that what they suffer from is actually a treatable disorder. Consider the rare neurological disorder known as pseudobulbar affect (PBA), which is characterized by uncontrollable, spontaneous episodes of crying or laughing that have nothing to do with how a patient is actually feeling.[185] Until they get a diagnosis of PBA, patients can't understand what is happening to them and struggle to get others to take them seriously. After Otsuka launched a treatment for PBA, the company funded a documentary that profiled several patients and ran ads to help others recognize their own plight and seek a proper diagnosis and treatment.[186] Because Otsuka's drug is the only FDA-approved option, simply raising awareness of the disease also drove awareness and utilization of their drug.

So if DTC advertising were exclusively restricted to campaigns that increased disease awareness and we outlawed the mention of specific drugs, only the companies that either sold the physician-preferred or only available treatment for a given condition would be motivated to run such ads. But what happens when a better drug comes on the market?

For example, patients with rheumatoid arthritis today are treated with antibodies that require injections or infusions. These drugs have a risk of causing infections because they strongly suppress the immune system. There are drugs in development that have a lower risk of infection, so let's assume that those drugs get approved. If DTC advertising were restricted to disease awareness with no mention of new drugs, word would spread slowly to patients about these new and better options. Even physicians who heard about the new drugs would not call all of their patients to get them to come in to change their prescription; it's more likely that they would wait until their patients' next appointments and possibly switch prescriptions at that time. It stands to reason that a patient who sees a traditional DTC ad for a new drug and proactively calls their doctor would be more likely to get the newer, safer therapy—and wouldn't that be a better result?

These are among the reasons why the FDA continues to allow DTC advertising in its current form.

## DTC Advertising and Generics

When Lyrica's patent expired in mid-2019, the FDA quickly approved nine low-cost generics of this neuropathic pain treatment, sparking the usual price competition.[187] The original drugmaker, Pfizer, is losing Lyrica's billions in annual sales, though no one should feel badly about that. Pfizer has made tens of billions of dollars on Lyrica since the drug first hit the US market in 2004 and will continue to market a longer-acting version of the drug for a few more years before it, too, goes generic. As discussed in Chapter 2, this is cause for celebration—another example of the biopharmaceutical industry fulfilling its end of the Biotech Social Contract.

This also means that Pfizer has no further incentive to market Lyrica, or to raise awareness of those shooting, burning, "pins-and-needles"-like sensations that should prompt a patient to talk to their doctor about neuropathy. No more budget for 60-second TV spots or glossy, four-page ads in *Time* magazine. The DTC advertising campaign is over.

This is standard practice in the industry and understandable from a financial standpoint. When a drug goes generic, the message that patients and physicians hear from the industry switches from a loud, "Let me teach you why you may need my expensive product," to an unspoken, "We'll sell you an inexpensive product if it occurs to you that you need it." Generic companies compete with one another purely on cost to serve whatever demand exists. Why would Teva, one of the companies that makes generic pregabalin (Lyrica's generic name), spend money on DTC ads touting pregabalin when pharmacies will just fill a patient's prescription with pills sourced from the lowest-priced manufacturer? Because of how generic drug companies compete, a smarter strategy is for Teva to keep its own costs as low as possible (i.e., not spend money on advertisements) and compete on price.

But considering the benefits of DTC advertising campaigns and the tremendous societal boon that generic drugs represent, it's a shame that there are almost no DTC advertisements for generic drugs and diseases that can be managed with them.

Insurance companies have some motivation to inform patients of diseases that can be managed inexpensively with generic drugs. Just as companies that offer flood insurance are motivated to help their customers prevent water damage by installing sensors and automatic shut-off valves, some health insurance companies try to educate patients on the dangers of high cholesterol and other conditions commonly managed with generics. A flyer in the mail or email may encourage patients to inform their doctors of symptoms that aid in a proper diagnosis and to take their medications as prescribed. If effective, these efforts save the insurance company money by preventing heart attacks, strokes, and other downstream consequences of these conditions that are much more expensive to treat. This practice might be much more common if our insurance system were truly motivated to reduce healthcare costs in the long run, but it's not. As discussed earlier, insurance companies are allowed by law to keep a fixed percentage of healthcare spending and therefore profit from the whole pie expanding. Their incentives are not yet aligned with making the healthcare system efficient. Hopefully with reforms, they could be. In any case, educational campaigns run by insurance companies do nothing for patients without insurance.

The closest we get to DTC ads for generic drugs are public service announcements (PSAs). For instance, the American Heart Association, American Stroke Association, and the AMA jointly funded a PSA to drive awareness of high blood pressure.[188] Because promoting generic drugs doesn't fit with anyone's business model (even non-profits have to have a business model to survive) there are unfortunately few examples.[189]

We know that individuals and society as a whole save money when branded drugs go generic, but are we better off if our awareness of the diseases they treat and our knowledge of their symptoms and treatments diminishes?

In most cases, society preserves the knowledge of how to use a drug by incorporating it into written medical guidelines that all physicians are taught and expected to follow. For example, knowledge of the proper use of statins, which have now all gone generic, is codified in medical textbooks and treatment guidelines. Increasingly, instructions on when to prescribe statins are coded into electronic medical data systems so that doctors are reminded to prescribe them when a patient's cholesterol is too high.

But there are some special cases in which patients don't know they need treatment until it is too late, and those treatments require more than just the training of physicians—they require a general societal understanding of the drug and when and how it might be used. In those cases, we may find ourselves unprepared to take custody of a newly generic drug, and the patent-burning party may prove bittersweet.

## After the Mortgage Is Paid Off

After a drug goes generic and DTC ads cease, if patient awareness wanes and diagnosis rates drop, then we fail to get the most out of an asset that society owns. Imagine that you buy a house with the help of a mortgage from a bank that provides free home maintenance for as long as you are paying the mortgage. If the plumbing breaks, you call the bank's service department. They even do preventative work, like sending a service team each year to winterize your pipes and clean out your gutters before the first freeze. After 15 years, you pay off the mortgage on your home, throw a mortgage-burning party to celebrate the occasion, and then realize that the responsibility for maintenance has now fallen on you. That's what happens whenever a branded drug goes generic: Society must preserve and disseminate its knowledge of how to use a drug, taking that duty over from a company that previously had the incentive and revenue stream to invest in public education and marketing. If we fail to engage, it's like paying off the mortgage on a house and then letting it fall into disrepair to the point that you have to rent another apartment. For example, not using drugs to prevent a heart attacks can lead to surgery, a "rent" expense, since surgery never goes generic.

---

## A Special Case: The EpiPen

A child with a severe allergy has accidentally eaten a peanut or been stung by a bee. Her throat is swelling shut, and every second counts. An epinephrine injection can hit pause on her body's reaction, buying time to get her to an ER.

For 40 years, epinephrine has been used to treat anaphylaxis. The drug was originally available in small glass vials, and users had to carry around a separate syringe.[190] If the need arose, a person had to insert the syringe into the vial, draw up the drug into the syringe, make sure to get the dose right, pause to push the air out of it, and then inject. Imagine a panicked parent doing this as his terrified child's throat swells, or an adult struggling to do this to herself while experiencing anaphylaxis. So little time, so many steps.

The EpiPen, approved in 1987, was the first product to put epinephrine into a pre-filled auto-injector. This was a meaningful upgrade that deserved the patent it received. But there was a significant secondary benefit to the rebirth of epinephrine as the branded EpiPen: The company selling it had a financial motive to educate society about anaphylaxis and the benefits of the auto-injector. The strange thing is that, for a long time, they didn't do so.

For its first 20 years on the market, the EpiPen was sold at a low price, less than $50 per device and was barely profitable. It was neither well known nor widely prescribed, and medical experts considered it underappreciated and under-prescribed.[191] When the specialty pharmaceutical company

Mylan acquired the (mostly generic) drug portfolio of the German company Merck KGaA in 2007,* EpiPen was part of the deal. Mylan's executives considered getting rid of the barely profitable product but decided to take another tack.[192]

Mylan recognized the potential in allergy preparedness and decided to raise awareness of anaphylaxis and, hence, increase the size of the market for the EpiPen. To fund all of this, they raised the *net price* of the EpiPen approximately 3-fold over the next decade (though public, media, and politicians focused on the more dramatic 6-fold *list price* increase, ignoring the growing rebates the company paid back to insurers).[193] The resulting marketing and lobbying campaign raised the awareness of the public, healthcare professionals, teachers, restaurant staff, airline employees, police officers, and many others about food allergies and insect stings, how to recognize anaphylaxis, and how and when to administer the EpiPen. Mylan also funded non-profits such as Food Allergy Research & Education (FARE) and gave free EpiPens to schools to get them started on

---

* Merck KgA's subsidiary Dey had itself acquired the rights to the EpiPen from Meridian Medical Technologies, which acquired it in a merger with Survival Technology, where it had been invented.

Wikipedia Contributors, "Epinephrine Auto-injector," *Wikipedia, The Free Encyclopedia*, accessed Oct. 15, 2019, https://en.wikipedia.org/wiki/Epinephrine_autoinjector.

allergy-preparedness, provided that they reordered annually (since EpiPens expire after a year). Many schools and restaurants now stock EpiPens and know how to use them, thanks in large part to Mylan's campaign.

The EpiPen grew to a nearly $1 billion/year blockbuster product by 2018. Critics derided Mylan's outreach efforts as self-serving,[194] but that is exactly the point: Higher prices provided the fuel and incentive for Mylan to do more good in terms of allergy awareness and preparedness in just one decade than other companies that owned the EpiPen had done over the prior two decades. In those companies' hands, the EpiPen cost much less, but it remained relatively unknown and underutilized, doing good for too few patients.

As the EpiPen's price climbed, an outcry arose from and on behalf of families who could not afford the EpiPen. Yet no one looked to America's insurance system, which failed to do what it was designed to do for those patients (as discussed in Chapter 4). A number of articles criticized Mylan for charging so much for what was considered a very old drug, not taking into account the importance and complexity of upgrading epinephrine from a vial to an autoinjector, as well as other improvements to the device. The complexity and value of these upgrades should have become clearer as other companies struggled to make comparable products that could successfully compete. Some companies just couldn't get their products past FDA review and in other cases had to recall them due to technical glitches uncovered after FDA approval.[195] Even Mylan had to recall some of their batches of the EpiPen due to manufacturing problems.[196] Drug-device combination products are technically challenging to manufacture to a high, consistent standard—errors can be fatal—but, as we'll see, it's not impossible.

From the standpoint of public awareness, Mylan was so successful that people thought it had a monopoly on epinephrine autoinjectors, although there was another cheaper autoinjector on the market called Adrena-click, whose manufacturer Impax (now Amneal) did little to promote it to patients or physicians.[197]

The criticism of Mylan also left out a number of important facts that paint a much more complete picture of how much better prepared our society is for that moment when a child with an allergy gets stung by a bee or accidentally eats a peanut. For example, many schools have created allergen-free tables in their cafeterias, which helps prevent the need for EpiPens from arising—and that's better than using them. Mylan's EpiPen campaign is not solely responsible for these and other preventative measures, but its educational value deserves to be weighed against the criticisms.

Going forward, who will fund the campaign to continue raising awareness of the seriousness of food allergies and anaphylaxis now that the EpiPen is going generic?[198] Anaphylaxis is a medical emergency that happens suddenly, often far from any physician. Parents, teachers, and many others outside of the healthcare system must be kept aware of the symptoms of anaphylaxis and be ready, willing, and able to administer a lifesaving dose of epinephrine. Attacks happen so rarely that it's hard for any patient to become an expert at recognizing the symptoms and knowing how to treat an attack, yet hesitating to give epinephrine when it is needed can be deadly.

In fifty years' time, physicians will still know when and how to prescribe epinephrine autoinjectors without any of the generic manufacturers having to invest in marketing, but who will pay for and do the outreach to the wider range of people that Mylan's campaign reached? Could a portion of the money that society will save from having inexpensive generic epinephrine autoinjectors be used to fund ongoing public education? Would such advertisements be as effective if carried out by the government or non-profit sector as they would be by a profit-motivated company? Or is legislation the answer?

Currently, thanks in part to Mylan's efforts, there is a law that encourages schools to consider adopting voluntary guidelines for food allergy preparedness. That's pretty weak, but importantly, the law allows undesignated EpiPens to be stocked at schools (otherwise, every EpiPen would have to be assigned to a particular patient based on a physician's prescription and could not be used to help other students). Laws nationwide could be strengthened to require schools and other institutions to stock epinephrine autoinjectors, routinely check them to make sure they aren't expired, and require they always have someone on hand who is trained to use them, just as public pools must have lifeguards on duty.

California passed such a law after media coverage of a student who died of anaphylaxis at a school.[199]

One solution might be for the government to require all generic epinephrine autoinjector companies to pay a fixed fee per device to a third-party marketing company that would be tasked with marketing these products to schools, airlines, restaurants, and other public places. The more autoinjectors sold, the more fees the marketing company would collect, reintroducing a profit motive. The generic companies would still compete on price to gain market share, with those that won the most market share providing the most funding towards marketing and education. The customers (or their pharmacies) would be the ones choosing which generic to buy based on price, but those prices would never be less than the cost of the product plus the fixed marketing fee. The marketing company would focus on volume, not price, since they would collect a fixed dollar amount per product sold.

## Pitfalls of the X-Prize Model of Paying for Drug Development

Instead of allowing companies to charge high prices for a long time for their new drugs, society could decide to incentivize drug development with a large upfront X-prize model, whereby a company that gets a drug approved gets a huge reward, and then the drug is immediately allowed to go generic.[200] It's like paying less for a home with cash upfront instead of a mortgage, and saving money by not having to pay interest.* A critical pitfall of the X-prize model is that it does away with the incentives to invest in the marketing and awareness campaigns needed to incorporate new medicines into the standard of care. That takes time and money. This might be fine for certain types of drugs, like antibiotics, in which case a small community of infectious disease specialists decide from the start how to use them judiciously to prevent the emergence of bacterial resistance. However, in the unlikely event that such an X-prize model were ever adopted

---

* Another key pitfall of the X-Prize model is that whoever has to pay the upfront cost on behalf of society (presumably the government) might struggle to come up with the money all at once. It's hard to plan for sudden expenses. That's why mortgages exist. In Chapter 8, I've included a sidebar on novel proposals to incentivize the development of antibiotics that illustrate that governments prefer a very different model from the X-Prize.

more broadly for medicines that do require promotion,* it would be prudent to pair it with the third-party marketing model I propose.

---

Sensible proposals like that take years to become policy, if they ever do. Meanwhile, the EpiPen is going generic, and I worry that the world is unprepared for what it will lose. When epinephrine autoinjectors are inexpensive once again and no one considers them worth marketing, I don't think we will be better off.

---

## Automated External Defibrillators (AEDs)

The points I'm making about preserving education apply equally well to automated external defibrillators (AEDs) developed to help people experiencing a heart attack. Just as the EpiPen can be life-saving for someone experiencing anaphylaxis, the odds of a patient recovering go up if someone properly applies an AED while waiting for first responders to arrive.[201] There is a patchy array of laws in effect in many states requiring certain businesses, such as health clubs and public spaces, to have AEDs available and people trained in their use.[202] Efforts to promulgate AED laws are funded by the handful of competing medical device companies that make these devices, but there is nothing to prevent free riders who just want to focus on selling at the lowest cost without investing in general awareness. Were the market to reward the lowest-cost companies, competitors might be forced to streamline their budgets, awareness of the importance and use of AEDs might fade, and we would all become a bit less safe.

---

* It's hard to imagine the entire industry operating this way or that it would lead to much cost savings. At the end of the day, drug development and proper marketing requires a certain number of people and spending and some profit to investors to keep them investing in new projects, so whether the industry collects its revenues all upfront for each success or over time (as it does now), the budget must be balanced. As discussed in Chapter 11, there's not much one can cut from the top-line before critical functions, whether R&D or marketing, are reduced.

## A Personal Note

As an investor in the biopharmaceutical industry, it's frustrating that after devoting years to helping bring about a new treatment for a disease—one that represents real progress—patients continue to go untreated because they don't know about it, their doctors don't know about it, or something else gets in the way. Sometimes a patient is embarrassed to discuss their condition or symptoms, as can be the case with depression, fibromyalgia (which many physicians dismissed as illegitimate for many years),[203] intimacy issues, or irritable bowel syndrome. Some may not even know that what they are experiencing is caused by a treatable disorder that they should discuss with their physician. I want the entire world to know about each newly approved drug as soon as it's available, and DTC advertising can help overcome many of the obstacles that prevent patients from getting the treatment they need.

As a father, this issue becomes even more personal, particularly the debate about the EpiPen and Mylan's outreach campaign. My family grapples with food allergies and lives with constant anxiety that a mislabeled snack could trigger a crisis. We are grateful for the current awareness of anaphylaxis and wish there were more.[204] Eating out with our children, whether at a restaurant or a friend's home, requires hypervigilance. My wife and I do not take for granted that our daughter's school takes allergies seriously and is staffed by people trained in how to use the EpiPen. It is no easy thing to put a price tag on that peace of mind.

But we also have insurance and are fortunate that we can afford our copayments. The fact that there are parents out there who don't have insurance or can't afford their out-of-pocket costs, who fear that they won't be able to afford a treatment that could save their child's life or even ease their child's discomfort, is unthinkable. One of my primary motivations for writing this book is to advocate for reforms that will make sure no parent has to live with that fear.

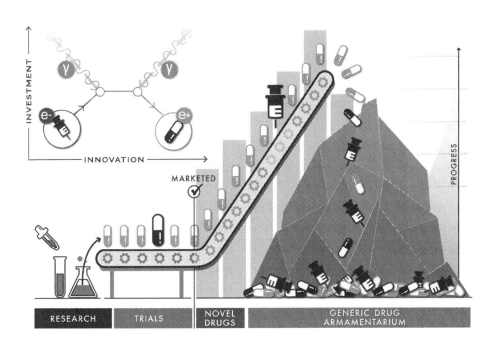

# 13

## INCENTIVIZING INCREMENTAL INNOVATION: PROPOSING SHORT EXCLUSIVITY EXTENSIONS INSTEAD OF LONG PATENTS

At age three, my daughter found that she enjoyed playing with the tester (needle and drug removed) of a new device-drug combination called Auvi-Q. This epinephrine delivery apparatus actually talked her through the few steps of using it correctly, and she got a kick out of showing everyone how to use it. For her this was a big improvement over an EpiPen that didn't talk to her and only came with written instructions, which she couldn't read. The device that she found amusing—a talking pen that gave step-by-step instructions—might end up saving lives. Yes, the EpiPen is easy to use. But in a moment of panic when seconds count, not everyone has the wherewithal to read and follow written instructions, no matter their age.

In addition, Auvi-Q is smaller than the EpiPen and shaped to fit more easily in a pocket. These might seem like minor improvements, but to a parent of a child with food allergies, these differences are meaningful (e.g., less risk of forgetting to take the bag with the EpiPen).

In accordance with the Biotech Social Contract, society is nearly finished paying off its mortgage on the EpiPen and, as generics come to market, they will eventually drive down prices. But if insurance companies refuse to cover Auvi-Q, patients will likely opt for a well-covered generic EpiPen, and Auvi-Q may fail commercially. And that leads to an important question: Is the upgrade represented by Auvi-Q worthy of another mortgage? Embracing and paying a premium for Auvi-Q's advantages would likely cost billions more over the next decade.

At the time development of the Auvi-Q first began, in the mid 2000s, researchers and investors couldn't have known that Mylan, the current producer of the EpiPen, would create such a large market for epinephrine autoinjectors. They probably expected that Auvi-Q's advantages would be worth a premium when it someday launched, though it's doubtful that they expected it to launch at the same time that the EpiPen would be going generic (and in fact, it didn't the first time around).[*] Auvi-Q is finally on the market, and its advantages will hopefully help it eventually garner a large share of the epi-autoinjector market, even if its manufacturer may have to lower the price to be closer to that of the EpiPen generics so that payers don't put up blocks. Importantly, it represents a permanent upgrade of our future generic armamentarium.

If Auvi-Q is a commercial success despite competition from generic EpiPens, then innovators will look to upgrade more such drugs in the future. For example, diabetics experiencing hypoglycemia can be rescued with a rapid dose of glucagon; there, seconds count too. And there are medications that can rescue someone experiencing a seizure. These all represent opportunities for optimizing the ease and speed of drug delivery outside of the hospital setting. It comes down to the value of increments of innovation.

What's the smallest increment of medical innovation that is worth its cost to society? And what's an adequate incentive to get to that innovation?

---

[*] The product was first launched in 2013 by Sanofi, which licensed the tech in 2009 from Kaleo, then called Intelliject. Sanofi voluntarily withdrew Auvi-Q from the market in 2015 amid manufacturing problems and weak sales, subsequently returning the product back to Kaleo.

Those questions underpin some controversy surrounding drug pricing. Is it innovative to turn a twice-daily pill into a once-daily pill or convert an intravenously infused (IV) drug into one that can be given subcutaneously, or combine two generic drugs into a single branded pill? If we want the new-and-improved version, we have to pay for it.*

But should we? Arguments against ignore several facts that are intrinsic to the Biotech Social Contract and belittle real and compelling advances.

## Convenience: Much More Than a Luxury

The more frequently patients have to take a pill, the less likely they are to remember to take all their pills. This is known as a problem of adherence (formerly and more paternalistically called "compliance"), and it has real-world consequences.† Moving from a twice-daily pill to a once-daily pill improves outcomes.[205]

Adherence is also compromised with pills that *must* be taken with food or *must* be taken on an empty stomach. A patient prescribed more

---

* We would not have to pay for it out of pocket if insurance were reformed to eliminate or cap out-of-pocket costs, but "we have to pay for it" would still mean that it would come out of society, factoring into insurance premiums and taxes. So let's say that the Auvi-Q needed to earn $2 billion over a decade ($200 million/year) in the US to justify its development cost. That would be roughly 60 cents per person per year (330 million people in the US). Sounds small. But there are many such technological upgrades to add up, and so it's worth considering the value of incremental innovation.

† It is a major flaw in the delivery of healthcare that there are trained professionals at every stage except, in most cases, the actual taking of the medication by the patient. For that step, there is no standardization; each patient is expected to look out for themselves, and yet that patient's physician and insurance plan and entire US healthcare system are judged by the outcome. That's why real-world outcomes are often worse than those generated by clinical studies in which investigators and their staffs closely watch patients to make sure they adhere to treatment. It doesn't matter how good the drug or how astute the physician; if the patient doesn't take the drug, the outcome is poor and reflects poorly on the drug, physician, and America's entire healthcare system. If we recognize the problem of adherence, we'll all appreciate the need for technological upgrades that improve convenience and adherence. Some of these are changes to the drugs themselves, but in some cases may be smartphone apps that remind patients to take their medication. Some companies are developing pills in which they embed sensors that signal when a patient has taken the pill, inform a physician whether a patient is taking their medication as prescribed. There's value in any approach that improves adherence. Interestingly, and this is a challenge for the FDA, there is no good way to show improved adhere in a well-conducted clinical trial because patients always adhere better when they are being closely watched. So you have to run a real-world clinical trial, which is easier said than done, because patients have to be informed that they are in a trial and so inevitably behave differently when watched. So if you hear someday about the FDA approving what seems like a slightly modified old drug with greater adherence properties, a lot more went into developing it and proving that it works as advertised than may seem on the surface.

than one medicine might face drug-drug interaction problems that would force them to stagger their various pills throughout the day and have to coordinate taking them with or without meals. It's easy to see how this can overwhelm at least some patients, especially those without a caretaker at home. These aren't merely inconveniences; these are barriers to adherence, and the more we can remove these barriers, the more patients will experience improved outcomes and avoid side effects and even death.

Turning pills that must be taken more than once a day into a once-daily pill, making large, hard-to-swallow pills smaller or coating them so that they are easier to swallow, making drugs that have to be taken with food (or on an empty stomach) able to be taken either way without compromising their rate of absorption into the bloodstream, combining multiple pills used to treat a disease into a single pill,* converting a pill that has to be swallowed to a film that dissolves in the mouth—all of these are valuable improvements. Imagine how welcome the pill-to-film improvement would be for a patient who can't swallow anything because they are suffering from chemotherapy- or migraine-associated nausea, or for a patient who has difficulty swallowing due to a neurological disorder such as Parkinson's, ALS, or multiple sclerosis.†

The incremental improvements are seemingly endless: IV drugs converted to subcutaneously administered medications allow for easier dosing—at a doctor's office or at home. Drugs that have to be drawn up from vials into syringes can be converted to pre-filled auto-injectors—then rendered stable at room temperature so that patients don't have to keep them in

---

* HIV was treated with three pills that were prescribed separately, but they were famously combined into a single pill, a triple cocktail. Individual components of these combination pills were replaced with better versions, reducing side effects, reducing drug-drug interactions, and increasing efficacy. The easier it is for patients to adhere to and tolerate their HIV medications, the less likely they are to develop resistance and to infect others. The branded drugs sold now are notably better than the ones that were first approved for HIV in the 1990s, and they will eventually go generic, leaving us far better equipped to inexpensively combat this disease than if we just stuck with the first generation of drugs.

† Migraines can cause severe nausea in some sufferers, such that they can't even swallow a small tablet with a bit of water—it just comes back up. The mortgage for this upgrade has been paid off; we now have generic migraine drugs that rapidly dissolve on the tongue without water.

refrigerators or carry them in coolers when they travel. Injected drugs with a lingering sting can be reformulated to make their injection less painful.*

Finally, consider insulin, which has been steadily improved over decades. For nearly a century, insulin extracted from animal pancreases was used to help diabetics regulate blood sugar, until the early 1980s, when recombinant human insulin was introduced. In the mid-1990s, insulin analogs came along and substantially replaced recombinant human insulin.† In the mid-2000s, these analogs were formulated in convenient, dose-adjustable, pre-filled syringes with needles so thin they could barely be felt. Recently, a more concentrated version hit the market, one that further improves convenience and tolerability by reducing the injected volume.

Today, controlling blood sugar requires less frequent injections, and those injections have faster onset and/or more reliable delivery profiles. Diabetics today experience better control of their blood sugar with less weight gain and lower risk of dangerous—potentially lethal—hypoglycemic episodes.‡

These improvements clearly have value, and they've often been accompanied by higher prices. The question of whether they are "worth it" compared to older human insulins has been debated extensively over the last decade.[206] Critics have suggested that insulin, a 100-year-old drug that once cost pennies, has been price-jacked by greedy companies, but this claim lacks merit. The insulin of 100 years ago and even 25 years ago is nothing like the products we have today[207]—and those newer products are beginning to go biosimilar,§ in accordance with the Biotech Social Contract.[208] Moreover, studies using conventional cost-effectiveness analyses found insulin analogs to be worth their higher costs,[209]—and these studies

---

* In 2018, 16 years after AbbVie first introduced Humira, its blockbuster therapy for rheumatoid arthritis and other auto-immune disorders, it launched an upgraded formulation that was less painful to inject.

† Recombinant insulin is human insulin produced from cells into which the gene for insulin has been genetically engineered (i.e., the cells' genetic code has been "recombined"). Insulin analogs are actually chemically different from human insulin, altered to make it better in certain ways.

‡ Hypoglycemia refers to low blood sugar, which can cause a person to lose consciousness, experience a seizure, or die.

§ Since biosimilars are the closest thing to generic versions of biologic drugs like insulins, I use "go biosimilar" to mean the same thing as for a conventional drug to "go generic." The idea is the same: the price drops due to competition among interchangeable versions of the same drug.

didn't even take eventual biosimilarization into account!* They assumed that high prices for branded insulin will stay high forever, which, as we know, is not the case. Imagine how much more favorable the analyses would look if they factored in the lower cost of biosimilars, the first of which have recently entered the US and EU markets.[210]

Would it be conscionable to make a patient use regular human insulins from over 20 years ago given how much better today's insulins are? If so, which patients exactly, to save the system money, should be exposed to greater risks of insulin shock or death? Physicians try to adhere to the Hippocratic Oath without letting their judgments be unduly influenced by cost, which is a luxury that our society can afford. No doubt, if patients didn't have insurance and had to pay out of pocket, physicians should prescribe whatever their patients could afford—better any insulin than no insulin. But the essence of the Biotech Social Contract is that a society as wealthy as America's can sustainably afford to make standard-of-care therapies available to all patients, rich and poor (and with few exceptions, to the poor in developing nations),† as long as those payments are investments (i.e., mortgage payments) into genericizable drugs.

## Assessing the Value of Incremental Improvements

As long as all improved versions of drugs eventually go generic, every upgrade is desirable. But it's reasonable to ask whether some of these upgrades could be had for less, if we could have a system that matches each quantum of innovation with a commensurate incentive. How do we evaluate upgrades and incremental improvements? That's the question that

---

* Here again, I use "biosimilarization" to refer to genericization (process of going generic) of a biologic drug like insulin. In other words, these studies didn't even take into account that insulin analogs would eventually become inexpensive.

† In terms of exceptions, I'm referring to drugs that have a high marginal cost of production, such as gene therapies and CAR-T therapies, such that even making them available to patients in the poorest developing countries would mean they are unaffordable (e.g., when a dose of a gene therapy costs $50,000 to manufacture). It's also functionally challenging to deliver some drugs that are inexpensive to produce but require cold storage, labor-intensive administration (frequent injections, infusions), or careful monitoring (e.g., have serious side effects that require hospitalization, frequent lab tests, or other therapies, such as administration of Epogen to treat drug-induced anemia or GCSF to treat drug-induced neutropenia).

drives politicians, patient advocates, journalists, health economics, physicians, and biotech executives to quarrel over which drugs are "worth it" and how to price drugs more intelligently. It's a critical question, and the answer reveals the inadequacies of our current systems for rewarding innovation.

In getting to that answer, we must not base the pricing debate on the affordability of any one drug for any individual patient. At the level of the individual, the cost of a drug is purely a function of how society structures its healthcare insurance system, and we covered that in Chapter 4. Here, we are focused on whether treatment upgrades are worth the cost when that cost is borne by society as a whole.

Keep in mind that every upgrade to a drug is patented, whether the innovation is the invention of an entirely new drug or a formulation tweak that makes an older drug more convenient. So the period of market exclusivity is typically over a decade. But the patent protection of the upgrade doesn't delay genericization of the older version. So while some upgrades result in the displacement of prior, potentially less-effective versions, many others co-exist and even compete with their older versions.

## The Old Competes with the New

When payers set higher copays for new versions that offer a small convenience (once-daily pill) and lower copays for the older generic versions (twice-daily pill) that are still effective when taken as prescribed, patients often prefer the generics and only some might pay the higher copay for extra convenience. Eliminating all copays would likely drive all patients to prefer the more convenient once-daily pill, which would result in a huge reward for the company for a modest innovation. So while patents govern how long a period of market exclusivity an upgraded version of a drug will have, it's good that insurance companies can regulate patients' access to the slightly better drug. A company, knowing that its branded once-daily pill will have to compete with generics of its off-patent twice-daily pill, will offer the payer rebates to get them to keep the copay relatively low for the once-daily brand. But switching away from a patent-based reward system for incentivizing small upgrades to a regulatory market exclusivity system discussed in this chapter would allow all patients to enjoy the benefits of the upgraded version of a drug without society paying too much. See the sidebar "Lyrica Competes with Itself" for a case study.

---

Since eventually the better version will also go generic, it makes sense to preserve incentives (i.e., some financial return) for companies to keep making incremental upgrade. But the question is how high that return needs to be. This is not the same as asking what the right amount of profit a company should get for inventing any new drug. Here I'm only talking about incremental upgrades that are relatively predictable, inexpensive, and fast.

Pursuing a cure for Alzheimer's would be too uncertain a venture to set the kind of reward in advance that we could confidently say would justify the risk and incentivize the industry to pursue it in earnest (except maybe an extremely high reward, akin to letting the winner set their own price for 10-15 years, which is what we have now). But skilled drug developers already know what it would take to turn a twice-daily pill into a once-daily one, and therefore it should be possible to size the reward for that upgrade to the cost, time, and risk of the work. Essentially, society should commission straightforward upgrades of older drugs with appropriately sized incentives instead of relying on patents for this incremental innovation, which sometimes result in too much reward and sometimes not enough.

## Enantiomers: Small Tweaks, Outsized Rewards

In the late 1980s and early 1990s, pharmaceutical companies figured out how to synthesize or purify especially pure versions of certain molecules known as chiral compounds. Chiral compounds are those for which multiple structural variants are possible using the same chemical formula. For example, your left and right hands are the same (four fingers and a thumb) and yet are structurally distinct such that your right hand won't fit into a left-handed glove. In chemistry, such variants are known as enantiomers of one another, which is to say mirror-image versions of one another, and they can act quite differently.

In some cases, drugs containing a mixture of enantiomers were not necessarily harmful; they were just less effective than drugs containing only the most effective enantiomer. In other cases, enantiomers might cause side effects, so a drug containing multiple enantiomers would not only be less effective, it might have serious consequences (as is the case with levodopa, a Parkinson's disease treatment, one enantiomer of which causes a blood disorder called granulocytopenia).

As with most innovation, what was once novel and special is eventually taken for granted as a reliable, inexpensive commodity. As with books, cars, computers, and phones, so with formulation technology and chemical synthesis techniques. This means that incremental drug innovations that previously were only rolled out as one-off upgrades are increasingly likely to be incorporated into the first versions of novel drugs. Chiral drugs that once might have been launched as mixtures of different enantiomers are more likely to be launched at the outset as a single, pure chemical.* Indeed, once companies were able to use this technology to make purer versions of drugs—at scale—the FDA strongly encouraged all companies to develop only the most therapeutically relevant enantiomer of their drugs.[211]

But sometimes small improvement can lead to disproportionate financial rewards. After its launch in 1989, Prilosec (omeprazole), a leading proton pump inhibitor for the treatment of heartburn† and a mixture of two enantiomers, generated billions of dollars in sales for AstraZeneca. As Prilosec reached the end of its patent life in 2001, AstraZeneca launched a purer version called Nexium (esomeprazole). It consisted of only the effective enantiomer, which meant that a 40mg dose contained twice the effective amount present in 40mg of Prilosec.[212]

Think of Prilosec being like a mixture of red and green M&Ms of which only the green ones are therapeutically active, and the red ones are useless, possibly even causing side effects. In this example, Nexium is like a drug consisting of just the green M&Ms. Not surprisingly, AstraZeneca was able to demonstrate that a 40mg dose of Nexium was more effective

---

* Basically, if to help a patient you need a drug that can reach into a right-hand shaped crevice in a problematic protein to turn it off, then don't go throwing in a mixture of right and left hands to do the job because you have no idea what those extra left hands are off doing throughout the body.

† Technically named gastroesophageal reflux disorder (GERD).

than 40mg of Prilosec, the highest marketed dose of Prilosec (which makes sense since 40mg of Prilosec includes only 20mg of Nexium green M&Ms diluted with 20mg of useless red M&Ms). AstraZeneca also formulated Nexium into a once-daily pill, which was a nice convenience. Once Prilosec went generic, physicians who wanted to prescribe a more effective treatment to patients for whom the 40mg dose of Prilosec wasn't enough had two options available to them: (a) They could risk prescribing an off-label (i.e., non-FDA-approved) 80mg dose of Prilosec (40mg of green M&Ms mixed with 40mg of the useless red M&Ms, the safety of which had not been formally demonstrated),* or (b) They could prescribe the FDA-approved 40mg dose of Nexium (40mg of pure green M&Ms).† As you would expect, most doctors and patients preferred Nexium, which remained a successful branded drug long after Prilosec went generic, generating over $50 billion of additional revenue for AstraZeneca—and drew not a small amount of public and payer ire over an old dog being paid so handsomely for its new trick.[213]

Competition within a drug class to launch a best-in-class product means a company can't afford to come to market with anything less than the best that it can do (try buying a new car without modern safety features like a rearview camera or ABS brakes). AstraZeneca was competing with other companies to treat heartburn. If it had been able to, AstraZeneca

---

* Before Nexium was approved, many physicians had no choice but to prescribe 80mg of Prilosec, twice the FDA-approved dose, to help patients who were not getting enough relief from just 40mg of Prilosec. After Nexium was approved, some physicians remained comfortable continuing to prescribe a high, off-label dose of generic Prilosec to save the patient and society money, but they did so while taking on potential legal liability if anything went wrong since there was a clinically proven, FDA-approved alternative. Therefore, many physicians preferred to prescribe 40mg of Nexium when a patient needed more than 40mg of generic Prilosec.

† Interestingly, although AstraZeneca's upgrade of Prilosec to Nexium was aligned with what the FDA was urging the entire industry to do, there would have been no reliable mechanism to reward AstraZeneca for creating Nexium had they not doubled its dose to give it an efficacy advantage over Prilosec. If AstraZeneca had merely tried to market Nexium 20mg, insurance companies could have only covered generic Prilosec 40mg and refused to reimburse for Nexium 20mg without clinical evidence that it was better. And had AstraZeneca merely doubled the dose of Prilosec to demonstrate that 80mg was more effective than 40mg and tried to keep marketing the 80mg dose as a new brand while 40mg of Prilosec went generic, physicians would have felt safe prescribing a double dose of the generic 40mg pill. So it was the combination of making Prilosec purer and doubling the dose to create Nexium 40mg that allowed AstraZeneca to profit from their incremental innovation. By comparison to improving efficacy by doubling the dose, converting Nexium 40mg into a once-daily pill was merely a nice convenience bonus.

would have launched Nexium, a once-daily, pure drug, from the start, instead of starting with a twice-daily, chirally mixed Prilosec. But the ability to make chirally pure drugs inexpensively at a large, commercial scale emerged after Prilosec's launch and therefore had to be worked into a future upgrade. Today, making pure drugs is much more straightforward. So while society paid for what seemed like small tweaks as many older drugs were re-launched in their purer forms as high-priced branded drugs, that novelty now comes standard and is paying off in new ways, sometimes enabling new drugs to come to market that couldn't even have been developed before.

For example, Johnson & Johnson's intranasally delivered depression drug esketamine (an enantiomer of the impure chiral drug ketamine) was approved in 2019, despite ketamine being DEA-monitored, only approved for hospital use (for anesthesia), and otherwise considered an illegal, commonly abused street drug.[214] And, although ketamine's anti-depressive properties have been understood for several years, J&J had to conduct a full clinical development program for esketamine—with all the usual costs that come along with that and, in this case, not without significant risk. So J&J took a decades-old dangerous anesthetic and repurposed it into a proven treatment for depression by employing intranasal formulation technology and chirally pure chemical synthesis to make it *safe enough* to approve for a relatively large population of patients (although its drug label still contains plenty of warnings). Yet, according to those who see esketamine as a low-risk reformulation of a variant of an old drug that some people snorted to get high and that was already suspected to help with depression, J&J merits the public ire that was once directed at Nexium and the EpiPen.[215]

## Incremental Incentives for Incremental Innovation

The question is this: Is $50 billion (the amount Nexium generated for AstraZeneca) a fair price for society to pay for a clinically proven, FDA-approved, once-daily, more effective derivation of a generic drug? Are there any ways by which society could have had it for less?

One way would be for the FDA to have offered to extend any company selling an impure chiral branded drug extra market exclusivity, let's say an extra six months of sales, in exchange for using newer manufacturing techniques to switch the drug to a pure enantiomer. At the time, Prilosec was the world's best-selling drug, with revenue peaking at more than $6 billion/year—so every extra six months of those sales would be extremely attractive to any company. And further upgrading the drug to a once-daily and developing a higher, more-effective dose could have been incentivized with additional, similarly short exclusivity extensions. In other words, AstraZeneca could have been incentivized to upgrade Prilosec to the pure, higher-dose, once-daily version that we know as Nexium 40mg for only an extra 18 months of Prilosec revenue.*

The idea of offering additional market exclusivity by regulatory fiat is not novel. Exclusivity periods of varying duration have been legislated to incent companies to test drugs in children, to develop drugs for small, special populations of patients, or to bring off-patent molecules to market in the US.

The Hatch-Waxman Act of 1984 and subsequent acts, such as the Food and Drug Administration Modernization Act (FDAMA) in 1997, recognized that sometimes a new patent is impossible or can't reliably encourage a company to develop a drug candidate into a product or to characterize it in ways that would benefit society. For example, FDAMA gave the FDA the ability to grant companies a six-month extension of an existing patent in exchange for running studies of their drugs to determine whether they could be safely and effectively used for children.

Consider that children have different metabolisms and are smaller, yet sometimes they need anti-depressants, analgesics, antibiotics, chemotherapy, and, increasingly, drugs for diabetes and hypertension. In many cases, it was not worth the expense and risk for companies to test their drugs in the much smaller pediatric population when it's so much easier to run trials in adults, the larger market.† So, for example,

---

* AstraZeneca would probably have just stuck with the Prilosec brand name.

† In this case, risk can refer to the possibility that a child experiences some adverse event in the clinical trial which might or might not be due to the drug being studied and then all physicians become more cautious using the drug in adults, putting the drug's sales in that large adult market at risk, even if the drug has already been proven to have a favorable benefit-risk profile in adults.

without trials incentivized by the FDA granting six months of extra exclusivity for pediatric studies, physicians would have to guess what dose of Lyrica should be given to a seven-year old for neuropathic pain, as opposed to being able to refer to the drug's label. It's far better that drugs go generic after we know how to use them properly, not only in adults but also in children.*

There are even some drugs that lack any patent coverage at the time they come to market. For example, there may be a drug that has been used in Europe for decades for a particular disorder that could also benefit American patients. However, no company would bother to go through the trouble of developing this drug for the US market, investing the money to run new trials to FDA standards, without some period of market exclusivity. Generics would simply be able to swarm in, preventing the company that did the work of bringing the drug to the US market from generating a return on its investment.

So for these cases and a number of others, the Orphan Drug Act of 1983, Hatch-Waxman Act, and, more recently, the Affordable Care Act of 2010, offered anywhere from 3-12 years of market exclusivity for a variety of drug categories, including biologics (12 years), drugs intended for an orphan market of under <200,000 patients (seven years), a small-molecule drug not available in any form in the US for a non-orphan market (five years), or a different dose or formulation of a drug that is already available in the US (three years).

Unlike pediatric exclusivity, which tacks six months onto the end of a period of patent protection, these other exclusivities run in parallel to a patent (and therefore are redundant if a company has a patent, which typically offers a longer period of market exclusivity). These FDA-granted exclusivities therefore only offer a fallback incentive in case there is nothing

---

* Once drugs are generic, there are essentially no incentives or mechanism for anyone to continue studying them to learn how they should be used in children or for new diseases except to find a way to convert them into a novel formulation or employ some other kind of incremental tweak, which would come with an entire new patent period, which may result in society paying more for that upgrade than what it would have cost had it been incentivized with a short exclusivity extension prior to the original drug going generic.

about a drug that the company can patent reliably to get the monopoly it needs to justify developing the drug.*

Given the rules of the game, AstraZeneca's Nexium strategy was logical. Unfortunately for society, relying on patents to incentivize Prilosec's incremental upgrades into Nexium instead of granting incremental exclusivity extension earned AstraZeneca far more profit than would have been enough to elicit those upgrades. To any proponent of a market-based economy (as opposed to a centrally planned one run by a government that claims to know the value of all things), this may sound heretical. But I picked the extreme risk/reward imbalance of the Prilosec/Nexium example in the hope that all capitalists would agree that this innovation could have been incentivized under a different scheme. Simply granting AstraZeneca six months of extra exclusivity for the whole Prilosec franchise to upgrade it to a pure enantiomer, six months more to upgrade it to a once-daily pill, and another six months to explore the safety and effectiveness of a higher dose would have generated an extra ~$9 billion for AstraZeneca, more than most drugs generate during their entire patent life. This new best form of Prilosec would have gone generic around 2003, twelve years earlier than Nexium actually did, which would have saved society over $40 billion.

## Lyrica Competes with Itself

Pfizer's original version of the pain drug Lyrica (generic name pregabalin) must be taken twice a day and went generic in 2019. Patents for the once-daily version of pregabalin, known as Lyrica CR, won't expire for another eight years. Insurance companies can leverage the availability of twice-daily pregabalin, deciding they won't cover Lyrica CR unless Pfizer drops the price to something close to the generic. In response, Pfizer will no doubt offer generous copay assistance to patients who are prescribed Lyrica CR and offer PBMs generous rebates to keep the drug on their formularies (i.e., society gets a discount thanks to Lyrica CR competing with pregabalin generics). Most patients will get regular

---

* Sometimes companies try to tweak the formulation of that drug so that they can get a patent, hoping to enjoy a longer period of exclusivity, but if the tweak is too modest, then the patent may be challenged in court by companies wanting to launch generics as soon as the Hatch-Waxman exclusivity expires.

pregabalin and some will get Lyrica CR. The goal, per the Biotech Social Contract, would be for Pfizer to generate enough revenue from Lyrica CR while it's still branded to have justified its development, after which time Lyrica CR too will go generic. What society most likely will wind up paying for this incremental upgrade will be modest compared to the investment necessary to get pregabalin in the first place (i.e., Pfizer's sales of the original Lyrica), and yet eventually everyone who needs pregabalin will be taking an inexpensive once-daily generic version. But what if Pfizer had been offered just six more months of exclusivity for Lyrica in exchange for letting Lyrica CR go generic at the same time? All patients who need pregabalin would already be enjoying the convenience and cost-effective efficacy of generic pregabalin CR.

## Seeking New Uses for Old Drugs

The Orphan Drug Act of 1983 was specifically passed to incentivize companies to develop drugs for smaller, orphan populations (up to 200,000 patients in the US).* When companies can invent a new drug to treat an orphan disease, they know they will have a long period of patent-protected market exclusivity but still might feel that the risks and costs of pursuing the program are too high. In these cases, the Act offers them tax breaks, research subsidies, a more open dialogue with the FDA on how to develop the drug, and accelerated review of their application to launch the drug earlier than would normally be possible.[216] If a drug has no patent protection, the law grants the company seven years of exclusivity. That's not bad, though Europe is more generous, offering ten years of exclusivity to any new drug.

---

* The term "orphan disease" referred to diseases that were considered too small (formally defined as <200,000 patients in the US) for anyone to pursue and were typically neglected by innovators who couldn't justify the cost and risk of pursuing treatments for them. Today, many orphan diseases are far from orphaned, in some cases with dozens of companies competing to figure out how to solve them, which offers hope to millions of patients. While the number of Americans suffering from any one orphan disease is small, there are approximately 7,000 of these rare disorders and an estimated 25-30 million Americans (7.6%-9%) suffer from one or more orphan diseases.

"FAQs About Rare Diseases," NIH, GARD, updated Nov. 30, 2017, https://rarediseases.info.nih.gov/diseases/pages/31/faqs-about-rare-diseases.

The Orphan Drug Act represents an example of how society through its government created a path in which the drug industry is incentivized to solve a societal problem. It works in some cases, but we need more such policies in place for situations where solely market-based incentives aren't enough to drive innovators and investors to develop a drug that is scientifically and technically developable.

For example, existing drugs are sometimes found to be useful for treating diseases for which they were not specifically developed. If a drug like this is nearing the end of its patent term, neither the current manufacturer nor future generic manufacturers would be able to financially justify risking capital on clinical trials to explore broader usage. Certainly a company in this situation might try to alter the original drug in some way and develop only this new version for the new indication.* But there is no guarantee that physicians will prescribe the modified drug as opposed to the old generic version for the new use. In this scenario, the government could offer the company a patent term extension in exchange for researching and testing its drug in a new indication. The length of the extension could even be tied to the drug's revenues; the lower the anticipated yearly revenues, the longer the extension would have to be to allow for the company to recoup costs.

In many cases, non-profits, including universities, the US National Institutes of Health (NIH), and other grant-giving groups, step in to fund studies for broader usage of older drugs. This helps society get more out of the generic armamentarium it already owns, which is hugely beneficial.†

Some might think non-profit funding is "purer" than profit-seeking investment because the latter leaves drug manufacturers beholden to shareholders, and that more drug development should be funded by non-profits. But it is not realistic to count on this kind of funding to have a wider impact on clinical development. The federal government contributes about 23% of

---

* Recall an earlier footnote on pg. 184 about Prilosec/Nexium. Only the combination of developing both a patentable pure enantiomer and testing a higher dose gave AstraZeneca the incentive to show that Nexium could treat heartburn better than Prilosec. Were Prilosec not a mixture of two enantiomers and therefore unable to be upgraded into a pure enantiomer, AstraZeneca might not have studied the higher dose to properly show that it was even more effective (though some physicians would have just used a higher dose off-label).

† See Prazosin case study in Chapter 15.

the total biomedical research dollars in the US, mostly through the NIH, but only a tiny fraction of that goes to clinical research.[217] Research funding from all other non-profit sources adds up to only 13% of the total.[218] The remaining 64% of biomedical research funding (80% of which is spending on clinical trials, as opposed to animal studies and basic research) is supplied by the biopharmaceutical industry.[219] There simply isn't enough non-profit funding to do what industry does.

Many drugs are invented entirely within companies. Most of those that do get their starts in NIH-funded laboratories offer only hints of activity in test tubes and mice. These compounds are often still too toxic to humans or so weak that a patient would have to take a higher dose than can be cost-effectively manufactured. Chemists that work for companies are experts at turning those "rough drafts" of drugs into much more potent, safer chemicals that are more likely to become well-tolerated, effective drugs, often through extensive and expensive trial and error.

## Why Can't Non-profits Do Everything?

In theory, a non-profit could raise money from donors to invest in R&D instead of a for-profit company offering a financial return to investors to inspire them to risk their money on funding its projects. Since profit margins for the biopharmaceutical industry run about 20%, if the industry converted entirely to a non-profit model (i.e., relying on donations instead of return-seeking investment), then branded drugs would cost society about a fifth less. That's not enough of a discount to make them affordable to individual patients; only proper insurance without onerous cost-sharing can do that.

But if you are still thinking that a 20% discount sounds attractive, keep in mind that, historically, capitalism has been a more reliable driver of innovation than altruism, which can be a bit patchy, relying on how good a donation makes a donor feel, as opposed to the powerfully motivating promise of greater financial security that investing offers. Hopefully, those who struggle to reconcile healthcare with profit-motive will recognize that, in the long run, as long as all expensive products eventually go generic (via contractual genericization if necessary) and insurance allows patients to afford what their physicians prescribe, the Biotech Social Contract is actually built on a sustainable, functional, utopian ideology.

## Humira—What If?

AbbVie's Humira is the most successful drug in history. Launched in 2002, it continues to generate nearly $20 billion/year (~$15 billion of that in the US) and isn't expected to go biosimilar in the US until 2023*—which means that, in essence, Humira will have enjoyed almost 21 years of market exclusivity. How has AbbVie been able to shield its flagship drug from biosimilar competition for so long? The answer, filing a thicket of patents for what some consider technicalities, has stirred a lot of controversy.[220]

Humira is an anti-TNF antibody initially developed to treat rheumatoid arthritis (RA). It wasn't the first of this class, but because it arrived as an auto-injector that made it relatively easy for patients to give themselves twice-monthly, subcutaneous shots, it was the most convenient. Other anti-TNFs had to be infused or injected more frequently. AbbVie then expanded the uses of Humira to include psoriatic arthritis (2005), ankylosing spondylitis in adults (2006), Crohn's disease in adults (2007), chronic plaque psoriasis in adults (2008), polyarticular juvenile idiopathic arthritis in children (2008), ulcerative colitis (2012), Crohn's disease in children (2014), and hidradenitis suppurativa (2015). In 2018, AbbVie launched an upgraded version of the auto-injector which causes fewer injection site reactions.

If the government had taken the approach suggested by this chapter (and Chapter 8) and granted AbbVie an extra six months for each of the eight new uses and the one tolerability upgrade, it would have tacked 4.5 additional years onto Humira's patent protection (i.e., as suggested in Chapter 8, delayed its Contract Generic Date by 4.5 years). That means Humira would have ended up enjoying a total of 19.5 years of exclusivity

---

* Europe has allowed some biosimilars on the market as of 2019. Biosimilars are expected in the US in 2023. Even then, Humira will enjoy orphan exclusivity for hidradenitis suppurativa until 2025.

for nearly all of its uses before the first biosimilars launch in the US. Given that each six months is worth $7.5 billion in sales to AbbVie, that's a lot of incentive.[221]

But if Humira actually starts to "go biosimilar" in 2023, then it would have enjoyed almost 21 years' market exclusivity. While that's not much longer than 19.5 years, considering that each year costs the US roughly $15 billion, the patent-based extension costs considerably more than the incentive scheme I propose.

I picked Humira as an example because it is the top-selling branded drug in the US and easily drives home the point of how delays to the introduction of biosimilars and generics can cost society dearly. But the incentives I propose should be strong enough to encourage companies to upgrade drugs with lower sales as well. The 20th best-selling drug in the US in 2018 was the HIV treatment Truvada with $2.6 billion in sales that year, still a lot (a six-month extension for this drug would offer a reward of $1.3 billion in additional revenues).[222] If we introduced this new scheme just for drugs that sell over $1 billion/year in the US, which I estimate would apply to less than 100 drugs and yet would have the most impact on overall US drug spending,[223] then six months of additional branded life would amount to at least $500 million of revenue per upgrade.* For drugs with lower sales or where an upgrade might be straightforward but still cost a lot, longer extensions might be necessary to entice companies to invest in upgrades. Companies would negotiate for the length of their extension with the FDA up front,† before incurring additional development costs, so there would be room to tailor the incentives to the specific cost and benefit of the upgrade.

As for Humira, AbbVie has certainly stretched the Biotech Social Contract by exploiting many features of our patent and regulatory system, illuminating where society is vulnerable. Still, Humira is a remarkable drug with many uses that helps a large number of patients manage a variety of

---

* This does not mean $500 million of profit, though these are the highest profit-margin products for the industry and so I would estimate every $500 million more of revenues could generate at least $300 million of after-tax profits.

† Or, as proposed in Chapter 8, a new Generic Drug Contracting Bureau.

diseases and should be much more affordable within a decade as a valuable addition to our generic (biosimilar, in this case) armamentarium.*

## Changing Incentives with Cautions

Some drugs sell relatively poorly but have the potential to be much more useful, either through an upgrade or through expansion of the market— sometimes both! The EpiPen is a perfect example, as discussed in detail in the previous chapter. If the suggestion in this chapter had been applied to the EpiPen, the government might have offered a company earning modest revenues on epinephrine another six months or even three years of extended market exclusivity in exchange for making the upgrade to the EpiPen. But considering how poorly epinephrine was selling at the time, that might not have been enough. Even three years is not enough time to both invest in expanding the market by educating physicians, parents, and schools, as Mylan did, and then generate an adequate return before generics come in. Had we relied on short market-exclusivity extensions to incentivize that upgrade, the EpiPen might not ever have been invented and society would still be unaware and unprepared for anaphylaxis. That would be counterproductive. The current patent-based system was necessary to allow a long enough period of exclusivity so that a string of companies, ultimately Mylan (and maybe continuing to Kaleo and its Auvi-Q), could figure out how to unlock its utility.

Indeed not all upgrades are easy, so we should be careful about assuming that what may seem like a small increment of innovation really can be incentivized with a modest extension of market exclusivity. There was a time when extending the release of a drug from a pill so that it can be taken once-daily instead of twice was in fact difficult.

Switching from a system that awards new patents to one that offers patent extensions or other additional exclusivities would admittedly not

---

* And if its price doesn't come down substantially due to biosimilar competition, as some fear, it would be a good candidate for contractual genericization.

Mark Trusheim et al., "Biologics Are Natural Monopolies (Part 2): A Proposal For Post-Exclusivity Price Regulation of Biologics," *Health Affairs*, April 15, 2019, https://www.healthaffairs.org/do/10.1377/hblog20190405.839549/full/.

be simple. Regulations with this aim would have to ensure that companies are incentivized to discover new uses for their drugs and drive changes in standards of care. This applies to both easily understood upgrades (e.g., converting a twice-daily drug into a once-daily; formulating an injectable drug at a more neutral pH so that it causes less irritation) and those that are challenging. They would require the regulator—and, indeed, maybe even the courts—to make distinctions between what is a difficult or complex upgrade, worthy of new patent protection and the lengthy monopoly that entails, and what is sufficiently incentivized by shorter exclusivities.

None of that will be easy, but that shouldn't stop us from trying (I propose a framework at the end of this chapter). Our current system allows companies to extend exclusivity beyond the intended scope of the Biotech Social Contract, yet sometimes fails to incentivize industry to explore new uses or upgrades for existing drugs. Who knows how many older drugs that are part of the generic drug mountain are trapped there in forms that are less convenient or less safe than they could be? How many conditions could be treated with drugs that we already have, if only there were enough incentive for companies to uncover their broader potential?

## How Payers Incentivize Innovation...or Fail to

The biopharmaceutical company Vertex has developed a set of drugs called potentiators and correctors to treat cystic fibrosis (CF). A potentiator called Kalydeco works very well on its own for the small sliver of CF patients with a certain genetic mutation of the disease. Vertex combined Kalydeco with a corrector molecule to create a combination treatment, Orkambi, that offers only a modest benefit for most other CF patients. Appreciating that Orkambi wasn't the best it could do, Vertex developed a triple combination of Kalydeco and two correctors that worked much better. This new cocktail, named Trikafta and approved in the US in late 2019, is profoundly transformative for the approximately 100,000 CF patients around the world.

Kalydeco costs roughly $300,000/year per patient in the US and less in European markets ($267,000 in the UK), where it is reasonably well covered for the small patient population that needs it.[224] But when it came to

Orkambi, which is reimbursed at $273,000 in the US, negotiations didn't go well in all European markets. Although Germany negotiated a price of $163,000, the UK rejected Vertex's proposed price. The company responded by publicly questioning the UK's support of biotech innovation and, according to some, even considered relocating its European offices and laboratories from the UK.[225] France, which pays the European rate for Kalydeco, insisted on a hugely discounted price for Orkambi (80% lower than other European countries). France and the UK seemed to be saying, "We're willing to pay your price, but only for drugs that work well." In response, Vertex canceled clinical trials of its newer triple combination agents in France on the basis that it would be unethical to test drugs on patients who might then not be able to access them once they are approved.[226]

But if France or the UK apply the same reimbursement standard to Trikafta once it's approved as it did to Kalydeco, Vertex should feel reassured that Trikafta will be reimbursed and continue to enroll French patients in trials even if France insists on playing hardball over the less effective Orkambi. For its part, France could have agreed to reimburse Orkambi for the next couple of years at the standard European rate, knowing that patients on Orkambi would indeed be upgraded to Trikafta once it was approved. The net result would have been a brief period of paying for at least some efficacy in the spirit of supporting innovation that had a high likelihood of yielding a much better treatment in the near future.

France and the UK acknowledged the value of Vertex's innovation by reimbursing Kalydeco at a high price (even if lower than in the US) for the few patients for whom it's appropriate and, rather than settling for a subpar first-generation combination therapy for the broader CF population, seem prepared to hold out for the good stuff.*

It might seem reasonable for a payer to take this approach to negotiating prices. After all, who wants to pay a premium for something that has limited efficacy? But it seems somewhat less reasonable when you consider

---

* Though the UK did eventually come to an agreement with Vertex.

Vertex, *Vertex Announces Agreement with NHS England for Access to All Licensed Cystic Fibrosis Medicines*, Oct. 24, 2019, accessed Nov. 1, 2019, https://investors.vrtx.com/news-releases/news-release-details/vertex-announces-agreement-nhs-england-access-all-licensed.

that these payers are deciding what they are willing to pay only after a company has incurred the expense of bringing the new therapy to market. On the other hand, if France had published, in advance of the development of Orkambi, how much it would be willing to pay for various degrees of benefit, it would have allowed Vertex to make an informed decision about whether to bring it to market in France. That might seem like a lot to ask.

In what other industry are innovators afforded such assurances by future customers? It's actually more common than you might think. For example, in the aviation and defense industries, in which companies may spend billions of dollars and many years developing expensive planes and technologies, pre-negotiated agreements are commonplace. Given the investment necessary to bring something new to market, companies in these fields have no choice but to line up customers in advance at pre-negotiated prices. That's also how the US government contracts with biotechnology companies to develop biodefense products such as pandemic vaccines.

Using pre-negotiated agreements would certainly help companies in the biopharmaceutical field make informed decisions about what to develop and where to bring it to market. The problem is that the calculations performed to arrive at a pre-negotiated price will likely undervalue the future benefit of a drug—especially if they employ conventional cost-effectiveness models that do not factor in eventual genericization. The UK's NICE, for example, does not take genericization into account when determining cost-effectiveness and negotiating prices for drugs.*

Making the methodology clear would be important so that patients who thought their government was underestimating the benefit of an increment of progress would have the opportunity to lobby their governments to reconsider its threshold for what it considered a meaningful and cost-effective benefit (or maybe what appears to be a small benefit on average is really a large benefit for an unpredictable few patients).

In the unique Vertex-France instance, Vertex was already supported by sales of Kalydeco and knew that it would soon launch the undeniably effectively Trikafta worldwide. Therefore, even if Vertex were to offer Orkambi

---

* The UK reimburses many drugs at prices above those NICE deemed cost-effective, which suggests that NICE's calculations are more of a negotiating tactic than a hard line.

globally at a low price in the intervening period, knowing that it could command higher prices once Trikafta got on the market, Vertex's innovation engine would likely not be significantly undermined, at most costing Vertex a few billion in Orkambi sales.

The fact that Vertex was in a position to potentially compromise on Orkambi pricing ought not to be seen as a broadly applicable precedent. Vertex was an anomaly, and on a global scale, France's tactics would rob the world of the benefits of real but incremental innovations potentially serving as the stepping stones to large advances. Most companies that have gotten an incrementally effective drug approved don't already know that their next drug will turn out to be far better, as fortunately turned out to be the case for Vertex. Therefore, failure to get reimbursement for their first version would likely result in those companies not being able to fund the rest of their pipelines.

Imagine if Orkambi were Vertex's first drug, that Trikafta did not yet have compelling proof-of-concept clinical data, and France's hardball tactics were the norm around the world, including the US. If this had been the case, Vertex's stock might have collapsed when news hit that Orkambi would not sell well, making it challenging to get the funds needed to advance Trikafta into trials and robbing patients suffering from cystic fibrosis and their families of the transformative potential of Vertex's ultimate innovation.

## When the Current Incentives Aren't Enough

Sometimes, even under the current system, there is not enough incentive to create a particular drug that would be useful to some patients. For example, a company might run out of money and never finish clinical trials of a new molecule. Later, it may dawn on someone that finishing development of the abandoned drug would still be a good idea. They might try to raise money from investors to restart trials, but the abandoned drug's patent may soon expire.

In Europe, the regulatory system simply grants any approved new drug a period of market exclusivity that lasts the longer of ten years or until its patents expire. In the US, if the patient population is small (orphan, <200,000 patients), the exclusivity period is seven years, per the Orphan Drug Act of 1983, but if it's a larger market, then the period is only five years, per the Hatch-Waxman Act of 1984.

Although Europe is more generous in its period of market exclusivity, it is notoriously ungenerous in its willingness to pay for drugs. Therefore, in many cases, both markets offer weak incentives. If a company were to pitch investors on the idea of funding development of a drug with dwindling patent coverage that would receive ten years of market exclusivity in Europe and five years in the US, investors might refuse unless the drug could be reformulated somehow and re-patented to provide a longer period of exclusivity for the US market where the company would expect to generate profits more reliably (as discussed in Chapter 10, due to America's unwillingness to deny). Absent such patentable tweaks, there's currently no path forward for funding development of the drug.

The US should adopt a policy like Europe's, simply granting a minimum of ten years of regulatory exclusivity to any approved novel drug.

In cases where a drug is already generic but isn't being developed for a promising new use, then even ten years of exclusivity for the new indication might not be motivating since investors would fear that physicians would simply prescribe the generic version for the new use. J&J was only able to justify developing intranasally delivered, chirally pure esketamine for depression despite the availability of generic, infused, impure ketamine (approved for anesthesia but not depression) precisely because of how extensively it upgraded the generic ketamine into a depression drug. While physicians can elect to treat patients with depression using generic, infused ketamine, most won't consider it an acceptable alternative to J&J's FDA-approved, intranasal, pure esketamine.

When an existing generic is already well-suited for a new use but just isn't approved for it yet, the FDA could offer different kinds of incentives to get companies to run trials for the new indication and submit it for approval so that it could be reflected in the drug's label. The agency already has an array of "priority review vouchers" that companies can earn when they develop drugs for tropical diseases or pediatric conditions, for example.[227] These vouchers typically let a company speed up FDA review of any drug it wants from the standard ten months to six months—and so they are valuable and tradable assets valued these days at around $100 million.* Similarly, a reward for getting an old generic approved for a new use could be an "extension voucher" for a six-month exclusivity extension for any other drug (though one would want to limit the number of such extensions one could put towards one drug or else AbbVie would buy them all to put towards Humira!).

## Funding Awareness of a Generic's New Use

For reasons discussed in Chapter 12, there would be no profit in marketing a generic drug for a new use, so how would doctors come to learn of it? An awareness campaign funded by the FDA could let both doctors and patients know about the inexpensive drug's new use. Of course, putting a government agency at the center of generic drug repurposing might mire the process in bureaucracy, but that would still be better than what we have now.† An alternative would be to contract with a third-party marketing firm to promote the drug for its new use in exchange for charging all generic manufacturers a fixed price per unit sold that they would then factor into their prices (akin to my proposal in Chapter 12 for how to keep promoting awareness of the EpiPen after it has gone generic). Society's total spending on the drug would go up by the amount of this added fee, which would fund the education campaign, but the generics companies would still compete with one another on price to win share of the now larger market (expanded by the new use of the drug).

---

* If a company is eager to start selling a drug that it thinks will generate $1 billion per year in sales, then it would be worth purchasing a priority review voucher for $100 million to bring that drug to market 4 months sooner, especially if it is competing with others to get to market first. These vouchers were worth more in the past when there were fewer of them, but drug developers responded to the incentive, developed a bunch of drugs the FDA wanted brought to market, and introduced enough vouchers into the market to bring down their price.

† In nearly all the cases of an old drug being brought to market for a new use, either the development was funded by a non-profit or NIH (which typically don't fund such efforts all the way through to FDA approval), or the company found something about that drug it could patent. That leaves a lot of untapped potential for repurposing old drugs.

As much as our current system of mostly patent-based incentives appears overly generous in rewarding incremental innovation, such innovation can be quite valuable in the long run, and we need the right incentives, no more no less, to encourage as much as of it as possible.

## Contractual Genericization: Proposing a Roadmap

Now that we have covered both contractual genericization in Chapter 8 and the use of brief monopoly extensions for standard incremental innovations in this chapter, we have the key elements to explore how contractual genericization might actually work.

First, we would need a regulator to ensure that all drugs go generic without undue delay, in accordance with the Biotech Social Contract. Let's say Congress passes a Contract Generic Drug Act, creating the Generic Drug Contracting Bureau (the "Bureau") to oversee this process.

Then, every time a company files for FDA approval of a new drug, it would register the patents protecting its drug with the Bureau and sign a contract to ensure the price of the drug drops when those initial patents expire without *undue* delay (allowing for due delays for legitimate upgrades, as we'll see). The purpose of this contract would be two-fold: 1) To serve as a failsafe* in case the price of the branded drug doesn't drop due to conventional generic competition,† and 2) To provide a mechanism for granting brief monopoly extensions to incentivize incremental upgrades of marketed branded drugs in lieu of the current, mostly patent-based system.

The contract would stipulate that if no generic manufacturer has received approval for a generic by the registered patent expiration date, the originator company would be obligated to drop the US price of its drug. I suggest that a fair contract generic price could be twice the cost

---

\* I'm not proposing a wholesale alternative to the current generics marketplace since encouraging conventional generics manufacturers to participate in the genericization processes would protect against shortages if the originator encounters a manufacturing problem. Also, competition among manufacturers can drive cost-reductions that lower prices more than if just one company kept making the drug at a regulated, fixed price.

† Which would be the case if a drug is ungenericizable (a natural monopoly), such as a gene or cell therapy, or in the case of a drug that is hard to genericize/biosimilarize (a natural oligopoly), as is potentially the case with biologics and complex drug-device combination products.

of production and distribution (i.e., a 50% gross margin),* where the price would remain indefinitely. Since the price would depend on company's costs, the Bureau would audit the financials of the production facility to confirm that they are properly reported. The idea would be that the production facility's costs would be set at no more than what it would cost if the facility were run as a standalone company.

If one or more generic manufacturers receives FDA approval of a generic by the time of the originator's patent expiration date, then the originator would be obligated to drop its price no later than two years after the patent expiration date. For every additional generic approved, the expiration grace period would be extended by three months to a maximum of three years, creating an incentive for the originator to help more generics come to market, which would help protect against supply shortages and give the free market a chance to bring prices down for drugs that can go generic the old-fashioned way. Still, the contract would remain in place to ensure that society pays no more than two-times the cost of production in the long term in case the free market doesn't get the job done.†

If the originator wants to make a straightforward incremental upgrade to the drug before it goes generic, the company could apply to the Bureau

---

* The specific pricing formula requires additional study and will be the subject of a future analysis. What matters is that the price be relatively low, simulating what society expects from a generic. The cost of producing most drugs is typically less than 10% of their branded net prices. Therefore, if a branded drug priced at $10/pill costs $1 to make, then limiting its contract generic price to $2/pill would result in 80% savings. If the pill costs 25 cents to make and its contract generic price were cut to 50 cents, that would result in 95% savings. However, in this case, I'm proposing that the price of the contract generic be based on the cost of both producing and distributing the drug, the latter being a small cost in most cases but potentially high in the case of special drugs that require special handling and storage conditions, such as radioisotopes, products that need to be shipped frozen, and living cells. Ultimately, the right markup might be higher or lower than I propose here. What's important is that it confer meaningful savings for society relative to the status quo, that the math be transparent, and that the contract generic price be consistently high enough to motivate companies to want to hold the contract and compete for who can service it at a low cost while still preserving quality.

† There would be no need for the contract to force a price cap on the originator if competition has already reduced the price to less than two times the cost of production. But the contract would remain in place in case the number of generics dwindles and the price creeps up. If the originator discontinues producing the drug because it is already conventionally genericized, the Bureau would transfer the contract to another active manufacturer of the drug to ensure that it remains a failsafe in case there are fewer competitors someday and the price starts to rise above the contract price. One way or another, every drug America relies on for which society has paid off the mortgage would be under contract with the Bureau to ensure that its price stays at or below a price pegged to its cost of production.

for a delay of genericization, indicating how long an extension it is seeking in order to incentivize development of the upgrade. The Bureau would publish a list of standard, precedented, and relatively common incremental upgrades that are comparatively straightforward to implement compared to developing a novel drug.[*] For expediency, applications would be considered automatically approved within 90 days unless the Bureau explicitly objects. For drugs with greater than $1 billion per year in US sales at the time of the upgrade's approval by the FDA, the Bureau would likely grant a short extension (for example, six months). For drugs with lower sales, it might grant a longer extension, possibly based on a formula linked to the drug's most recent sales (i.e., the lower, the longer).[†]

Because the industry would rely on timely decisions from the Bureau, the Bureau would need to be well-staffed with knowledgeable people.[‡] The funding for such an agency would come from the savings society realizes from implementing contractual genericization.

When deciding whether to recognize an upgrade as worthy of an extension, the Bureau could seek input from patients, physicians, and the FDA, just as the FDA often seeks input from many stakeholders when considering whether to approve a new drug and which warnings and uses to include in its label. If the Bureau rejects a company's application for an extension application because it does not consider the proposed upgrade sufficiently meaningful, the company would know that it shouldn't waste its time or money pursuing that upgrade. If the Bureau grants an extension for a proposed upgrade, then the company could decide to pursue its

---

[*] For example, a once-daily version of a twice-daily pill; a dissolving film version for people who struggle to swallow pills; a less painful and/or easier injectable formation; a pure enantiomer like Nexium of a chiral drug like Prilosec; demonstrating that a higher dose is more effective or a lower dose is safer but equally effective; uncovering a way to use the drug more safely, possibly by restricting its use with certain other drugs or in certain patients; an additional use of a drug to treat a new disease, and other examples discussed earlier in this chapter. The six-month pediatric extension that the FDA already grants to companies that study how their drugs can be used properly in children would also be included as worthy of a genericization delay, as it is now.

[†] Both the duration of extensions and the sales thresholds should be the subject of study and debate by all stakeholders. I include specific values here as placeholders to help the reader conceptualize how this could work.

[‡] While the FDA must have a large staff to review all approved drugs and thousands of drug candidates at various stages of testing, the Bureau would be primarily focused on the hundreds of already approved branded drugs and otherwise hard- or impossible-to-genericize drugs under contract, so I would expect it to be much smaller than the FDA.

development and, upon FDA approval of the upgraded version of the drug, would receive the agreed-upon extension of the contractual genericization date.

The originator would be eligible for as many extensions as the number of standard upgrades the Bureau and FDA approve. As discussed earlier, under this scheme, AbbVie's Humira would have earned nine six-month extensions (4.5 extra years): One for improved tolerability and eight for demonstrating that the drug can treat eight additional diseases.

Per the originator's contract with the Bureau, the company would agree to narrowly license the patents covering any upgrades to generics manufacturers so that they could launch generics of the upgraded drug on or after the new expiry date.* To the extent that generics companies struggle with the steps to create a generic, the FDA and Bureau would be able to direct the originator to transfer certain know-how to those manufacturers (e.g., trade-secrets for how to make the drug at a high quality).† It would be in the interest of the originator to have one or more other generics approved by the expiration date since that would delay the contractual genericization date by 2-3 years, during which time the originator would have to compete on price but might expect to be able to sell its product at a price higher than the relatively low price set by its contract. Absent any generic competition by the extended contractual genericization date, the contract would require the upgraded drug to drop in price.

Since the cost of production might rise over time and the market for the drug might shrink, a company under a contract would have the right to submit audited financials to the Bureau showing that its costs per dose are rising and argue that it needs to raise its price.

There might come a day when the originator may not want to keep making its drug at this low cost. If there are already generics on the market and the price of those drugs is already less than the originator's contract

---

* The intent of the license would be to allow generic companies only to make that particular drug. The license would not allow other companies to use the invention taught in the patent for their own purposes, such as to make their own novel drugs. My aim is to interfere with the patent system as little as is necessary to enable contractual genericization while preserving it to stimulate innovation.

† As part of its mandate to regulate monopolies, the Federal Trade Commission (FTC) already has the legal right to compel technology transfer from a monopoly to a competitor. So what I'm proposing here is a standard tool for ensuring a competitive free market.

generic price, then society would have no need for the originator to keep making its drug.* But if the drug is not conventionally genericizable or if there are too few generics to keep the price as low as twice the cost of production, then the originator would not have the right to stop production. The originator would have to either continue to manufacture the drug at the contract generic price or sell the contract to a qualified manufacturer.

It would make sense for the Bureau to work closely with a few vetted contract manufacturers that already produce drugs on behalf of many drug companies.† Somebody has to be ready to take over a manufacturing facility from an originator that proves unable or unwilling to meet the requirements of its contract for low-cost, high-quality production. In fact, the Bureau could periodically put the right to take over production of each contract generic out to bid, obligating the originator to sell the contract (at a price pre-defined in the generic contract) to the one that most credibly promises to make the drug to a high quality standard and sell it at a lower cost, unless the originator can match the price. Society's right to benefit from the drugs on which the mortgage has been paid off must be honored.

A company with a drug under contract may want to develop a new drug based on the first one but involving complex, non-standard upgrades and considerable development risk (e.g., a novel chemical variant with new properties or an oral formulation of an injectable drug). The originator would be able to seek confirmation from the Bureau that it recognizes the new drug's novelty at any point during the drug's development, including before the company has started funding expensive clinical trials, so that it knows whether it could look forward to the incentive of a

---

* In case the competitive markets someday fail (e.g., generics manufacturers drops out and price competition eases), the Bureau would technically always want a company to hold the genericization contract for a drug. Therefore, if the originator discontinues production, the Bureau would transfer the contract to any other qualified company making the drug. If the price climbs, that company would be obligated to make the drug at no higher than the contract price. It would make sense for there to be a high-quality, fallback company that is always there to take over a contract that no one else wants, though if the contract sets the contract price properly, someone should always want to make a drug since profits should be guaranteed.

† I can even imagine that there may arise a non-profit manufacturer or else a for-profit one based in a low-tax haven (akin to funds that acquire drug royalties) that specializes in low-cost manufacturing and manages to outbid most others to take over many genericization contracts. It's better for society that drugs like Daraprim end up with such a low-cost manufacturing specialist under a genericization contract than price-jacked in the hands of a Turing.

long patent-protected period of branded pricing. But if the Bureau doesn't consider the drug novel, the company could either (a) Stop wasting time and money on its development; (b) Enlist the help of physicians, patients, and the FDA to make the case that the new drug is distinct enough and challenging enough to merit the longer exclusivity than the incremental extension process permits;* or (c) Accept an exclusivity extension of the original drug.

If the Bureau recognizes the new drug's novelty, the company would register its patents with the Bureau before FDA approval and receive a new exclusivity expiration date, subject to extension based on future approved standard upgrades. In that case, the originator would still be obligated to honor the contract on its first drug and therefore the novel version would have to compete with its low-cost predecessor, just as Lyrica CR has to compete with generic pregabalin. If the second drug is meaningfully better than the first and sells well despite its predecessor being generic, society should be glad to pay off the mortgage on this advance, since it too will someday go generic and offer lasting value.

This rough framework for how contractual genericization could work would surely benefit from input from all relevant stakeholders, including the FDA, payers, and the biopharmaceutical industry.

---

* The FDA already has experience determining when there is an unmet need and using incentives to encourage companies to develop everything from antibiotics for rare kinds of infections to treatments for pediatric diseases.

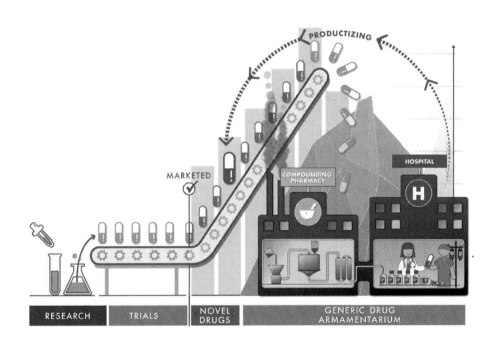

RESEARCH

TRIALS

NOVEL
DRUGS

MARKETED

PRODUCTIZING

COMPOUNDING
PHARMACY

HOSPITAL

H

GENERIC DRUG
ARMAMENTARIUM

# 14

## PRODUCTIZING HOMEBREWS: STEALING OR A SERVICE TO SOCIETY?

Sometimes creative physicians invent ways of treating patients with techniques and new formulations of old drugs without the help of drug companies. These are often referred to as "homebrew" therapies, and they are usually unpatented. Bone marrow transplant, in vitro fertilization, and any basic surgery are examples of treatments that were invented by physicians and spread through the medical community.

Prescribing progesterone to prevent preterm birth is an example of a homebrew therapy. Progesterone has long been available as a pharmaceutical, used both for birth control and fertility treatment. Some physicians discovered that they could just have a compounding pharmacy make this generic drug into an injectable solution for $20 per dose to prescribe to certain pregnant women at risk of delivering prematurely to help them carry their babies to term. The medical community ran a few of its own studies, the most influential being an academic study published in 2003 that showed that injected progesterone was better than placebo at preventing preterm births.[228] For the most part, physicians felt confident that it worked and that they knew how to prescribe it and to which patients.

But the FDA prefers that all medicines be manufactured properly to a standard called Good Manufacturing Practice (GMP) and subjected to one or more rigorous clinical trials. A company called KV Pharma obliged by manufacturing injectable progesterone and submitting it for FDA review with the available clinical data. In 2011, contingent on the company committing to running a confirmatory clinical study, KV Pharma received accelerated FDA approval for a branded version of progesterone they called Makena. As an orphan drug, Makena earned seven years of market exclusivity protection. KV Pharma launched Makena at a high list price, $1,500-per-dose (up to $30,000 per pregnancy), with all of the usual room in that number for negotiation with payers.

KV Pharma's list price was met with swift public condemnation. The drug was portrayed as an example of profiteering and price-jacking, since the company was perceived to be reaping profits without having risked anything. Amid the backlash, KV tried to assuage critics by lowering Makena's list price to $690 per dose. It didn't work.[229] The FDA, swayed by public opinion, broke with normal policy and publicly conveyed that it wouldn't stand in the way of compounders continuing to make progesterone for physicians intent on boycotting Makena.[230] After investing resources into bringing it to market and conducting the ongoing confirmatory study, KV Pharma's seven-year term of exclusivity was suddenly not so exclusive. KV Pharma went bankrupt shortly thereafter and in 2014 was acquired by AMAG Pharmaceuticals, which then relaunched Makena at $550 per dose.[231]

That price was obviously still much higher than what compounding pharmacies were charging for injectable progesterone, but the playing field had shifted. Regulators had begun to turn against compounding pharmacies due to substandard and contaminated products produced by some of them (see Chapter 9). Sales of Makena grew to more than $300 million per year before generics launched in 2018.[232]

The real lesson that this case study can impart became clear later. The confirmatory trials for Makena dragged out longer than anticipated, due to slow enrollment, largely because US patients could get the marketed product instead of enrolling in the trial and risking getting a placebo. But in 2019, the results became available, and, surprisingly, it turned out that progesterone is no better at preventing preterm birth than placebo. In addition, some in the healthcare industry had begun to raise concerns that the 2003 study, the one that had sparked the routine use of progesterone for prevention of preterm birth in the first place, was flawed.[233] Women in the placebo arm of that study had a much higher rate of preterm birth than would have been ordinarily expected, possibly because the placebo arm, by pure chance, had more women who had experienced two or more prior preterm births. It seemed possible that the long-held belief in progesterone's efficacy may have rested on a statistical fluke.[*] Worse yet, another study suggested that using progesterone might increase a woman's risk of gestational diabetes.[†]

Ultimately, the FDA's insistence on proper clinical evidence shed light on the shortcomings of an old homebrew remedy. It's not clear whether physicians will stop using Makena, or whether it will be removed from the market altogether.[‡] But one thing is clear: Makena was never the risk-free, exploitative profit opportunity critics made it out to be. Society needed the proper confirmatory study that would never have come about had it

---

[*] Incidentally, KV Pharma's one-time peer Columbia Labs conducted a study of intravaginal progesterone in women at risk of preterm birth because of premature cervical shortening—this was thought to be another seemingly no-brainer patient population that was already commonly treated with off-label intravaginal progesterone. Columbia's study seemed to show their drug worked but the FDA refused to approve the drug because its effect was only evident in patients enrolled outside of the US, not those in the US.

[†] David B. Nelson, "17-Alpha Hydroxyprogesterone Caproate Did Not Reduce the Rate of Recurrent Preterm Birth in a Prospective Cohort Study," *AJOG* 216, no. 6 (2017): 600, https://www.ajog.org/article/S0002-9378(17)30294-6/fulltext.

[‡] In late 2019, an FDA advisory panel offered the agency conflicting advice about whether the drug should remain on the market until yet another study determines Makena's efficacy or lack thereof. AMAG argued that because Makena is now widely prescribed in the US, they had to enroll their placebo-controlled study mostly outside of the US, where prenatal standard of care is different (though that hardly makes it clear why Makena wouldn't work for those patients).

AMAG, *AMAG Pharmaceuticals Announces Topline Results from the Prolong Trial Evaluating Makena*, March 8, 2019, accessed Nov. 1, 2019, https://www.amagpharma.com/news/amag-pharmaceuticals-announces-topline-results-from-the-prolong-trial-evaluating-makena-hydroxyprogesterone-caproate-injection/.

remained a homebrew therapy.* That KV Pharma was lambasted and run into bankruptcy may dissuade other companies from developing similar kinds of drugs where we have anecdotal but not definitive evidence that they might work. That would be unfortunate: These companies provide a valuable service, and the benefits of productizing homebrews extend well beyond confirming whether or not they really work.

## Homebrews and the Biotech Social Contract

Makena's is a story that begins as a seeming exception to the Biotech Social Contract. The outrage over Makena's pricing was similar to the public's anger at Turing for price-jacking Daraprim (Chapter 9). Using the mortgage analogy, it's as if KV Pharma was a bank trying to collect mortgage payments from society on a house that society had built on its own. Hadn't society bypassed drug companies to solve its own problem, compounded its own treatment, and run its own studies? So why should a company and investors now get to profit? And yet, this story ends by illustrating how the biotech industry still has an important role to play when it comes to homebrews.†

There are several reasons why society should want most homebrews to be properly productized. Firstly, as shown by the Makena case study, a treatment that is "easy and proven" is often neither as easy nor as proven as we think. When subjected to proper clinical studies, homebrew therapies, even those that have been used for a long time, can turn out to not work as reliably as we thought. Running rigorous clinical studies is expensive, and without funding from the biopharmaceutical industry—and subsequent,

---

* One could argue that the FDA shouldn't have granted KV Pharma accelerated approval, but, given that the preponderance of evidence suggested that the drug worked, the FDA's mandate was to make it available for patients while incentivizing its proper testing. Accelerated approval has been a boon to patients and companies in many cases; it may simply turn out that Makena wasn't one of them.

† When drug companies productize a homebrew, they not only confirm that it works but they also standardize the therapy so that it is manufactured consistently and in a clean, sterile environment, which is particularly important in the case of injected drugs. By submitting the GMP-manufactured drug for FDA-approval, they also create a roadmap by which the drug can later go generic, bringing the cost down closer to the cost of the original homebrew or possibly even lower (since there are efficiencies at economies of scale compared to having disparate compounding pharmacies serving individual patients).

though temporary, high prices for the approved drug—those trials are unlikely to be run for homebrew treatments.

Homebrews have a benefit-risk profile, yet it's not spelled out in an FDA-approved label. A proper trial generates data that inform the drug's label so that all physicians can understand how to best use it.

Insurance companies often reject coverage of homebrews, claiming they are experimental. A company would have a department that would help the physician advocate for a patient to get reimbursement, pointing out to the insurance company all the ways that a patient meets the criteria for treatment spelled out in the drug's label. Patients and physicians appreciate that.

There's also a misconception about homebrew treatments being inexpensive. Consider that the US spends over $4 billion per year on stem cell transplants to treat approximately 22,000 patients, without much involvement from biotech companies (although biotech products are used to treat side effects of transplants, such as anemia).[234] IVF and assisted reproduction generates over $5 billion in revenue per year. Those revenues don't attract as much attention because they are spread across a hundred transplant centers, hundreds of IVF clinics, and countless physicians. Unlike for a blockbuster drug, there is no single, for-profit entity to focus on if the costs are deemed too high. Yet a product selling $4 billion or more per year in the US falls within the top ten of all drugs.[235]

The large homebrew industry is largely unregulated, unlabeled, and sometimes inadequately validated. When companies are able to productize a homebrew, they shine a light on assumptions, generate data on the benefit-risk profile of the product that goes into the label, and then help appropriate patients get affordable access as best they can.

But productizing homebrews has other benefits. The initial, homebrew version of most treatments is only the beginning of what's possible. Next-generation, productized versions of homebrew therapies are often more effective, safer, or much easier for patients to take. Take homebrew fecal transplants, for example.[236] This procedure, which is becoming standard-of-care for patients who suffer from recurrent *C. difficile* infections of their GI tracts, involves transplanting liquefied fecal matter from a healthy donor to the patient via enema. A non-profit helps process stool donations from healthy donors and helps patients find a match.[237]

Several companies are attempting to identify the exact bacterial species that helps patients with *C. difficile* and create standardized pills that would deliver the same or better results, which will obviate the transplanting of actual feces from one person to another. That's a goal worth aiming for, but it requires considerable R&D funding (on the scale of hundreds of millions of dollars) and expertise that is common in industry but less common in academia and the non-profit sector.

A similar effort to upgrade stem cell transplants is now ongoing. Over many decades, physicians in the US have performed several hundred thousand stem cell transplants (mostly bone marrow transplants) to treat cancer and genetic disorders. The procedure involves transferring cells from a healthy donor to a sick patient. Patients must be carefully matched to donors with similar genetics, which is often done through the use of a non-profit-run registry. Perfect matches are rare, and even close-but-not-perfect matches can require extensive, lifelong immune-suppression to prevent the donor's cells from attacking the recipient's tissues, which can expose the patient to high infection risk and other problems. At the start of the procedure, the transplant recipient must undergo bone marrow "conditioning" to make room in the bone marrow for the new stem cells to engraft. This involves putting patients through aggressive chemotherapy treatment that wipes out their immune systems and leaves them severely anemic, requiring a long hospital stay. Many biopharmaceutical companies are working on ways to mitigate the severity of the conditioning process and modify the transplanted cells and treatment protocol so that little or no immune suppression is needed. If successful, these advances would revolutionize this often-curative procedure, making it both safer and available to many thousands more patients each year. The benefits are clear and, as with other homebrews-turned-branded-therapies, the resultant price would initially be higher than the homebrew. But provided the insurance industry does its job, patients would be able to afford it. And paying this mortgage would end up forever lowering transplant-associated rent.

Thirdly, once previously homebrew-only therapies are manufactured to precise GMP standards and FDA approved, it becomes possible to think about someday genericizing them in the traditional sense or through contractual genericization (see Chapter 8). In the long run, society would receive an upgrade at a relatively lower cost. Consider how inefficient it is to have a thousand different compounding pharmacies making injectable progesterone for individual patients compared to the economies of scale of centralized manufacturing by several generics manufacturers. On the other hand, if a first-generation homebrew technology like stem cell transplant or fecal transplant remains the purview of a scattered community of physicians and/or modestly funded non-profits, no one will make the heavy investments needed to transform those technologies into something that might end up having an even lower cost once it is standardized, optimized, and genericized.

## Homebrew Solutions

There are actually not many examples of productized homebrews and they don't make up much of America's drug budget. For all the headlines it sparked, Makena generated relatively modest sales, $322 million in 2018, which represented <0.1% of drug spending in the US. But for argument's sake, if society wanted to upgrade many more homebrews, might there be another way of doing it without leaving it up to the private sector to take the initiative? Maybe there is an alternative approach that would save society money. We could, for example, have the government do it. I think this tempting solution would currently be bureaucratic overkill, but let's game it out.

Say we expanded the FDA's mandate (and budget, of course) to include the gathering of data on the safety and effectiveness of homebrew therapies (like a commonly compounded drug or an off-patent drug being used in a novel way). The agency could, essentially, ask itself to approve the drug and assign it a label, standardizing it for society. If trials are necessary, the FDA could contract with research organizations to carry them out, particularly if they are low-risk trials meant to confirm what was already conventionally believed. The FDA could put GMP manufacturing out for bid and grant the right to market the drug to whichever company commits to doing so competently at the lowest branded price. Having the government take on these tasks, which are normally carried out by the private sector, might sound like a radical idea, but it mimics how the Defense Department bids out biodefense projects, such as the development and manufacturing of pandemic flu vaccines.

Let's look at how this strategy might have played out, were it applied to Emflaza (generic name deflazacort), a steroid that has been on the market outside of the US since 1985. It's not exactly a case of productizing a homebrew, but it's similar in that US patients could get deflazacort if they smuggled it in from abroad, where it is already generic. In 2017, a biotech called Marathon sped Emflaza through FDA approval for the treatment of Duchenne Muscular Dystrophy (DMD). The company based its application on existing data, did not run a new clinical trial, and then launched Emflaza at a high price. Media coverage and public reaction to what was perceived as Marathon attempting to wrest a profit from an existing drug without undertaking any risk led to what may look like the company's downfall, though in truth it was acquired for a handsome price by PTC Therapeutics, which re-launched the drug at a lower (but still high) price.* PTC sold $92 million of Emflaza in 2018.

Arguably the FDA could have offered any one of the generic manufacturers of deflazacort a deal: In exchange for agreeing to sell deflazacort at a modest price in the US, the FDA would do the work of packaging their existing data for review and granting approval for its use in treating DMD. No profit-seeking middleman needed! Of course, a generic company wouldn't then invest in physician and patient education. A better strategy would be for the FDA to put a contract out for bid to companies like PTC to get the right to sell the drug; whichever company offered to credibly market the drug for the lowest cost would win the chance to do so.

---

* The theme from KV and Marathon seems to be that ostensible retribution for price gouging simply shifts a drug's profitability elsewhere, to an acquiring company. Society will overpay for productized homebrews if this becomes a validated strategy, with those companies willing to do the dirty work of getting such drugs approved and anchoring pricing "negotiations" at a very high launch price being paid to take the heat by future acquirers who keep their hands clean, swooping in like "white knights" to lower the price a bit and collect future profits. The end result is the same—someone profits from doing the work, except it costs extra to pay for all that financial machination.

Emflaza and Makena represent comparatively straightforward cases of productizing homebrews that the FDA might be able to coordinate on its own if society really thought it was worth the trouble. But more advanced upgrades such as those involving next-generation fecal transplant and stem cell transplant technologies require a level of innovation that's best left to the private sector.

In any case, once these drugs are properly manufactured, tested, and FDA-approved, regardless of how much or little risk is involved, they will eventually go generic and remain a part of our treatment armamentarium—instead of never having been FDA-approved at all.

# 15

# BENEFIT-RISK BALANCE: LESSONS FROM THE OPIOID CRISIS

**The opioid crisis is a national disaster that continues to devastate thousands** of individuals, families, and communities. Given the scope of the crisis, there is a good chance that you have been affected by it or know someone who has, and there are overwhelming odds that you have seen, heard, or read about it somewhere over the last several years. In seeking to understand the roots of the crisis, much of the coverage has assigned much of the blame to the irresponsible greed of Purdue Pharmaceuticals, the maker of OxyContin, and much of that is indeed warranted.

You won't find any defense of Purdue here. Public records reveal that Purdue's executives either encouraged or tolerated profit-seeking without regard for patient safety, akin to heroin dealers preying on their customers.[238] They marketed a drug they knew to be dangerous as being safer than it was, hid data that would have revealed its dangers, and knowingly reaped the revenues associated with the non-medical use and diversion of its product.[239] Agencies such as the FDA and the Department of Justice are in charge of regulating potential abuses like this, and even back in 2003, the Drug Enforcement Agency (DEA) reported that "the company's aggressive methods, calculated fueling of demand, and the grasp for major market share very much exacerbated OxyContin's widespread abuse and diversion."[240] Still, Purdue got away with it for way too long, and countless lives have been destroyed as a result. Currently pursuing bankruptcy and facing a proposed $10 billion settlement, Purdue is the most conspicuous of several companies facing numerous lawsuits over their roles in fueling and stoking the opioid crisis.[241] Also accused are other opioid manufacturers Teva Pharmaceutical, Johnson & Johnson,* Mallinckrodt, and Endo, as well as pharmaceutical distributors McKesson, AmerisourceBergen, and Cardinal Health,† and pharmacies like CVS, Walgreens, and Walmart for observing and profiting from, but not stopping, some pharmacies from ordering far more pills than could possibly have been intended for legitimate uses.[242]

Hopefully, these lawsuits and future settlements will not only deter drug companies from engaging in improper marketing and distribution but also help people and communities affected directly or indirectly by the current crisis.‡ Though for thousands upon thousands of families, it is too late.

It is imperative that something like this never be allowed to happen again. In order to prevent future crises, we must understand what went wrong, how the system broke down, who is to blame, what we can learn from it, and what we can do about it. Assigning all the blame to a single cause—such as irresponsible marketing—would be oversimplifying a complex problem and not deriving full value from the vital lessons we should learn from it.

## Benefit-Risk

All drugs have benefits and risks, and both can vary from patient to patient, depending on the nature or severity of the disease, other illnesses or drugs a person is taking, and many other factors. We often evaluate drugs based

---

* J&J has entered multiple settlements of opioid lawsuits, including a $4 billion agreement in October 2019.

† Those three distributors account for the overwhelming majority of market share and in October 2019 were said to be paying $18 billion in a settlement of major opioid litigation.

‡ The settlements announced also include companies providing free addiction-treatment drugs, services, and supplies valued at $25-30 billion.

upon their benefits and efficacy—what they purport to do and how well they do it. But when a physician is deciding whether or not to prescribe a drug to a patient or the FDA is deciding whether or not to approve a drug for release, they base their decision on both benefits and risks. That's also why all advertisements that mention a drug must mention both the benefits and the risks. Drug-associated risks can be annoying (e.g., mild constipation) or they can be dangerous (e.g., addiction), even lethal (e.g., respiratory depression).*

The FDA approved and physicians prescribe blood pressure-lowering drugs like lisinopril because the benefits are significant (preventing strokes, heart attacks, and kidney damage) and, for most patients, outweigh the risks (which can include cough, dizziness, and headaches). But to someone with normal blood pressure, such drugs do not offer benefit—only risk. So the FDA requires that drug developers demonstrate which types of patients are likely to benefit and to what degree they would benefit before deciding whether to approve it, how it is to be prescribed, and to whom. That information appears on the drug's label, and from there, it's up to physicians to determine whether a patient meets the requirements for treatment with that drug. If yes, then the drug is said to be "indicated for" that patient and the physician can prescribe the drug and is said to be using the drug "on-label," meaning in accordance with how the FDA intended. Sometimes, a physician prescribes a drug for a patient or a purpose not expressly approved by the FDA. This kind of usage is known as "off-label." Either way, no patient is supposed to be able to obtain a prescription drug unless a doctor has written a prescription for it; this is a critical check in our healthcare system.

When a company produces a particularly dangerous drug or one that carries the risk of addiction, the FDA can also require the company to take extra precautions to ensure that patients only get the doses they are supposed to, and that drugs are not diverted to people who shouldn't take them. If a drug is particularly liable to be abused (e.g., opioids, amphetamines, and even anabolic steroids), the DEA also plays a role in deciding how dangerous they are and enforcing proper distribution.

---

* Constipation, addiction, and respiratory depression are examples of opioid side effects.

The bottom line is that all of these factors—whether a drug's benefits outweigh its risks, whether it is potentially addictive, what's on the drug's label, to whom it should be prescribed, and how it is distributed—exist in a balance that must be calibrated for each drug to achieve a favorable benefit-risk profile. In the case of opioids, the balance was (and despite recent efforts to improve, still is) so miscalibrated that hundreds of thousands of lives were destroyed. Sometimes the harm came directly from patients abusing duly prescribed opioid drugs and other times from patients, having become addicted and then cut off from access to prescription opioids, turning to illegal and more potent narcotics, such as heroin and illegally manufactured fentanyl. These illicit opioids don't come with labels, aren't standardized from one dose to the next, and can easily result in potentially lethal overdoses in even the most experienced users.

Societies worldwide have long struggled with the benefit-risk profile of opioid drugs. And while modern medicine is better and safer in countless ways than in centuries past, the opioid crisis we have today was exacerbated not just by companies knowingly engaging in improper marketing but also, perversely, by the hubris of the drug industry, the FDA, and highly trained physicians, all of whom were over-confident in their technology, data, and judgment.

Let's unpack that last statement and start with an example of how freely physicians can exercise their judgment when treating their patients.

## Physicians' Choice: Off-label Drug Use

When sorting out whether a drug is appropriate for a patient, all a doctor has to do is compare the patient's medical record and diagnosis with a drug's label, and then determine if the two match up—right? In practice, it isn't always so straightforward.

In some cases, the physician thinks that a drug can help someone for whom it is not strictly indicated, so they prescribe it "off-label," as discussed above. That can happen without any company promoting its off-label use and without patients even asking for it, though sometimes patients might ask, and pharmaceutical companies have been fined in the past for improper off-label marketing.[243] But why would a physician use a drug in a way that the FDA has not approved? Perhaps the physician knows, from her own experience, that the drug has more uses than the ones listed on its label. Some physicians even conduct their own clinical studies to find new uses for existing drugs and publish their results. In this way, off-label uses can eventually gain traction in the medical community as word spreads. These uses can sometimes make their way into medical guidelines, even though these new uses haven't been granted FDA approval.

## Prazosin—A Case Study In Off-label Use

Prazosin was first approved in 1976 to treat high blood pressure. These days, it is less commonly prescribed for that purpose because better and safer drugs, like lisinopril, have come along. However, prazosin is used off-label to treat enlarged prostate glands, red scorpion stings,* and nightmares associated with post-traumatic stress disorder (PTSD).[244] Prazosin's benefits in treating PTSD-related nightmares were discovered serendipitously long after it was generic, when a physician at the Department of Veterans Affairs (VA) observed that a patient taking the drug to treat an enlarged prostate (its main off-label use at the time) also experienced relief from trauma-associated nightmares.[245] Since then, a number of studies have demonstrated its benefit-risk in that indication, but you won't find the words "trauma" or "nightmare" on the label.[246]

In this case, the fact that prazosin has long been generic is important for two reasons. One, it means that no one is marketing prazosin for any purpose—either on- or off-label—so physicians looking for ways to treat patients with PTSD nightmares must rely on other physicians, research papers, the internet, or even patients, in order to learn of prazosin's utility.† Two, once a patient has been prescribed prazosin off-label, insurance companies will probably pay for it without checking whether the patient actually has high blood pressure, the on-label

---

* Red scorpion venom activates proteins called alpha-receptors, so the realization that prazosin functions by blocking alpha-receptors led to the idea that it could help treat people who have been stung.

† Of course, with no DTC campaign in effect, patients are less likely to know about it. Furthermore, psychiatrists and other specialists who deal with trauma are more likely to know about prazosin's off-label usage than primary care physicians (PCPs), which means that patients who might benefit from this treatment might require a referral to expensive specialists from their PCPs before this treatment is even discussed.

condition. As an inexpensive generic, prazosin costs the payer so little that it's not worth it for the payer to worry about it being over-prescribed or over-used. Still, in the case of nightmares associated with PTSD, if an insurance company did push back, a physician could point to the abundance of scientific studies and medical guidelines that justify such usage—and the insurance company would likely relent.

---

The bottom line is that medicine has long had a tradition of physicians exercising their own judgment about how a drug can best be used, informed but not necessarily constrained by what the FDA has approved a drug for and what its label says.

But sometimes it's important to put guardrails around how a drug is prescribed and make sure only specific patients get it under carefully monitored conditions, helping to shift the benefit-risk balance away from a drug's risks.

## Risk Evaluation and Mitigation Strategies

Some drugs are so dangerous, but so essential for patients, that the FDA approves them with special restrictions and careful monitoring of side effects and off-label use. These Risk Evaluation and Mitigation Strategies (REMS) are intended to tip the benefit-risk of a drug away from the risks so that patients can still benefit. Congress created the formal concept of REMS for the FDA to administer in the Food and Drug Administration Amendments Act of 2007, but prior to that moment companies still ran similar risk management programs to protect patients from harm and themselves from liability.[247]

In Chapter 9, I discussed Jazz Pharmaceuticals and its use of REMS to prevent generics of its narcolepsy drug Xyrem (brand name for sodium oxybate) from entering the market. But there's another story behind Xyrem that is pertinent to the opioid crisis and will help shed some light on how the FDA thinks about protecting the public from a drug's risks.

When prescribed and used properly, Xyrem helps patients diagnosed with narcolepsy to experience a profoundly deep, restorative sleep, which can be of great benefit to patients so exhausted from waking up countless times throughout the night that they otherwise can fall asleep at random moments during the day.

But the risks associated with Xyrem are varied and extreme. For one, sodium oxybate-induced sleep is so deep that patients are rendered oblivious to their surroundings and often have no memory of what transpired while they were unconscious. This can make them vulnerable to sexual predators, which is why sodium oxybate—or "GHB," as its active component is more commonly known—is considered a date-rape drug. The incidence of sexual assault involving GHB and other sedatives is disturbingly common.[248] In addition, at high doses, it can cause a feeling of euphoria, which can lead to addiction, and it can even suppress a person's ability to breathe. Hundreds of deaths have been reported in association with GHB use.[249] In 2000, as its risks became more obvious and its use more widespread,[250] the DEA classified GHB as a Schedule 1 drug, in the same category as heroin, LSD, ecstasy, and synthetic marijuana.[251]

In 2002, the FDA approved Xyrem for narcolepsy with a strict risk-management program that would later be converted to a REMS program. Today, Jazz tracks every physician who prescribes Xyrem and every patient to whom it's prescribed, mails the drug directly to patients (it doesn't go through a local pharmacy), has the patient or a representative sign for the package (it's never left unattended), and calls patients or their caregivers to explain the dangers of the medication and how to use it properly.[252] Jazz also had to get the DEA's approval to produce Xyrem, which requires Jazz to account for every drop it makes and provide proof to the DEA that none has been diverted from the manufacturing plant.

These precautions work well. A 2009 study found that out of 26,000 patients worldwide who had received Xyrem in the prior nine years, there were only ten cases (0.04%) of patients abusing the drug (e.g., getting high, or driving soon after taking it) and two cases of sexual assault (0.008%).[253] But GHB is a simple molecule that can be made from widely available ingredients, using fewer steps than it takes to make crystal meth, and recipes are available on the internet. So while Jazz's REMS helped to keep patients and the public safe from Xyrem, it could do nothing to mitigate the harm of all the illicitly produced GHB available on the street. There are 1,000-2,000 GHB-related ER visits and hundreds of cases of GHB-related date rape in the US alone each year.[254]

As Jazz continued to study new uses for Xyrem, it turned out that the drug could also help patients suffering from fibromyalgia, a syndrome involving a combination of fatigue and pain that some researchers theorized was caused in part by patients sleeping so poorly that, in their exhausted state, they experienced normal stimuli, such a breeze across their skin, as pain. Jazz submitted extensive clinical trial data to the FDA seeking approval to expand Xyrem's label to include the treatment of fibromyalgia, but in 2010 the FDA rejected the application out of concern for the public's safety.

Very few patients suffer from narcolepsy, with maybe 50,000 diagnosed in the US and only 14,700 taking Xyrem as of the middle of 2019, while closer to ten million suffer from fibromyalgia.[255] And even though Jazz promised it would take the same precautions when distributing Xyrem to patients with fibromyalgia, an expansion of the label might have increased the amount of Xyrem that Jazz shipped by over 100-fold. The FDA's advisors feared that such a dramatic expansion of the supply would substantially increase the chances that the drug would be used inappropriately and that many more people might end up victimized with the help of an FDA-approved pharmaceutical.[256]

The agency's caution with respect to Xyrem reflected an increased awareness of the harms the FDA knew it had helped unleash by authorizing the broad use of opioids years earlier.

With an understanding of benefit-risk tradeoffs, the levers that drug companies, physicians, and FDA have to control this balance, and concepts covered in earlier chapters like insurance design, we can look specifically at how these factors contributed to the opioid crisis.

## Opioids: A Brief History

Opium has exacted a heavy toll throughout history. For millennia, humans have cultivated poppies and dried their milky, morphine-rich sap into opium, which has been smoked, swallowed, snorted, and, more recently, injected for recreational purposes, to alleviate pain, forget grief, or help children fall asleep.[257] Ancient Sumerians called it "joy," though the drug has a dark side and a bloody history.

In 1805, Friedrich Wilhelm Adam Serturner, an assistant pharmacist in Prussia, isolated crystals of a pure molecule from poppy juice and published a study claiming that it could induce sleep. Through self-experimentation, he discovered that, at low doses, the drug could relieve pain, at higher doses, it could induce euphoria, and at even higher doses, cause drowsiness and confusion. He named it Morphium after the Greek god of dreams; today, we call it morphine, and we call the class of drugs to which it belongs "opioids."

These chemicals mimic natural endorphin molecules that our bodies release in response to physical discomfort or threat, which, in turn, suppress pain (e.g., why accident victims often don't feel pain immediately after an accident, only after some time when endorphins have worn off) and even induces a state of euphoria (e.g., "runner's high"). Chemicals of this class include morphine, heroin, fentanyl, and oxycodone, all of which interact with receptors on neurons in slightly different ways.

The isolation of morphine was a transformative advance. Physicians who had been hesitant to prescribe raw poppy juice or opium, for fear that the variation in potency from batch to batch could lead to overdose, could now administer a precise amount of pure morphine to patients. Serturner was widely recognized for his breakthrough and is counted among the founders of pharmaceutical science. But opium would not be tamed then. In an ending fit for a Greek tragedy, Serturner died addicted to the substance he'd discovered.[258]

Since the time of morphine's discovery, we've continued to search for safer variants. When heroin was discovered towards the end of the 19th century, it was declared to be non-addictive, which of course turned out to be devastatingly inaccurate. Unfortunately, this has proven to be a recurring theme throughout the history of opioids.

As opioids became indispensable tools for managing severe post-surgical pain or the pain of patients suffering from terminal cancer, which torments patients as it eats away at their bones and other organs, the dangers of addiction and overdose weren't always fully understood—even among the medical community. Opioids were known to be dangerous and addictive if not used properly, but following surgery, these drugs were thought to be safe because their administration was temporary. In the case of cancer, the side effects and risk of addiction didn't seem as scary in the face of impending death, though as cancer treatments improved, patients could end up on opioids for years, blurring the line between treating patients who are living and those who are dying.

In 1980, a widely cited short letter in *The New England Journal of Medicine* reported that an analysis of nearly 40,000 hospitalized patients found that "despite widespread use of narcotic drugs in hospitals, the development of addiction is rare in medical patients with no history of addiction."[259] This, too, would turn out to be false, but physicians found the idea appealing that opioid drugs,* when properly prescribed to patients in their care, would not lead to addiction. The medical community's over-confidence that it had tamed opioids would contribute to their broader use to help patients suffering from chronic pain.

## The Seeds of a Perfect Storm

The seeds of today's opioid crisis were sown in 1995, due in large part to two key developments.

First, physician and President of the American Pain Society Dr. James Campbell gave an address declaring that, along with blood pressure, pulse rate, temperature, and rate of breathing, pain should be considered the 5th vital sign.† This meant that, besides looking for objective measures of ill health, doctors should ask their patients if they are feeling pain and then try to treat it. This may seem surprisingly obvious today, but that's the whole point: When a patient didn't proactively complain, asking about pain hadn't been standard practice, but now it would be.[260] The VA, for

---

* This drug classes included methadone, hydromorphone, hydrocodone, oxymorphone, oxycodone, and fentanyl, many of which were available in various formulations and combinations.

† The American Pain Society was named as a defendant in the major opioid litigation and subsequently declared bankruptcy in 2019.

example, took Dr. Campbell's encouragement to heart, publishing a "Pain as the 5th Vital Sign Toolkit" in 2,000.*

Also in 1995, the FDA approved Purdue Pharma's OxyContin, an extended-release formulation of the opioid oxycodone that was meant to be taken in pill form once every 12 hours to manage pain. It was designed to release oxycodone slowly, so that the patient would get a smooth, constant dose. Prior to this, nearly all opioids, with the exception of a long-acting morphine drug called MS Contin, were formulated as immediate-release (in that they released their contents all at once, not gradually) and had to be taken every 4-6 hours. The FDA thought OxyContin would be safer and less likely to lead to abuse, later explaining:

> *At the time of approval, FDA believed the controlled-release formu-lation of OxyContin would result in less abuse potential, since the drug would be absorbed slowly and there would not be an immediate "rush" or high that would promote abuse. In part, FDA based its judgment on the prior marketing history of a similar product, MS Contin, a controlled-release formulation of morphine approved by FDA and used in the medical community since 1987 without signif-icant reports of abuse and misuse.[261]*

The FDA went so far as to permit the following to appear on OxyCon-tin's prescription label:

> *Delayed absorption, as provided by OxyContin tablets, is believed to reduce the abuse liability of a drug.[262]*

In an environment that was placing renewed emphasis on pain man-agement and with the FDA indicating that OxyContin was a preferred—if not the preferred—opioid, Purdue launched a vigorous promotional cam-paign and conducted additional clinical studies to show the utility of opi-oids to treat chronic non-cancer pain. Then, they got permission from the FDA to print on the label that their opioids could be used for all pain that

---

\* Therein quoting Campbell: *"Vital Signs are taken seriously. If pain were assessed with the same zeal as other vital signs are, it would have a much better chance of being treated properly. We need to train doctors and nurses to treat pain as a vital sign. Quality care means that pain is measured and treated."*

couldn't be adequately managed in other ways. Buying into the perception that OxyContin had the most favorable benefit-risk of any opioid in the long history of opioids, Purdue marketed its product as the weapon of choice in the war on pain with what court records now show to have been an indecent and illegal zeal, overstating OxyContin's efficacy and lying about its risks.[263]

The company pushed non-specialist primary care doctors to prescribe the drug off-label for less severe pain indications, significantly outspending rivals like Johnson & Johnson, which marketed the competing medicine Duragesic. To spread the word, more than 5,000 doctors, nurses, and pharmacists attended all-expenses-paid resort-based speaker-training conferences during the first five years OxyContin was marketed.[264] Some of these healthcare professionals were then paid by Purdue to extol the virtues of using OxyContin for various pain indications (nearly 2,500 physicians were on the company's "speakers bureau" list by 2002). Purdue sponsored or directly financed more than 20,000 pain-related "educational programs" between 1996 and 2002 and spent nearly $5 million in advertising in medical journals in 2001 alone.[265] Though the company avoided DTC advertising on television, it built or sponsored a variety of pain-focused consumer-facing websites. The company's aggressive tactics quickly made OxyContin a blockbuster, generating over $1 billion in sales per year within five years of its launch.

And while all this would have been legal if Purdue had only made FDA-approved and true marketing claims and physicians disclosed all of these payments in gifts, as is now mandated by the Sunshine Act, Purdue crossed many lines. In 2007, Purdue Pharma and three of its senior executives were investigated and fined $634 million—still one of the largest financial penalties on record—for misleading doctors about the safety of its product.[266] This included making fraudulent claims that OxyContin was less addictive, less subject to abuse, and less likely to cause withdrawal symptoms than other pain medicines.[267] Still, cumulative OxyContin revenues have exceeded $35 billion, the majority of which were generated after that 2007 $634 million fine.[268]

A big problem was that OxyContin wasn't nearly as hard to abuse as everyone seemed to think. In order to achieve an immediate release of its contents, all someone had to do was chew up a pill or crush it into a powder and snort it. Despite reports that MS Contin had been similarly abused, the FDA somehow didn't see any of this coming.[269] Referring to the approval of OxyContin in 1995, the FDA said recently:

> *There was no evidence to suggest at the time that crushing the controlled-release capsule followed by oral ingestion or snorting would become widespread and lead to a high level of abuse.[270]*

Granted, at that time, MS Contin was not widely prescribed—nowhere near the level of OxyContin would be—so reports of abuse were infrequent and didn't receive much attention. To be fair, the FDA did not anticipate OxyContin being prescribed so broadly for less-than-severe pain, as it would turn out to be. But in retrospect, the regulatory checks then in place failed to assess the risks of OxyContin and to put sufficient guardrails in place.*

Before long, the evidence of abuse became irrefutable. From 1999 to 2007, the number of opioid-related deaths in the US climbed from approximately 8,000 to over 18,000, with prescription opioids involved in most cases.[271] The number of people addicted to opioids and seeking relief from the agony of withdrawal caused the street value of OxyContin to soar, to the extent that many pharmacies were forced to fortify their security. When they couldn't get OxyContin, many even turned to heroin.

There were enough cases of patients reporting getting hooked on opioids following what seemed like legitimate medical use, such as a prescription to help manage post-surgical pain or chronic lower back pain, that it didn't matter that most patients weren't actually overdosing on their own prescriptions. The fact was that pharmaceuticals that had been developed in the US, approved by the FDA, aggressively marketed by a company, recommended by medical associations, and prescribed by physicians

---

* At this point, you may see the parallel to Xyrem, which was more like MS Contin when used just for the small population of narcolepsy patients but threatened to be more like OxyContin if approved for fibromyalgia. In 2010, when considering whether to approve Xyrem for fibromyalgia, the FDA exhibited far more caution than it did in 1995 with regard to opioids.

were contributing to a rising death toll, and there was plenty of blame to go around.

Each key stakeholder responded in a different way, with consequences that would tragically drive America's opioid-related death toll far higher, to 47,600 in 2017, for reasons we'll explore below.

## The FDA's Response

About five years after OxyContin came to market, the FDA removed the claim that delayed absorption might reduce abuse from its label. By 2003, they'd added to opioid labels stronger and more prominent language that cautioned users about the risk of addiction.[272]

OxyContin's marketing materials now say:

> *Although the risk of addiction in any individual is unknown, it can occur in patients appropriately prescribed OxyContin. Addiction can occur at recommended doses and if the drug is misused or abused.*

In 2007, the year Purdue was fined $634 million for misleading doctors about OxyContin, Congress granted to the FDA the power to regulate REMS programs. From then on, the FDA would only approve opioids in conjunction with REMS, and it retroactively imposed that requirement on opioids already on the market.

## Physicians' Response

For a long time, it was common for anyone released from the hospital after a surgery to get a prescription for generic Vicodin (hydrocodone plus acetaminophen),* generic Percocet (oxycodone plus acetaminophen), or some other opioid—often enough for a whole month when only a few days' worth would have been enough.[273] With increased awareness of the opioid crisis, and in some cases in responses to new laws limiting prescription opioid use, physicians reduced the doses they prescribed, the number of

---

* Acetaminophen is the active ingredient in Tylenol.

pills per prescription, and the number of times they extended a patient's prescription.[274] Some stopped prescribing opioids entirely to avoid liability. Patients suffering from severe pain complained that they now had a harder time getting treated because other patients were abusing opioids.[275]

Overall, the number of opioid prescriptions has come down since its peak in 2010, but it is still much higher now than in the 1990s because physicians continue to operate with an imperative to treat patients' pain and they have few alternatives. Try as they may to comply with medical guidelines to make the most of non-opioid drugs, physicians are constrained by those drugs' benefit-risk profiles. Some of those non-opioid drugs are too weak to manage severe pain and/or cause serious side effects. For example, naproxen, ibuprofen, and aspirin can cause serious internal bleeding of the stomach and GI tract.[276] At high doses, acetaminophen (Tylenol) causes liver failure. These purportedly safer options send hundreds of thousands of patients to the ER each year and kill several thousand.[277] So when a physician is trying to help a patient already on non-opioid alternatives that is still suffering from severe pain, simply increasing the dose of these drugs is not as clear-cut a solution as it might seem.

In addition, a healthy physician-patient relationship is grounded in trust. To deny a patient in pain a prescription for an opioid because the physician worries that she might abuse it would undermine that trust. With a "not my patients" mindset, some physicians acknowledged that addiction was a problem but that it was happening to patients being treated by other, less responsible physicians.[278]

## The Drug Industry's Response

Realizing that the benefit-risk profile of prescription opioids still posed a significant problem, the biopharmaceutical industry responded by attempting to upgrade opioids to prevent abuse and reduce the likelihood of overdose with new ideas and technologies.[279] Their goal was the same one chemists had long chased, to develop an abuse-resistant opioid, one that would neither lead to addiction nor overdose.

One idea involved mixing an opioid with niacin, a relatively safe drug that causes an unpleasant feeling of heat and flushing if someone were to crush or chew the pill, or take too many. But someone intent on abusing that opioid could counteract the effects of niacin with aspirin, so that one didn't make it to market. Purdue itself upgraded OxyContin to be more abuse-deterrent by making its shell harder, which made it extremely difficult to chew. It also constructed a core that would cause the drug to turn to gel if mixed with a solvent, deterring its abuse via injection. Once the FDA approved the new OxyContin in 2010, Purdue pulled its older version off the market, and the FDA said it would not grant approval to any future generics without abuse-deterring features.[280] Still, the new OxyContin's abuse-deterrent features could be defeated and other companies attempted to develop more advanced versions. A drug named Xtampza ER featured new technology that caused the pill to release its painkiller only as slowly as intended—even when crushed or chewed—and also made it nearly impossible to snort or inject.*

Innovators and their investors had thought that if they created even more advanced types of opioid medications that would make it harder for patients to abuse, the FDA might reward these advances by both approving them and removing other, more-easily abused versions from the market. But that didn't happen. Having already fallen for OxyContin's false promise of being a much safer opioid, the FDA wasn't about to again give physicians any excuse to underestimate the risks of any new opioids. The FDA set a high bar for any claims that a drug was harder to abuse and pointed to evidence that each new type of opioid drug, whatever its technological defenses, could technically still be manipulated by a determined abuser, maybe by using solvents to dissolve pills or a hammer to crack a hard, outer shell.

---

* Drugs tend to dissolve faster when their surface-to-volume ratio increases, which is what happens when a pill is crushed into a powder. Consider that granular sugar dissolves faster than a sugar cube. So making a drug that dissolves at the same rate regardless of its surface-to-volume ratio took some skill, though this breakthrough did not seem to be appreciated in the opioid marketplace.

## Insurance Companies' Response

Insurance companies, under no obligation to favor newer abuse-deterrent opioids over older generic ones and with an eye on their own bottom line, still set low copays for generic opioids and high ones for branded versions, nudging patients away from newer technologies. Purdue offered PBMs rebates on OxyContin, so even when a drug like Xtamptza ER came along that would be harder to abuse, insurance steered physicians and patients considering a long-acting opioid towards OxyContin. Insurance companies may have felt justified in not valuing incremental, abuse-deterring upgrades based on cost-effectiveness analyses published by academics that suggested they weren't worth it, but such studies fail to consider the lives that will continue to be saved long after upgraded versions go generic.[281]

Nor did many physicians, secure in their "not my patients" mindset, feel compelled to switch to prescribing abuse-deterrent opioids. Selecting an abuse-deterring branded for a patient meant both insinuating that the patient might become a drug abuser and sticking them with a higher copay as the cost of this mistrust.

Other than OxyContin, the few other abuse-deterrent opioids that the FDA approved did not sell well, and investors began to pull back from funding similar projects.[282] Investors and innovators either didn't know how high the FDA's bar was for considering an upgraded opioid meaningfully safer than OxyContin or didn't see a way to achieve that goal. But even if there had been a technological way to make opioids non-abusable, that would not have helped everyone already addicted to them. In fact, just the limited abuse-deterrent features built into OxyContin had immediate, lethal, unintended, yet predictable consequences.

## All Roads Lead Here

Operating under a false sense of security, the FDA, physicians, and drug companies directed countless patients towards an on-ramp to addiction for over a decade.[283] As they realized their mistakes and made changes, the death rate from prescription opioids began to fall.[284] But tighter prescribing rules and the switch to abuse-deterrent opioids in 2010 pushed great numbers of people addicted to OxyContin into the street, where they began to overdose in unprecedented numbers on more potent, adulterated, and unmarked opioids, especially heroin and illicit synthetic fentanyl.[285] By 2010, a study even showed a rise in the rate of hepatitis C infections associated with the uptick in people injecting heroin.[286] The only way to help all of the people who had become addicted was to treat their addiction.

Fortunately, there has been some progress in the development of treatments for opioid abuse. Drugs like naloxone counteract opioids to save the life of someone experiencing overdose, and milder opioids like buprenorphine more safely blunt cravings to help patients manage symptoms as they fight to get clean. And thanks to the steady decriminalization of drug possession, it has become easier to treat users as patients suffering from an addiction disorder instead of as criminals. However, we still need insurance reforms to ensure that effective treatments for addiction are as accessible and affordable to all patients as the opioids to which they first became addicted.[287]

There can be no diminishing the responsibility that Purdue and other drug companies bear for unethical marketing tactics, along with some physicians who knowingly sold prescriptions to addicts and distributors that did nothing to stop some pharmacies from dispensing more opioid prescriptions than there were people in their neighborhoods.[288] They ruined lives. Hopefully large financial fines and settlements and even criminal convictions will drive lasting reforms. But if that's all we take away from the opioid crisis, then we've not learned enough.

I think we have to acknowledge that these bad actors did not so much cause the crisis as inflame what began with good people making well-intentioned decisions.

## Unattainable Balance

Even if Purdue had only marketed OxyContin exactly as the FDA allowed in 1995, we would still be dealing with an opioid crisis. The on-label benefit-risk of OxyContin and opioids in general failed to convey how addictive this class of drugs has always been, even when prescribed by well-meaning physicians to patients in real pain. We lied to ourselves about the dangers of pharmaceutical opioids for decades, not unlike how we lied to ourselves about the dangers of smoking and, more recently, vaping,* by first assuring ourselves these products were safe and later realizing they weren't.

That doesn't mean that pharmaceutical-grade opioids haven't been profoundly useful medicines. While I would like to believe that I would not have defended the benefits of cigarettes in the 1970s, as cigarette companies notoriously did, I do now defend the importance of opioid drugs in the treatment of pain.[289] I appreciate that well-meaning physicians and FDA staff thought they were helping millions of patients suffering from pain by making opioids more accessible.†

As long as we continue to need opioids to manage pain, we'll struggle to manage the addiction they inflict. Despite all the attention to the opioid crisis, changes to drug labels, and tightening of both marketing and prescribing practices, in 2017, about 11 million people in the US misused these drugs—a third of these under a prescription from a doctor and nearly half by obtaining, buying, or stealing the drug from a friend or relative with a prescription.[290] Opioid labels can be written to urge even more caution, though they are already intimidating, just as the FDA still continues to push for more gruesome labels for cigarettes.[291] And I have no doubt that there are still physicians who aren't prescribing opioids in the most responsible way and need training in some cases or policing in others. But even if there were a single best way to use these drugs, it would still carry a risk of addiction.

One way or another, I think all roads would have eventually led us to this point where we must acknowledge that we have not yet found a way

---

* We failed to appreciate how vaping, though much better for current smokers than cigarettes (assuming they can't just quit), would get a generation of kids addicted to nicotine with a myriad of flavors and advertisements portraying vaping as hip. In retrospect, vaping should have been more tightly regulated, as it's starting to be, with more effort to keep it away from kids and discouraging all non-smokers from picking it up.

† The FDA clearly has learned hard-won lessons through the opioid crisis. When in 2010 the agency decided not to approve the use of Xyrem to treat the large population of patients suffering from fibromyalgia, regulators probably had the opioid crisis on their minds. Those who wanted to abuse GHB would still be able to do so by getting it on the black market, but the FDA did not want to compound the problem by allowing millions of patients with fibromyalgia to be prescribed a version of that drug. I don't know if the FDA was right in making that decision; fibromyalgia can be a debilitating, painful condition with few available treatments. But based on that decision, I see the FDA making an effort to do right by society.

to manage severe pain that doesn't also risk destroying lives. Perhaps it's because I'm a scientist and have witnessed what we can achieve with biotechnology, but the only solution I see to both treating pain and resolving the opioid crisis lies in biomedical innovation.

## Now Where?

Going forward, we must go beyond simply trying to make opioids harder to abuse. We must gain a greater understanding of the biology of how we experience pain and invest in the development of new types of drugs to reduce pain without addiction. That work is already happening at university laboratories and companies around the world. Whether investors will back these efforts depends on whether they believe that those who succeed in making a non-addictive pain drug will be rewarded, which requires not only physicians wanting to prescribe the drug, but insurance companies being willing to pay for the drug without imposing a higher copayment than for generic opioids.

It wouldn't even take anything as dramatic as new legislation imposing drug price controls to rob us of the benefits of non-addictive pain drugs. Just consider how counterproductive it would be—how potentially harmful to society—if, once OxyContin goes generic, insurance companies encouraged patients to save money by taking that instead of making a new non-addictive alternative at least as affordable.

This is a critical moment, and if we fail to uphold the Biotech Social Contract to encourage the drug industry to solve pain management in a better way, we'll pay for our short sightedness with many more generations pushed into addiction by old opioid pharmaceuticals.

# 16

## A CALL TO ACTION

**So what exactly is novel about the Biotech Social Contract? What am I** saying that hasn't been said before by others?

Most importantly, it is the idea that, on a societal level, spending on branded drugs is not an expense tied to products delivered today, but an investment in the growth of a large and growing generic drug mountain that will serve humankind inexpensively for the rest of time. High out-of-pocket costs imposed by insurers are what violate the contract on an individual level. They deny many patients the appropriate treatments their physicians prescribe. Not only is this bad for patients, but, by making it harder for companies to commercialize their innovations, poor insurance coverage and high out-of-pocket costs endanger our investment in a vital, affordable resource that will improve the lives of future generations.

In a way, this whole book has been my attempt to reframe the entire drug pricing debate.

When the public's reaction to branded drug prices being unaffordable for patients leads to talk of price controls, the biotech industry's response is usually something like:

"But we must be allowed to charge high prices in order to keep developing new drugs, because they are expensive and risky to develop. Price controls will hurt R&D and reduce the number of new drugs that we can make."

All of that is true, but this response has failed to answer the underlying question of affordability, both for the patient and society! The answer does not mention the long-term value of generics, nor does it make the case that patients can't afford drugs because their insurance doesn't want them to (if they even have insurance).

I propose the following response:

No, price controls on novel drugs are not the answer. To allow patients to afford what their physicians prescribe, we must ensure that all patients have insurance coverage and eliminate or cap their copayments and deductibles. Society should not be asking its most vulnerable members to shoulder, through high out-of-pocket costs, a disproportionate share of our collective investment in biomedical innovation. To incentivize and fund the development of drugs that will eventually go generic and improve our standards of care for the rest of time, drug companies must charge temporarily high prices for new drugs, but those costs should be borne by society as a whole via universal, comprehensive insurance and not passed on to patients at the pharmacy counter. Insurance that makes treatments that a doctor prescribes unaffordable is not insurance at all. So the answer to making drugs affordable for patients is that we need to reform insurance in America to make it function as the insurance it's supposed to be. As for price controls on novel drugs, they would only temporarily solve affordability of the drugs we have today but would then counter-productively slow or halt the expansion of our generic drug armamentarium, which would leave future generations with healthcare that is no better than what we have today and more expensive than it could be. Drugs going generic is the cost-containment mechanism we have long had and the only one we should rely on and optimize to ensure that drugs are cost-effective in the long run.

## Call to Action

To preserve the Biotech Social Contract, I call for:

1. In exchange for legislation to solve patient affordability by reducing their out-of-pocket costs, the drug development industry

must offer to society contractual genericization of otherwise non-genericizable drugs (Chapter 8). I proposed contractual genericization for the first time in an article on *Medium* just after Christmas 2017,[292] and then described it again in *BioCentury* a year later in December 2018.[293] Others called for it in April 2019 in a post on *Health Affairs*.[294] If this is a start, then I admit it feels slow, but as I point out in Chapter 8, non-genericizable drugs currently represent a very small fraction of our total drug budget, so we have time to implement contractual genericization. I include a step-by-step framework for how contractual genericization could work at the end of Chapter 13.

2.  A system of incentivizing upgrades of existing drugs that leverages shorter regulatory exclusivity extensions for the whole drug franchise rather than entirely new patents on straightforward, low-risk improvements. I describe how short extensions could integrate with contractual genericization at the end of Chapter 13.

3.  A proposal for how society can take over marketing from companies when certain non-standard products like the EpiPen go generic (Chapter 12).

4.  Caution when referencing US prices to those in Europe or elsewhere, since the likely result would, paradoxically, raise US prices (Chapter 10).* I also reframe the relationship between the US and other countries by focusing on America's goals, arguing that whatever the rest of the world pays for branded drugs is a subsidy that makes drugs more affordable for America. The conventional view is that the US subsidizes drugs for other countries, which makes it sound like we can stop doing that by just paying less, overlooking the negative consequence of such policies to American patients.

5.  Mortgage-based cost-effectiveness modeling using a long time-horizon that takes into account the fact that a drug is only

---

* Others objected to reference pricing, arguing it would lower drug costs in the US and therefore reduce funding for innovation, which would only be true if the US imposed absolute price controls in addition to reference pricing, as has also been proposed.

expensive for a relatively brief time but yields benefit forever after, often permanently reducing the utilization of healthcare services (which not only don't go generic but rise rapidly in cost; Chapters 1 and 4).*

Ideas that I've discussed that have been proposed elsewhere are:

1. Capping or eliminating cost-sharing and ensuring that everyone has insurance, thereby allowing all patients to afford what their physicians prescribe and resolve a major point of controversy (Chapters 1 and 4).

2. Strategies to prevent price-jacking of sole-source generics, such as (a) requiring that companies provide samples to generic competitors and coordinate REMS and (b) guaranteed purchase contracting (functionally similar to contractual genericization), which could also be useful in cases of there being so few generic or biosimilar competitors that the price remains well above the cost of production (Chapter 9).

3. Reforming drug rebate practices so that payers are not better off encouraging higher list prices to misleadingly maximize room for rebates (Chapter 7).

4. Helping physicians make the best use of their time with patients by reducing time wasted on redundant data entry and enabling them to delegate more. The US should also train more primary care physicians and teach patients how to be more effective advocates for their own care (Chapter 12).

5. Installing a European-style 10-year exclusivity period (up from 5-7 years) for any new drug approved in the US that no longer has patent protection to incentivize investment in the drug's development (Chapter 13).

---

* For example, Lipitor would have looked much more cost-effective in its early years had one divided fifteen years of costs by a century's worth of effectiveness.

6. Creating a market exclusivity extension voucher system to incentivize companies to upgrade the drug labels of old generics with data on how to put them to new uses (Chapter 13).[295]

7. Addressing the opioid crisis by making addiction treatment more widely available and affordable and investing in non-addictive drugs that treat pain.

8. Fostering trade negotiations between the US and other wealthy nations to encourage other countries, particularly wealthier ones, to contribute more towards supporting the global drug development industry. We can encourage them to pay for more branded drugs (not deny their own patients) and to approve reimbursement for branded drugs more quickly (Chapter 10). In today's political climate, such discussions may seem hard to imagine, but they would not be unprecedented.

Specifically, there are some direct actions that scientists, executives, and other members of the drug industry can take to promote the Biotech Social Contract.

1. Continue to advocate for universal health insurance and capping or (ideally) eliminating out-of-pocket costs, which BIO and PhRMA already do. This is the first and only real answer to the question of how patients are supposed to afford high drug prices.

2. Celebrate the mountain of generic drugs that innovation has created. Whenever the discussion about drug prices shifts from what patients can afford to what society can afford, explain that drugs that go generic are far more cost-effective than any other aspect of healthcare. What society pays for branded drugs is an investment towards owning them as generics. Towards this end, our industry should celebrate the ongoing value and cost-effectiveness of generics with a Public Domain Day for Drugs (Chapter 2).

3. Advocate for internal reforms to ensure that drugs go generic without undue delay and stay affordable. When drug pricing

discussions veer inevitably towards patent games and price-jacking, acknowledge these problems (Chapters 8 and 9) and embrace possible reforms, such as contractual genericization.

4.  Write articles and opinion editorials that call for insurance reform to help patients afford medicines.* Use these to rebut the usual, flawed arguments against drug prices in America (e.g., America can pay what Europe pays).

5.  When companies model the cost-effectiveness of a drug, they should create mortgage-based models that project over an extended timeframe so as to capture the impact of genericization, instead of carelessly adopting conventional models that only judge a drug by its branded price, presuming it will always be that high.†

## A Note to Members of the Biopharmaceutical Industry

The biopharmaceutical industry has long been and continues to be on the right side of history, turning biomedical knowledge into useful products. We treat and cure diseases for a living. Our inventions ease pain, prolong life, and make it possible for people to enjoy any other creative and joyful pursuit. Drugs are not without their risks, and we have caused harm along the way (Chapter 15), but the benefit-risk profile of all that the drug industry has accomplished is by any objective standard a positive one. As long as we continue to learn from our mistakes and make each generation of medicines better than the last, we'll be driving forward important progress.

---

* Here's one I wrote in response to a drug and insurance reform bill put forward by Speaker of the House Nancy Pelosi: https://www.statnews.com/2019/09/23/patients-losers-pelosi-drug-prices-plan/.

† Some might say that no one believes any cost-effectiveness calculations that a biased drug company publishes, and I can see how that would be true. That still doesn't mean that, when a drug company presents its own argument for cost-effectiveness, it should play by others' flawed rules by omitting the value of future generic versions of its drug. For all talk of bias, anyone would be welcome to look at a mortgage-based model and assess it on its merits. Then cost-effectiveness researchers that treat genericizable drugs as if they will be branded forever can present their arguments for why it's appropriate to pretend that they will be expensive forever.

Healthcare in the US has become exceedingly expensive. Total healthcare spending, approaching 20% of GDP, is an enormous cost burden on society, families, and individuals. But there is no way that branded drugs, at just 1.3% of GDP, can't be made affordable to everyone through proper insurance.

That people are angry with the rising costs and perpetual inefficiencies of hospitals and clinics should be no surprise. Even if insurance paid for everything and eliminated out-of-pocket costs, insurance premiums and health-related taxes to cover healthcare services would remain high.

But medicines that keep people out of the hospital, spare them surgeries, and will someday go generic are part of the solution to high healthcare costs and represent only a minor societal expense. Were we to stop innovating and all current drugs went generic, society would indeed "save" money in the near term: Healthcare spending would drop by 5-7%. But resigning ourselves to what we have now without striving for better solutions for our children is a terrible way to save.

So if you work or will someday work at a biotechnology or pharmaceutical company, know that your work is important, valuable, and much more cost-effective than critics currently appreciate. And with insurance reforms, all patients will be able to afford what you can invent.

All it takes for our industry to honor the Biotech Social Contract is to ensure that our revenues continue to be linked to innovation as directly as possible, as the patent system intends them to be. That means that all drug companies must make sure that their drugs go generic without undue delay, shunning lifecycle management tactics that do not benefit patients.

What is and what isn't a legitimate basis for seeking to delay genericization can be subjective, and every company may have a bias towards believing that it's doing the right thing. But the world is watching and judging the entire industry by its response to any one company's actions.

While no one company might be expected to voluntarily deny itself lawful profits, for the preservation of the whole industry, it is important that we collectively—at the level of organizations like BIO and PhRMA—support regulations to bring about contractual genericization of off-patent drugs that remain natural monopolies (e.g., someday gene therapies) or even natural oligopolies (e.g., biologics with few biosimilars) to ultimately make them as inexpensive as they can be. The drug industry should make its money from innovation, not long tails of profits from old drugs.

Clipping those long tails will impact a few companies in the near-term. Indeed, the reforms I'm proposing fundamentally pit innovators who value the first 10-15 years of a new drug's sales against the more mature companies milking older drugs, potentially creating a rift within the industry. But to safeguard the drug development industry from the kinds of blunt price controls being discussed today, it's important that we offer society a better model by which all drugs can become cost-effective in the long run.

Especially if tail-limiting regulation (e.g., contractual genericization) were to come paired with vital insurance reforms to allow all patients to afford the medicines we create, we must be prepared to make such essential trades to uphold the Biotech Social Contract. Doing so will benefit present and future patients in America and around the world.

## Calling Every Reader to Action

As a parent, child, sibling, spouse, grandparent, or friend to someone who currently needs or someday may need medical care, your view of the drug pricing debate counts. This is personal, or at least someday it will be.

It's up to each of us how we talk about drug pricing at the dinner table. If we write or comment on social media, it's up to us what we say on this topic. It's up to each of us how we vote. Those are some of the ways we can make a difference.

There are now scientists exploring every crack in the façades of thousands of diseases and disorders, like water searching for weaknesses in a rock so that it might, by expanding and contracting with the seasons, break it apart from within. As innovators move from idea to idea, backed by investors supporting small companies or by the revenues of larger companies, they will fail countless times. But some will succeed. In time, human ingenuity will seep through every fissure and disintegrate yet another healthcare challenge, just as decades of concerted effort resulted in a cure for hepatitis C. We are tackling cancer and heart disease and diabetes with the same determination.

America has always been a country of hardworking, risk-taking innovators. We wanted to put people on the moon and we did. We have invented our way to a remarkable modern world, and what we can accomplish with our sights set on disease is nothing short of extraordinary.

Even as America struggles to compete with other countries in manufacturing and other sectors, we remain a leader in biomedical innovation. We're good at it. We should keep doing it.

If you, a family member, or someone you know is a scientist working for a biotechnology company, you should be proud. America should be proud.

And yet, until we have made the fruits of all that effort accessible and affordable to all Americans, we can't be happy or proud. That is the lesson amidst the public outrage over drug costs.

So now you understand the role of insurance in determining whether what society can afford is affordable to any one patient. You must decide the degree to which insurance companies and government plans should be allowed to cut holes in the safety net they are promising while still calling the product "insurance." I hope that this book has equipped you with the knowledge to recognize policies that really can make healthcare affordable for patients while preserving innovation.

Upholding the Biotech Social Contract is up to each of us.

# ACKNOWLEDGMENTS

**This book would not have been possible without the support of my colleagues,** my editors and thought partners, and my wife. At RA Capital, I'm grateful to my co-founder and partner Raj Shah, who has encouraged me to write and speak out; our lead graphics artist Erin Clutter, who masterfully captured the essential elements of each article; and a former member of our writing team, Aaron Hiltner, who helped me turn our dialogues into early drafts of articles that later became the core of this book. I could always count on my editor, Chris Morrison, for thought partnership, making the cuts that needed to be made, and pushing me to finish. When my attention went elsewhere, my sense of duty to respond to Chris' comments were often the impetus to find the time to keep writing. Chris was later joined by Lari Bishop and Brian Saliba, two editors I trusted to examine the book from a lay perspective (Chris and I both being biotech insiders). Lari and Alex expertly shepherded the manuscript to its final form. I thank Christina Lilliehook and Rachel Carter for their attentive proofreading, and the team at *the*BookDesigners for their creative work on the cover.

I deeply appreciate the thought partnership and writing talents of Anthony Bower and Jessica Sagers, my co-authors of articles of which portions are included in chapters on international drug reference pricing and a public domain day for drugs, respectively. Thank you to Amitabh Chandra and John Stanford for their thoughtful suggestions as I neared the finish line. And a special thank you to my fellow biotech investor Alex Karnal for pressure-testing how contractual genericization might really play out and the impact of different kinds of price controls on innovation. I am also grateful to everyone who asked me probing questions when I've spoken about what I saw as the Biotech Social Contract, especially the students in the classes I've taught; it is their questions that I tried to address in so many footnotes, caveats, explanations, and analogies that made it into this book.

I'm deeply thankful to Richard Aldrich, a businessman, investor, and entrepreneur with a rare talent for bringing out the potential in others, for his generous, no-nonsense mentorship, for launching my career as a scientist-investor, and for his unwavering support of my professional experiments.

I dedicate this book to my wife Anna, for her unwavering support and setting an example for me by her scholarship. And to my parents, Evelina and Alex, who challenged me to always question received wisdom (at some cost to themselves). Also, to my brother Joseph, sister-in-law Jennifer, brother-in-law Danny, and Mary Grace, for all their spirited discussions at our gatherings. And to their children, Penelope, Zane, Levit, Bella, Music, and Julian, and to my children, Olivia and Valentin, who all have made the distant future and well-being of future generations so much more personal for me. And, finally, to Joanna Haas, who as a physician and drug developer was an exceptionally well-qualified thought partner and, as my mom-in-law, was someone I could trust to not hold back. This book has been both a personal journey and a family adventure.

# ENDNOTES

## Part 1: The Biotech Social Contract

1   Blue Cross Blue Shield, Health of America Report, *Planned Knee and Hip Replacement Surgeries Are on the Rise in the U.S.* (Blue Cross Blue Shield Association, 2019), https://www.bcbs.com/sites/default/files/file-attachments/health-of-america-report/HoA-Orthopedic%2BCosts%20Report.pdf.

2   Department of Research & Scientific Affairs, *Annual Incidence of Common Musculoskeletal Procedures and Treatment* (American Academy of Orthopaedic Surgeons, 2014), https://www.aaos.org/research/stats/CommonProceduresTreatments-March2014.pdf;

R. Andrews et al., *HCUP Projections: Mobility/Orthopedic Procedures 2003 to 2012* (Rockville: U.S. Agency for Healthcare Research and Quality, 2012), http://hcup-us.ahrq.gov/reports/projections/2012-03.pdf;

Qian Gu PhD et al., "Surgery for Hip Fracture Yields Societal Benefits That Exceed the Direct Medical Costs," *Clinical Orthopaedics and Related Research* 472 (2014): 3536-3546, accessed Oct. 15, 2019. doi: 10.1007/s11999-014-3820-6, https://link.springer.com/content/pdf/10.1007%2Fs11999-014-3820-6.pdf;

Lane Koenig et al., "Estimating the Societal Benefits of THA After Accounting for Work Status and Productivity: A Markov Model Approach," *Clinical Orthopaedics and Related Research* 474, no. 12 (2016): 2645-2654, accessed Oct. 15, 2019. doi: 10.1007/s11999-016-5084-9, https://www.ncbi.nlm.nih.gov/pmc/articles/PMC5085951/;

SM Kurtz and KL Ong et al., "Impact of the Economic Downturn on Total Joint Replacement Demand in the United States: Updated Projections to 2021," *The Journal of Bone & Joint Surgery America* 96, no. 8 (2016): 624-30, accessed Oct.15, 2019. doi: 10.2106/JBJS.M.00285, https://www.ncbi.nlm.nih.gov/pubmed/24740658.

3   Cynthia Cox and Rabah Kammal, "How Has U.S. Spending on Healthcare Changed Over Time?" *Peterson-Kaiser Family Foundation Health System Tracker*, Dec. 20, 2018, https://www.healthsystemtracker.org/chart-collection/u-s-spending-healthcare-changed-time/#item-administrative-costs-have-risen-over-time-but-have-recently-moderated_2017.

4   J Conway et al., "Lisinopril and Enalapril in Hypertension: A Comparative Study Using Ambulatory Monitoring," *Journal of Human Hypertension* 4, no. 3 (1990): 235-9. https://www.ncbi.nlm.nih.gov/pubmed/2163450.

5   AstraZeneca, *1999 Annual Report*, accessed Oct, 15, 2019, https://ddd.uab.cat/pub/infanu/40172/iaASTZENa1999ieng.pdf.

6    David H. Kreling et al., *Prescription Drug Trends: A Chartbook Update* (Madison, WI: The Kaiser Family Foundation, 2001), http://files.kff.org/attachment/report-prescription-drug-trends-a-chartbook-update.

7    Alexander Gaffney, "How Many Drugs Has FDA Approved in Its Entire History? New Paper Explains," *Regulatory Focus*, Oct. 3, 2014, https://www.raps.org/regulatory-focus%E2%84%A2/news-articles/2014/10/how-many-drugs-has-fda-approved-in-its-entire-history-new-paper-explains

8    Arthur A. Patchett et al., 1983, Aminoacid Derivatives as Antihypertensives, US Patent 4,374,829A, filed Feb, 17, 1981, and issued, Feb. 22, 1983.

9    Chie Hoon Song and Jeung-Whan Han, "Patent Cliff and Strategic Switch: Exploring Strategic Design Possibilities in the Pharmaceutical Industry," *SpringerPlus* 5, no. 1 (2016): 692, accessed Oct. 15, 2019. doi: 10.1186/s40064-016-2323-1, https://www.ncbi.nlm.nih.gov/pmc/articles/PMC4899342/.

10   Peter Kolchinsky, "Let's Throw a Patent- Burning Party," *Wall Street Journal*, Sept. 30, 2018, https://www.wsj.com/articles/lets-throw-a-patent-burning-party-1538329275.

11   "Health Spending," OECD Data, Organisation for Economic Co-operation and Development, accessed Oct. 15, 2019, https://data.oecd.org/healthres/health-spending.htm;

     Centers for Medicare and Medicaid Services, *National Health Expenditure Projections, 2015-2025*, accessed Oct. 15, 2019, https://www.cms.gov/Research-Statistics-Data-and-Systems/Statistics-Trends-and-Reports/NationalHealthExpendData/Downloads/Proj2015.pdf

12   Centers for Medicare and Medicaid Services, *National Health Expenditures 2017 Highlights,* accessed Oct. 15, 2019 https://www.cms.gov/Research-Statistics-Data-and-Systems/Statistics-Trends-and-Reports/NationalHealthExpendData/downloads/highlights.pdf

13   Peter Kolchinsky and Jessica Sagers, "We Need a Public Domain Day to Highlight When Drugs Go Off Patent," *STAT*, Feb. 14, 2019, https://www.statnews.com/2019/02/14/public-domain-day-drug-patent-expiration/.

14   Glenn Fleishman, "For the First Time in More than 20 Years, Copyrighted Works Will Enter the Public Domain," *Smithsonian.com*, Jan, 2019, https://www.smithsonianmag.com/arts-culture/first-time-20-years-copyrighted-works-enter-public-domain-180971016/.

15   Lila Bailey, "Join Us for a Grand Re-Opening of the Public Domain," *Internet Archive Blogs* (blog), Dec. 5, 2018, https://blog.archive.org/2018/12/05/join-us-for-a-grand-re-opening-of-the-public-domain-january-25-2019/.

16   "Hep C Drugs: Is Your Plan Really Benefiting From Your PBM'S 'Deal'?," National Prescription Coverage Coalition, accessed Oct. 15, 2019, http://nationalprescriptioncoveragecoalition.com/hep-c-drugs-is-your-plan-really-benefiting-from-your-pbms-deal/

17   Eric C. Schneider and David Squires, "From Last to First—Could the U.S. Health Care System Become the Best in the World?" *The New England Journal of Medicine*, July 14, 2017, http://www.nejm.org/doi/full/10.1056/NEJMp1708704.

18   PDCI Report Series, *Generic Drug Prices: A Canada US Comparison* (Palmer D'Angelo Consulting Inc., 2002), http://www.who.int/intellectualproperty/events/en/R&Dpaper2.pdf;

     OJ Wouters et al., "Comparing Generic Drug Markets in Europe and the United States: Prices, Volumes, and Spending," *Milbank Quarterly* 93, no 3 (2017): 554-601, accessed Oct. 15, 2019. doi: 10.1111/1468-0009.12279,

     https://www.ncbi.nlm.nih.gov/pubmed/28895227;

     Irene Papanicolas et al., "Health Care Spending in the United States and Other High-Income Countries," *JAMA* 319, no. 10 (2018): 1024-1039, accessed Oct. 15, 2019. doi: 10.1001/jama.2018.1150,

     https://jamanetwork.com/journals/jama/article-abstract/2674671;

Shanoor Seervai, "The Truth About Waiting to See a Doctor in Canada," *The Commonwealth Fund*, October 30, 2018, https://www.commonwealthfund.org/publications/podcast/2018/oct/truth-about-waiting-see-doctor-canada.

19    "Generic Drugs," US Food & Drug Administration, accessed Oct. 15, 2019, https://www.fda.gov/drugs/buying-using-medicine-safely/generic-drugs;

OJ Wouters et al., "Comparing Generic Drug Markets."

20    Bridie Taylor, "Treatment of Hepatitis C Has More Than Doubled Since 2013. Yet 99% of People Are Still Being Denied the Life-Saving Cure," *World Hepatitis Alliance*, July 28, 2016, http://www.worldhepatitisalliance.org/news/jul-2016/treatment-hepatitis-c-has-more-doubled-2013-yet-99-people-are-still-being-denied-life.

21    ORC International Poll, *Poll 4* (March 8, 2017), distributed by CNN, http://i2.cdn.turner.com/cnn/2017/images/03/08/rel4d.-.budget.pdf.

22    Vinod Thomas, "Will More Infrastructure Spending Increase US Growth?" *Brookings* (blog), Dec. 13, 2016, https://www.brookings.edu/blog/future-development/2016/12/13/will-more-infrastructure-spending-increase-us-growth/.

23    Gary Claxton et al., "Payments for Cost Sharing Increasing Rapidly Over Time," Peterson-KFF: Health System Tracker, Peterson Center on Healthcare and Kaiser Family Foundation, April 12, 2016, http://www.healthsystemtracker.org/brief/payments-for-cost-sharing-increasing-rapidly-over-time/#item-start.

24    *Overview of the ICER Value Assessment: Framework and Update for 2017-2019* (ICER, 2019) https://icer-review.org/wp-content/uploads/2017/06/ICER-value-assessment-framework-Updated-050818.pdf.

25    William S. Smith, "The U.S. Shouldn't Use the 'QALY' in Drug Cost-Effectiveness Reviews", *STAT*, Feb. 22, 2019, https://www.statnews.com/2019/02/22/qaly-drug-effectiveness-reviews/.

26    Chie Hoon Song and Jeung-Whan Han, "Patent Cliff and Strategic Switch."

27    Rob Wright, "Allergan's Brent Saunders Shares a Social Contract," *Life Science Leader*, Sept. 1, 2017, https://www.lifescienceleader.com/doc/allergan-s-brent-saunders-shares-a-social-contract-secret-0001.

28    Samantha Artiga et al., "The Effects of Premiums and Cost Sharing on Low-Income Populations: Updated Review of Research Findings," *KFF*, June 1, 2017, https://www.kff.org/medicaid/issue-brief/the-effects-of-premiums-and-cost-sharing-on-low-income-populations-updated-review-of-research-findings/;

Jeffery T. Kullgren et al., "A Survey of Americans with High-Deductible Health Plans Identifies Opportunities to Enhance Consumer Behaviors," *Health Affairs* 38, no. 3 (2019). accessed Oct. 15, 2019. doi: 10.1377/hlthaff.2018.05018, https://www.healthaffairs.org/doi/abs/10.1377/hlthaff.2018.05018?journalCode=hlthaff

29    IQVIA Institute for Human Data Science, *Medicine Use and Spending in the U.S.: A Review of 2018 and Outlook to 2023* (Parsippany, NJ: IQVIA, 2019), https://www.iqvia.com/-/media/iqvia/pdfs/institute-reports/medicine-use-and-spending-in-the-us---a-review-of-2018-outlook-to-2023.pdf?&_=1557542013851;

Micah Hartman et al., "National Health Care Spending in 2016: Spending and Enrollment Growth Slow After Initial Coverage Expansions," *Health Affairs* 37, no. 1 (2017), accessed Oct. 15, 2019. doi: 10.1377/hlthaff.2017.1299, https://www.healthaffairs.org/doi/full/10.1377/hlthaff.2017.1299.

30    Teresa A Coughlin et al., "Uncompensated Care for the Uninsured 2013: A Detailed Examination," *KFF*, May 30, 2014, https://www.kff.org/uninsured/report/uncompensated-care-for-the-uninsured-in-2013-a-detailed-examination/.

31    "How Much Does Health Insurance Cost Per Month?" Health Markets, accessed Oct. 15, 2019, https://www.healthmarkets.com/content/how-much-does-health-insurance-cost-month

32    Emily Gee and Topher Spiro, "Excess Administrative Costs Burden the US Health Care System," *Center for American Progress*, April 8, 2019, https://www.americanprogress.org/issues/healthcare/reports/2019/04/08/468302/excess-administrative-costs-burden-u-s-health-care-system/ ; https://www.nytimes.com/2018/07/16/upshot/costs-health-care-us.html.

33    Katie Keith, "Two New Federal Surveys Show Stable Uninsured Rate," *Health Affairs*, Sept. 13, 2018, https://www.healthaffairs.org/do/10.1377/hblog20180913.896261/full/.

34    IQVIA Institute for Human Data Science, *Medicine Use and Spending in the U.S*

35    IQVIA Institute for Human Data Science, *Medicine Use and Spending in the U.S.*

36    Samantha Artiga et al., "The Effects of Premiums and Cost Sharing on Low-Income Populations.";

      Robyn Tamblyn et al., "Adverse Events Associated with Prescription Drug Cost-Sharing Among Poor and Elderly Persons," *JAMA* 285, no. 4 (2001): 421-429, accessed Oct. 15, 2019. doi: 10.1001/jama.285.4.421,

      https://jamanetwork.com/journals/jama/fullarticle/1108322

37    Abhijeet Yadav et al., "Variations in Health Insurance Policies Regarding Biologic Therapy Use In Inflammatory Bowel Disease," *Inflammatory Bowel Diseases* 23, no. 6 (2017): 853-857, accessed Oct. 15, 2019. doi: 10.1097/MIB.0000000000001153, https://www.ncbi.nlm.nih.gov/pubmed/28509816.

38    Shubha Bhat et al., "Advocating for Patients with Inflammatory Bowel Disease: How to Naviagte the Prior Authorization Process," *Inflammatory Bowel Diseases* 25, no. 10 (2019): 1621-1628, accessed Oct. 15, 2019. doi: 10.1093/ibdizz013, https://www.ncbi.nlm.nih.gov/pubmed/30753551/.

39    Samantha Artiga et al., "The Effects of Premiums and Cost Sharing on Low-Income Populations.";

      Robyn Tamblyn et al., "Adverse Events Associated with Prescription Drug Cost-Sharing."

40    David Ovalle, "Insurance Adjusters, Appraisers Took Kickbacks for Inflated Mechanic Bills, Hialeah Cops Say," *South Florida Sun Sentinel*, Oct. 1, 2010, https://www.sun-sentinel.com/news/fl-xpm-2010-10-01-fl-adjusters-appraisers-charged-20101001-story.html.

41    Samantha Artiga et al., "The Effects of Premiums and Cost Sharing on Low-Income Populations."

42    Robyn Tamblyn et al., "Adverse Events Associated with Prescription Drug Cost-Sharing."

43    DHHS, *National Health Expenditures 2017 Highlights* (CMS ,2017), https://www.cms.gov/Research-Statistics-Data-and-Systems/Statistics-Trends-and-Reports/NationalHealthExpendData/Downloads/highlights.pdf;

      IQVIA Institute for Human Data Science, *Medicine Use and Spending in the U.S.*

44    "Personal Income in the United States from 1990 to 2018," Statista, accessed Nov. 1, 2019, https://www.statista.com/statistics/216756/us-personal-income/;

      Kimberly Amadeo, "FY 2018 Federal Budget: Enacted Versus Trumps Budget Request," *The Balance*, https://www.thebalance.com/fy-2018-trump-federal-budget-request-4158794.

45    Juliette Cubanki et al., "How Many Medicare Part D Enrollees Had High Out-of-Pocket Drug Costs in 2017?" *KFF*, https://www.kff.org/medicare/issue-brief/how-many-medicare-part-d-enrollees-had-high-out-of-pocket-drug-costs-in-2017/.

46    "Incorporating the Effects of the Proposed Rule on Safe Harbors for the Pharmaceutical Rebates in CBO'S Budget Projections—Supplemental Material for *Updated Budget Projections: 2019-2029*," (analysis, Washington D.C., 2019), www.cbo.gov/system/files/2019-05/55151-SupplementalMaterial.pdf.

47    Scott Gottlieb, "Capturing the Benefits of Competition for Patients" (speech, Washington, DC, March 07, 2018) US Food & Drug Administration, https://www.fda.gov/NewsEvents/Speeches/ucm599833.htm.

48    BC Editorial Board, "Back to School: Breach of Contract,"
      *Biocentury*, Sept. 1, 2017, https://www.biocentury.com/biocentury/
      strategy/2017-09-01/25th-back-school-issue-repair-social-contract.

49    Pan Foundation Issue Brief 8, *Capping Out-of-Pocket Drug Costs for Medicare Beneficiaries* (Pan
      Foundation, 2018), https://panfoundation.org/files/PAN-Issue-Brief-8_Capping-Out-of-
      Pocket-Drug-Costs-for-Medicare-Beneficiaries.pdf.

50    Amber Porterfield et al., "Electronic Prescribing: Improving the Efficiency and Accuracy of
      Prescribing in the Ambulatory Care Setting," *Perspectives in Health Information Management*
      11, no. 1 (2014), accessed Oct. 15, 2019. https://www.ncbi.nlm.nih.gov/pmc/articles/
      PMC3995494/.

51    "Medical Loss Ratio," Centers for Medicare & Medicaid Services, accessed Oct. 15, 2019,
      https://www.cms.gov/CCIIO/Programs-and-Initiatives/Health-Insurance-Market-Reforms/
      Medical-Loss-Ratio.html

52    Peter Kolchinsky, "How to Save $200 Billion and Cure Hepatitis C," *Exome*, July 22, 2013,
      https://www.xconomy.com/boston/2013/07/22/how-to-save-200-billion-and-cure-hepatitis-c/.

53    Stephen Barlas, "Are Specialty Drug Prices Destroying Insurers and Hurting Consumers?" *P&T*
      39, no. 8 (2014): 563-66, accessed Oct. 15, 2019. https://www.ncbi.nlm.nih.gov/pmc/articles/
      PMC4123806/.

54    Chie Hoon Song and Jeung-Whan Han, "Patent Cliff and Strategic Switch."

55    FTC Staff Study, *Pay-for-Delay: How Drug Company Pay-Offs Cost Consumers Billions* (Federal
      Trade Commission, 2010), https://www.ftc.gov/sites/default/files/documents/reports/pay-
      delay-how-drug-company-pay-offs-cost-consumers-billions-federal-trade-commission-staff-
      study/100112payfordelayrpt.pdf.

56    Bill Briggs, "Surgery Prices Surge with Innovation and Consolidation
      Under Obamacare," *NBC News*, Aug. 31, 2014, https://pnhp.org/news/
      surgery-prices-surge-with-innovation-and-consolidation-under-obamacare/;

      Michael Rosenblatt, "The Real Cost of 'High-Priced' Drugs," Harvard Business Review, Harvard
      Business Publishing, Nov. 17, 2014, https://hbr.org/2014/11/the-real-cost-of-high-priced-drugs.

57    Lev Facher, "Democrats' New Logic on Drug Pricing: Developing Slightly Fewer Medicines is
      OK If It Means Lower Prices," *STAT*, Oct. 28, 2019, https://www.statnews.com/2019/10/28/
      democrats-new-logic-drug-prices-biomedical-innovation/.

58    Kimberly Leonard, "Budget Breakers," *US News & World Report*, Sept.
      24, 2015, https://www.usnews.com/news/the-report/articles/2015/09/24/
      expensive-drugs-a-drag-on-consumers-and-government.

59    John F. Kennedy, "Special Message to the Congress on Urgent National Needs" (speech,
      Washington, DC, May 25, 1961) NASA, https://www.nasa.gov/vision/space/features/jfk_
      speech_text.html.

## Part 2: How to Keep Drug Prices in Check

60    Lunawati L. Bennett and Chris Fellner, "Pharmacotherapy of Gaucher Disease: Current and
      Future Options," *P&T* 43, no. 5 (2018): 274-280, 309, accessed Oct. 15, 2019. https://www.ncbi.
      nlm.nih.gov/pmc/articles/PMC5912244/.

61    Geeta Anand, "Why Genzyme Can Charge So Much for Cerezyme," *The Wall Street Journal*,
      Nov. 16, 2005, https://www.wsj.com/articles/SB113210882766198549.

62    Samuel D. Waksal, "Pay Only for Drugs That Help You," *The New York Times*, March 6, 2012,
      http://www.nytimes.com/2012/03/07/opinion/pay-only-for-drugs-that-help-you.html;

Charles Ornstein and Ryann Grochowski Jones, "The Drugs That Companies Promote to Doctors Are Rarely Breakthroughs," *The New York Times*, Jan. 7, 2015, https://www.nytimes.com/2015/01/08/upshot/the-drugs-that-companies-promote-to-doctors-are-rarely-breakthroughs.html;

Austin Frakt, "How Patent Law Can Block Even Lifesaving Drugs," *The New York Times*, Sept. 28, 2015,

https://www.nytimes.com/2015/09/29/upshot/how-patent-law-can-block-even-lifesaving-drugs.html.

63    Donna Young, "'Orphans' Hit Historic High At US FDA; More 'Me-Too' Drugs Urged," *SRA*, Dec. 16, 2015, https://pink.pharmaintelligence.informa.com/PS118484/Orphans-Hit-Historic-High-At-US-FDA-More-MeToo-Drugs-Urged.

64    Scott Gottlieb, "Capturing the Benefits of Competition for Patients."

65    IQVIA Institute for Human Data Science, *Medicine Use and Spending in the U.S.: A Review of 2018 and Outlook to 2023* (Parsippany, NJ: IQVIA, 2019), https://www.iqvia.com/-/media/iqvia/pdfs/institute-reports/medicine-use-and-spending-in-the-us---a-review-of-2018-outlook-to-2023.pdf?&_=1557542013851.

66    Wikipedia Contributors, "Red Queen's Race," *Wikipedia, The Free Encyclopedia,* accessed Oct. 15, 2019, https://en.wikipedia.org/wiki/Red_Queen%27s_race.

67    "Hep C Drugs," National Prescription Coverage Coalition, accessed Oct. 15, 2019

68    IQVIA Institute for Human Data Science, *Medicine Use and Spending in the U.S.*

69    Noam N. Levey, "Rising Health Insurance Deductibles Fuel Middle-Class Anger and Resentment," *Los Angeles Times,* July 17, 2019, https://www.latimes.com/politics/la-na-pol-health-insurance-angry-patients-20190628-story.html#null.

70    Neeraj Sood et al., "Follow the Money: The Flow of Funds in the Pharmaceutical Distribution System," *Health Affairs,* June 13, 2017, https://www.healthaffairs.org/do/10.1377/hblog20170613.060557/full/.

71    Bob Herman, "Inside a Drug Pricing Contract," *Axios,* updated March 15, 2018, https://www.axios.com/inside-express-scripts-pbm-contract-8be2f09d-cbfa-4275-9855-7bc9c4fcc1a7.html.

72    "UnitedHealthcare Launches Expansion of Direct-to-Consumer Pharmacy Discounts to Millions of Americans," UnitedHealth Group, March 6, 2018, http://www.unitedhealthgroup.com/Newsroom/Articles/Feed/UnitedHealthcare/2018/0306DirecttoConsumerPharmacyDiscounts.aspx?r=1.

73    Brooke Wright, "Trending in Benefit Design: Copay Accumulator Programs," *Hiro* (blog), Feb. 5, 2018, https://www.hirc.com/blog/trending-benefit-design-copay-accumulator-programs.

74    Robert Goldberg, "Reduce Drug Prices By Eliminating PBM Rebates," *The Hill* (blog), Feb. 14, 2017, http://thehill.com/blogs/congress-blog/healthcare/319479-reduce-drug-prices-by-eliminating-pbm-rebates.

75    "Wyden Calls for Increased Drug Pricing Transparency to Lower Costs," United States Senate Committee on Finance, March 15, 2017, https://www.finance.senate.gov/ranking-members-news/wyden-calls-for-increased-drug-pricing-transparency-to-lower-costs.

76    Carolyn Y. Johnson, "The Real Reason the US Spends Twice as Much on Health Care as Other Wealthy Countries," *The Washington Post*, March 13, 2018, https://www.washingtonpost.com/news/wonk/wp/2018/03/13/the-real-reason-the-u-s-spends-twice-as-much-on-health-care-as-other-wealthy-countries/?utm_term=.0bb0bf775941.

77    "Which Firms Profit Most from America's Health-Care System," *The Economist*, March 15, 2018, https://www.economist.com/news/business/21738934-it-not-pharmaceutical-companies-which-firms-profit-most-americas-health-care-system.

78    Fiona Scott Morton and Lysle T. Boller, "Enabling Competition in Pharmaceutical Markets," (Hutchins Center Working Paper, Yale School of Management, 2017), https://www.brookings.edu/wp-content/uploads/2017/05/wp30_scottmorton_competitioninpharma1.pdf.

79    Zachary Brennan, "Biosimilars in the US: Lower Costs, Increased
      Patient Access, IMS Report Finds," *Regulatory Focus*, June 20, 2016,
      http://www.raps.org/Regulatory-Focus/News/2016/06/20/25166/
      Biosimilars-in-the-EU-Lower-Costs-Increased-Patient-Access-IMS-Report-Finds/.

80    QuintilesIMS, *The Impact of Biosimilar Competition in Europe* (QuintilesIMS, 2017), http://www.
      medicinesforeurope.com/wp-content/uploads/2017/05/IMS-Biosimilar-2017_V9.pdf.

81    Scott Gottlieb, "Health & Wealth: Biocentury's Interview with FDA
      Commissioner Scott Gottlieb," Interview by Steve Usdin, *Biocentury*, June 23,
      2017, https://www.biocentury.com/biocentury/politics-policy-law/2017-06-23/
      biocentury%E2%80%99s-interview-fda-commissioner-scott-gottlieb.

82    Andrew W. Mulcahy et al., *The Cost Savings Potential of Biosimilar Drugs in the United states*
      (Rand Corporation, 2014), https://www.rand.org/content/dam/rand/pubs/perspectives/PE100/
      PE127/RAND_PE127.pdf.

83    Chie Hoon Song and Jeung-Whan Han, "Patent Cliff and Strategic Switch.";
      Zachary Brennan, "Biosimilars in the US: Lower Costs";
      Benjamin Yu, "Greater Potential Cost Savings with Biosimilar Use," *The American Journal of
      Managed Care* 22, no. 5 (2016): 378, accessed Oct. 15, 2019, http://www.ajmc.com/journals/
      issue/2016/2016-vol22-n5/greater-potential-cost-savings-with-biosimilar-use.

84    "NHE Fact Sheet," CMS.gov, accessed Oct. 15, 2019, https://www.cms.gov/research-statistics-
      data-and-systems/statistics-trends-and-reports/nationalhealthexpenddata/nhe-fact-sheet.html;
      IQVIA Institute for Human Data Science, *Medicine Use and Spending in the U.S.*

85    Dan Stanton, "First US Biosimilar Gradually Eroding Amgen's Market Share, Sandoz,"
      *BioParhma Reporter*, Jan. 29, 2016, https://www.biopharma-reporter.com/Article/2016/01/29/
      Sandoz-s-biosimilar-Zarxio-gradually-eroding-Amgen-s-Neupogen-sales.

86    "Hepatitis C Treatments Give Patients More Options," US Food & Drug Administration,
      updated March 4, 2017, https://www.fda.gov/ForConsumers/ConsumerUpdates/ucm405642.
      htm.

87    Anne Casselman, "Identical Twins' Genes Are Not Identical," *Scientific American*, April 3, 2008,
      https://www.scientificamerican.com/article/identical-twins-genes-are-not-identical/.

88    Charlotte Hu, "Pharmaceutical Companies Are Backing Away From
      a Growing Threat That Could Kill 10 Million People a Year by 2050,"
      *Business Insider,* July 21, 2018, https://www.businessinsider.com/
      major-pharmaceutical-companies-dropping-antibiotic-projects-superbugs-2018-7.

89    Ike Swetlitz, "Gottlieb Pitches 'Subscriptions' to Incentivize Pharma to Make New Antibiotics,"
      *Stat*, Sept. 14, 2018, https://www.statnews.com/2018/09/14/gottlieb-idea-antibiotic-resistance/;
      "Wanted: A Reward for Antibiotic Development," *Nature Biotechnology* 36, no. 555 (2018),
      accessed Oct. 15, 2019. https://www.nature.com/articles/nbt.4193.

90    Phil Taylor, "UK Unveils New Antibiotic Buying Plan, Pharma
      Incentives," *PMLive,* Jan. 24, 2019, http://www.pmlive.com/pharma_news/
      hancock_proposes_new_antibiotic_buying_plan_for_nhs_1276081.

91    Preston Atteberry et al., "Biologics Are Natural Monopolies (Part 1): Why Biosimilars Do Not
      Create Effective Competition," *Health Affairs,* April 15, 2019, https://www.healthaffairs.org/
      do/10.1377/hblog20190405.396631/full/;
      Mark Trusheim et al., "Biologics Are Natural Monopolies (Part 2): A Proposal For Post-
      Exclusivity Price Regulation of Biologics," *Health Affairs*, April 15, 2019, https://www.
      healthaffairs.org/do/10.1377/hblog20190405.839549/full/.

92    Joshua D. Schiffman et al., "Early Detection of Cancer: Past, Present, and Future," *ASCO
      Educational Book*, 25 (2015): 57-65, accessed Oct. 15, 2019. doi: 10.14694/EdBook_
      AM.2015.35.57, https://www.ncbi.nlm.nih.gov/pubmed/25993143.

93    Lee Cooper, "A Radical Proposal for Preventing Rare Genetic Diseases," *Wired*, June 5, 2017, https://www.wired.com/2017/06/radical-proposal-preventing-rare-genetic-diseases/.

94    Carolyn Y. Johnson, "This Old Drug Was Free. Now It's $109,500 a Year," *The Washington Post*, Dec. 18, 2017, https://www.washingtonpost.com/news/wonk/wp/2017/12/18/this-old-drug-was-free-now-its-109500-a-year/.

95    Jaroslav Flegr et al., "Toxoplasmosis—A Global Threat. Correlation of Latent Toxoplasmosis with Specific Disease Burden in a Set of 88 Countries," *PLoS One* 9, no. 3 (2014): e90203, accessed Oct. 15, 2019. doi: 10.1371/journal.pone.0090203, https://www.ncbi.nlm.nih.gov/pmc/articles/PMC3963851/.

96    Jeffrey L. James, "Neglected Parasitic Infections in the United States: Toxoplasmosis," *The American Journal of Tropical Medicine and Hygiene* 90, no. 5 (2014): 794-99, accessed Oct. 15, 2019. doi: 10.4269/ajtmh.13-0722, https://www.ncbi.nlm.nih.gov/pmc/articles/PMC4015566/.

97    Jaroslav Flegr et al., "Toxoplasmosis—A Global Threat,"
James B. McAuley, "Congenital Toxoplasmosis," *Journal of the Pediatric Infectious Diseases Society* 3, suppl. 1 (2014): S30-35, accessed Oct. 15, 2019. doi: 10.1093/jpids/plu077, https://www.ncbi.nlm.nih.gov/pmc/articles/PMC4164182/.

98    Joseph Lykins et al., "Understanding Toxoplasmosis in the United States Through 'Large Data' Analyses," *Clinical Infectious Diseases* 63, no. 4 (2016): 468-75, accessed Oct. 15, 2019. doi: 10/1093/cid/ciw356, https://academic.oup.com/cid/article/63/4/468/2595100/Understanding-Toxoplasmosis-in-the-United-States.

99    GlaxoSmithKline, *GlaxoSmithKline Annual Report 2010*, accessed Oct. 15, 2019 https://www.gsk.com/media/2691/annual-report-2010.pdf.

100   https://www.google.com/search?ei=XseoXdC1NOG1ggflmLoI&q=corepharma+gsk+daraprim+-turing+price+2010;
Jonathan D. Alpern et al., "High-Cost Generic Drugs—Implications for Patients and Policymakers," *The New England Journal of Medicine* 371 (2014): 1859-62, accessed Oct. 15, 2019. doi: 10.1056/NEJMp1408376,
http://www.nejm.org/doi/full/10.1056/NEJMp1408376?viewT#t=article.

101   Zachary Brennan, "Generic Drug Backlog at FDA: A Dive Into the Confusing Numbers," *Regulatory Focus,* Nov. 1, 2016, http://www.raps.org/Regulatory-Focus/News/2016/11/01/26106/Generic-Drug-Backlog-at-FDA-A-Dive-Into-the-Confusing-Numbers/.

102   Andrew Pollack, "Drug Goes From $13.50 a Tablet to $750, Overnight," *The New York Times*, Sept. 20, 2015, https://www.nytimes.com/2015/09/21/business/a-huge-overnight-increase-in-a-drugs-price-raises-protests.html.

103   Trueman W. Sharp to Abbreviated New Drug Applications, memorandum, Jan. 17, 2017, "Decision to Waive the Requirement for a Single, Shared System REMS for Sodium Oxybate Oral Solution," https://www.fda.gov/media/102913/download.

104   "FDA Approves a Generic of Xyrem with a REMS Program," US Food & Drug Administration, updated Jan. 19, 2017, https://www.fda.gov/drugs/drug-safety-and-availability/fda-approves-generic-xyrem-rems-program.

105   Jayne O'Donnell, "FDA Chief Says Drug Makers Are Gaming the System to Slow Generic Competition; Vows Action," *USA Today,* Aug. 15, 2017, https://www.usatoday.com/story/news/politics/2017/08/15/fda-chief-says-drug-makers-gaming-system-slow-generic-competition-vows-action/568698001/.

106   "Daraprim Prices, Coupons and Patient Assistance Programs," Drugs.com, accessed Oct. 15, 2019, https://www.drugs.com/price-guide/daraprim.

107   Shefali Luthra, "'Pharma Bro' Shkreli is in Prison, But Daraprim's Price is Still High," *Kaiser Health News*, May 4, 2018, https://khn.org/news/for-shame-pharma-bro-shkreli-is-in-prison-but-daraprims-price-is-still-high/.

108  Adam Feuerstein, "Martin Shkreli's Drug Company is Losing Money—And Its Salesforce Feels Cheated," *Stat*, Sept. 18, 2019, https://www.statnews.com/2019/09/18/martin-shkrelis-drug-company-is-losing-money-and-its-salesforce-feels-cheated/.

109  Zachary Brennan, "Gottlieb: 'End the Shenanigans' on Delaying Generic Drug Competition," *Regulatory Focus*, Nov. 8, 2017, http://raps.org/Regulatory-Focus/News/2017/11/08/28846/Gottlieb-End-the-Shenanigans-on-Delaying-Generic-Drug-Competition/;

US Congress, House, *Creating and Restoring Equal Access to Equivalent Samples Act of 2019*, HR 965, 116th Cong., 1st sess., introduced in House May 10, 2019, https://www.congress.gov/bill/116th-congress/house-bill/965/text.

110  Though, if one were very specific about particular formulations, the number is over 300;

Zachary Brennan, "More Competition: Senator Proposes Priority Reviews for Some Generics, New Voucher Program," *Regulatory Focus*, March 3, 2016, http://www.raps.org/Regulatory-Focus/News/2016/03/03/24466/More-Competition-Senator-Proposes-New-Priority-Reviews-for-Some-Generics-New-Voucher-Program/.;

FDA, *List of Off-Patent, Off-Exclusivity Drugs Without and Approved Generic* (FDA, 2017), https://www.fda.gov/media/105829/download.

111  Meghana Keshavan, "With One Manufacturer and Little Money to be Made, Supplies of a Critical Cancer Drug Are Dwindling," *Stat*, Feb. 20, 2019, https://www.statnews.com/2019/02/20/supplies-bladder-cancer-drug-bcg-dwindling/.

112  Matthew Cohen et al., "Policy Options for Increasing Generic Drug Competition Through Importation," *Health Affairs*, Jan. 7, 2019, https://www.healthaffairs.org/do/10.1377/hblog20190103.333047/full/.

113  Zachary Brennan, "More Competition."

114  https://www.katherineeban.com/

115  Kevin Kelleher, "The Biotech Bubble May Finally Have Popped," *Time*, Sept. 29, 2015, https://time.com/4053640/biotech-bubble/.

116  Peter Loftus, "Cancer Drug Price Rises 1,400% with No Generic to Challenge It," *The Wall Street Journal*, Dec. 25, 2017, https://www.wsj.com/articles/cancer-drug-price-rises-1400-with-no-generic-to-challenge-it-1514203201?mg=prod/accounts-wsj.

117  Rachel Nall et al., "The Cost of HIV Treatment," *Healthline*, March 4, 2019, https://www.healthline.com/health/hiv-aids/cost-of-treatment#current-drug-costs.

118  "Competitive Bidding: What is Competitive Bidding," FindRFP, accessed Oct. 15, 2019, https://www.findrfp.com/Government-Contracting/competitive-bidding.aspx.

119  Wikipedia Contributors, "New England Compounding Center Meningitis Outbreak," *Wikipedia, The Free Encyclopedia*, last updated Nov. 8, 2019, https://en.wikipedia.org/wiki/New_England_Compounding_Center_meningitis_outbreak.

120  "Hepatitis C," World Health Organization, July 9, 2019, https://www.who.int/news-room/fact-sheets/detail/hepatitis-c.

121  Q4 2019 Earning Results, *Gilead*, Feb. 4, 2019, http://investors.gilead.com/static-files/d37c8017-5ae2-40d1-b8e3-371604c33341.

122  Q4 2019 Earning Results, *Gilead*

123  Michael Mezher, "European Commission Says Compulsory Licensing Can Only Happen at National Level," *Regulatory Focus*, June 26, 2015, https://www.raps.org/regulatory-focus%E2%84%A2/news-articles/2015/6/european-commission-says-compulsory-licensing-can-only-happen-at-national-level.

124  Dr. Anupam B. Jena, "US Drug Prices Higher Than in the Rest of the World, Here's Why," *The Hill*, Jan. 19, 2018, http://thehill.com/opinion/healthcare/369727-us-drug-prices-higher-than-in-the-rest-of-the-world-heres-why;

QuintilesIMS Institute, *Outlook for Global Medicines Through 2021* (Parsippany, NJ: QuintilesIMS Institute, 2016), https://morningconsult.com/wp-content/uploads/2016/12/ QuintilesIMS-Institute-Global-Outlook-FINAL.pdf

125 "Pharmaceutical Spending," OECD Data, Organisation for Economic Co-operation and Development, accessed Oct. 15, 2019 https://data.oecd.org/healthres/pharmaceutical-spending. htm#indicator-chart

126 Irene Papanicolas et al., "Health Care Spending in the United States."

127 Irene Papanicolas et al., "Health Care Spending in the United States."

128 William H. Shrank et al., "Waste in the US Health Care System Estimated Costs and Potential for Savings," *Jama* 322, no. 15 (2019): 1501-09, accessed Oct. 15, 2019. doi: 10.1001/ jama.2019.13978, https://jamanetwork.com/journals/jama/articlepdf/2752664/jama_ shrank_2019_sc_190005.pdf.

129 Panos Kanavos et al., "Higher US Branded Drug Prices and Spending Compared to Other Countries May Stem Partly from Quick Uptake of New Drugs," *Health Affairs* 32, no. 4 (2013), accessed Oct. 15, 2019. doi: 10.1377/hlthaff.2012.0920, https://www.healthaffairs.org/doi/ full/10.1377/hlthaff.2012.0920.

130 Ariel D. Stern et al., "The Impact of Price Regulation on the Availability of New Drugs in Germany," *Health Affairs* 38, no. 7 (2019): 1182-87, accessed Oct. 15, 2019. doi: 10.1377/ hlthaff.2018.05142, https://www.ncbi.nlm.nih.gov/pubmed/31260362.

131 Ariel D. Stern et al., "The Impact of Price Regulation," 1182-87.

132 *Summary of Feedback: PHARMAC's Proposal to Decline a Funding Application for Eculizumab* (PHARMAC, 2013), https://www.pharmac.govt.nz/assets/eculizumab-2013-08-analysis-of- feedback.pdf;

"Your Support Is Invaluable," PNH Support Association of NZ, accessed Oct. 15, 2019, http:// www.pnhsanz.org.nz/advocacy1.html.

133 Lydia O'Neal, "How to Stop Drug Prices from Rising? New Study Points to Single-Payer Health Care System," *International Business Times*, June 19, 2017, https://www.ibtimes.com/political-capital/ how-stop-drug-prices-rising-new-study-points-single-payer-health-care-system.

134 Dana O. Sarnak et al., *Paying for Prescription Drugs Around the World: Why Is the US an Outlier?* (The Commonwealth Fund, 2017), https://www.commonwealthfund.org/sites/default/files/ documents/___media_files_publications_issue_brief_2017_oct_sarnak_paying_for_rx_ib_v2.pdf.

135 "Health Care That Works Harder," Express Scripts, accessed Oct. 15, 2019, https://www.express- scripts.com/corporate/.

136 Jerome H. Reichman, "Compulsory Licensing of Patented Pharmaceutical Inventions: Evaluating the Options," *Journal of Law, Medicine & Ethics* 37, no. 2 (2009): 247-63, accessed Oct. 15, 2019. doi: 10.1111/j.1748-720X.2009.00369.x., https://www.ncbi.nlm.nih.gov/pmc/ articles/PMC2893582/pdf/nihms204056.pdf.

137 Kristina M. Lybecker and Elisabeth Fowler, "Compulsory Licensing in Canada and Thailand," *Journal of Law, Medicine & Ethics* (2009): 222-39. https://www.wardhealth.com/file/1734/ download?token=FMWb6w26;

*"The Campaign for Use of Compulsory Licensing in Thailand," Make Medicines Affordable, Feb. 18, 2015,* http://makemedicinesaffordable.org/en/ the-campaign-for-use-of-compulsory-licensing-in-thailand/.

138 McKenna Moore, "Russian Drugmaker Granted License to Produce Celgene Copycat," *Fortune*, July 11, 2018, http://fortune.com/2018/07/11/celgene-russia-nativa-revlimid/;

"Legal Scene Set for Russian Drugmaker to Get Compulsory License on Sutent," The Pharmaletter, April 30, 2019, https://www.thepharmaletter.com/article/ legal-scene-set-for-russian-drugmaker-to-get-compulsory-license-on-sutent.

139  Swathi Iyengar et al., "Prices, Costs, and Affordability of New Medicines for Hepatitis C in 30 Countries: An Economic Analysis," *PLoS Med* 13, no. 5 (2016): e1002032, accessed Oct. 15, 2019. doi: 10/1371/journal.pmed.1002032, https://www.ncbi.nlm.nih.gov/pmc/articles/PMC4886962/pdf/pmed.1002032.pdf.

140  Daniel A. Goldstein et al., "A Global Comparison of the Cost of Patented Cancer Drugs in Relation to Global Differences in Wealth," *Oncotarget* 8, no. 42 (2017): 71548-71555, accessed Oct. 15, 2019. doi: 10.18632/oncotarget.17742, https://www.ncbi.nlm.nih.gov/pmc/articles/PMC5641070/.

141  K.E. Young, "The Perverse Impact of External Reference Pricing (ERP): A Comparison of Orphan Drugs Affordability in 12 European Countries. A Call for Policy Change," *Journal of Market Access & Health Policy* 5, no. 1 (2017), accessed Oct. 15, 2019. doi: 10.1080/20016689.2017.1369817, https://www.tandfonline.com/doi/full/10.1080/20016689.2017.1369817.

142  The Council of Economic Advisers, *Reforming Biopharmaceutical Pricing at Home and Abroad* (Washington DC: Executive Office of the President of the US, 2017), https://www.whitehouse.gov/wp-content/uploads/2017/11/CEA-Rx-White-Paper-Final2.pdf.

143  Zoltán Kaló et al., "International Comparison of Pharmaceutical Expenditure in Middle Income Countries—Methodological Questions," *Value in Health* 15, no. 4 (2012), accessed Oct. 15, 2019, https://www.ispor.org/research_pdfs/40/pdffiles/PHP44.pdf.

144  Dr. Anupam B. Jena, "US Drug Prices Higher.";
QuintilesIMS Institute, *Outlook for Global Medicines Through 2021.*

145  Jerome H. Reichman, "Compulsory Licensing of Patented Pharmaceutical Inventions," 267-73.

146  Phillip L. Swagel to Honorable Frank Pallone Jr., official email, Oct. 11, 2019, "Effects of Drug Price Negotiation Stemming from Title 1 of H.R. 3, the Lower Drug Costs Now Act of 2019, on Spending and Revenues Related to Part D of Medicare," https://www.cbo.gov/system/files/2019-10/hr3ltr.pdf.

147  "2018 ASP Drug Pricing Files," CMS, US Centers for Medicare & Medicaid Services, modified Nov. 30, 2018 https://www.cms.gov/Medicare/Medicare-Fee-for-Service-Part-B-Drugs/McrPartBDrugAvgSalesPrice/2018ASPFiles.html.

148  US Congress, House, *Lower Drug Costs Now Act of 2019,* HR 3, 116th Cong., 1st sess., introduced in House Sept., 19, 2019, https://www.congress.gov/bill/116th-congress/house-bill/3/text?q=%7B%22search%22%3A%5B%22hr3%22%5D%7D&r=1&s=2.

149  Peter Kolchinsky, "Patients Will Be the Losers as Pelosi's Paln to Control Drug Prices Nearly Strikes Out," *Stat*, Sept. 23, 2019, https://www.statnews.com/2019/09/23/patients-losers-pelosi-drug-prices-plan/.

150  Ariel D. Stern et al., "The Impact of Price Regulation," 1182-87.

151  Jerome H. Reichman and Catherine Hasenzahl, *Non-voluntary Licensing of Patented Inventions.* (Geneva, Switzerland: ICTSD & UNCTAD, 2003), https://www.ictsd.org/downloads/2008/06/cs_reichman_hasenzahl.pdf.

152  Rebecca E. Wolitz, "New GAO Report on Drug Industry Profits," *SLS* (blog), Jan. 10, 2018, https://law.stanford.edu/2018/01/10/new-gao-report-on-drug-industry-profits/.

153  "Biopharmaceutical Spotlight," Select USA, International Trade Administration, accessed Oct. 15, 2019, https://www.selectusa.gov/pharmaceutical-and-biotech-industries-united-states;
European Federation of Pharmaceutical Industries and Associations, *The Pharmaceutical Industry in Figures* (Brussels, Belgium: EFPIA, 2018), https://www.efpia.eu/media/361960/efpia-pharmafigures2018_v07-hq.pdf;
Mateji Mikulic, "Global Pharmaceutical Industry—Statistics & Facts," *Statista*, Aug. 13, 2019, https://www.statista.com/topics/1764/global-pharmaceutical-industry/.

## Part 3: Beyond Conventional Thinking

154   US Congress, House, *Lower Drug Costs Now Act of 2019.*

155   Phillip L. Swagel to Honorable Frank Pallone Jr., official email, Oct. 11, 2019, "Effects of Drug Price Negotiation."

156   Lyrica, "Lyrica TV Commercial, 'Beach Day,'" iSpot.tv, 2018, video, 1:00, accessed Oct. 15, 2019, https://www.ispot.tv/ad/dfvu/lyrica-beach-day.

157   "Background on Drug Advertising," US Food & Drug Administration, last modified June 19, 2015, https://www.fda.gov/drugs/prescription-drug-advertising/background-drug-advertising.

158   "Basics of Drug Ads," US Food & Drug Administration, last modified June 19, 2015, https://www.fda.gov/drugs/resourcesforyou/consumers/prescriptiondrugadvertising/ucm072077.htm.

159   Carolyn McClanahan, "Dinosaur Doctors and the Death of Paternalistic Medicine," *Forbes*, Feb. 19, 2013, https://www.forbes.com/sites/carolynmcclanahan/2013/02/19/dinosaur-doctors-and-the-death-of-paternalistic-medicine/#3a1e1aeb6af3.

160   Brian C. Drolet and Candace L. White, "Selective Paternalism," *Virtual Mentor* 14, no. 7 (2012): 582-8, accessed Oct. 15, 2019. doi: 10.1001/virtualmentor.2012.14.7.oped2-1207, https://journalofethics.ama-assn.org/article/selective-paternalism/2012-07.

161   Albert W. Morris et al., "'For the Good of the Patient,' Survey of the Physicians of the National Medical Association Regarding Perceptions of DTC Advertising, Part II, 2006," *Journal of the National Medical Association* 99, no. 3 (2007): 287-93, accessed Oct. 15, 2019. https://www.ncbi.nlm.nih.gov/pubmed/17393955.

162   Milton Packer MD, "Does Anyone Read Medical Journal Anymore?" *Medpage Today*, March 28, 2018, https://www.medpagetoday.com/blogs/revolutionandrevelation/72029.

163   Thomas Sullivan, "Nearly Half of US Physicians Restrict Access by Manufacturer Sales reps—New Strategies to Reach Physicians," *Policy & Medicine*, May 6, 2018, https://www.policymed.com/2013/10/nearly-half-of-us-physicians-restrict-access-by-manufacturer-sales-reps-new-strategies-to-reach-physicians.html.

164   MedData Point, *MedData Point Shares Physician Opinions on DTC & DTP Pharmaceutical Advertising* (MedData Group), https://www.meddatagroup.com/wp-content/uploads/MedDataGroup_PhysOpinions_on_Pharma_Advertising.pdf.

165   Jerome R. Hoffman and Michael Wilkes, "Direct to Consumer Advertising of Prescription Drugs," *BMJ* 318 (1999): 1301-2, accessed Oct. 15, 2019. https://www.ncbi.nlm.nih.gov/pmc/articles/PMC1115695/pdf/1301.pdf.

166   Farah Ahmad, "Are Physicians ready for Patients with Internet-Based Health Information?" *Journal of Medical Internet Research* 8 no. 3 (2006): e22, accessed Oct. 15, 2019. doi: 10.2196/jmir.8.3e22, https://www.jmir.org/2006/3/e22/pdf.

167   Christine A. Sinsky, "Infographic: Date Night with the EHR," *NEJM Catalyst,* Dec. 12, 2017, https://catalyst.nejm.org/date-night-ehr/.

168   AMA, *AMA Calls for Ban on DTC Ads of Prescription Drugs and Medical Devices,* Nov. 17, 2015, accessed Oct. 15, 2019, https://www.ama-assn.org/content/ama-calls-ban-direct-consumer-advertising-prescription-drugs-and-medical-devices.

169   "Direct-to-consumer Advertising Under Fire," *Bulletin of the World Health Organization* 87, no. 8 (2009): 565-644, http://www.who.int/bulletin/volumes/87/8/09-040809/en/.

170   Rebecca Ruiz, "Ten Misleading Drug Ads," *Forbes*, Feb. 2, 2010, https://www.forbes.com/2010/02/02/drug-advertising-lipitor-lifestyle-health-pharmaceuticals-safety.html#78c288248c58.

171   "Irritable Bowel Syndrome," Mayo Clinic, accessed Oct. 15, 2019, https://www.mayoclinic.org/diseases-conditions/irritable-bowel-syndrome/diagnosis-treatment/drc-20360064;

        Elizabeth Landau, "Food Allergy Diagnosis 'An Inexact Science,' *CNN*, May 11, 2010, http://www.cnn.com/2010/HEALTH/05/11/food.allergies.definition/index.html;

"Depression," National institute of Mental Health, US Department of Health and human Services, accessed Oct. 15, 2019, https://www.nimh.nih.gov/health/topics/depression/index.shtml.

172 Jane E. Henney, "Challenges in Regulating Direct-to-Consumer Advertising," *JAMA* 284, no. 17 (2000): 2242, accessed Oct. 15, 2019. doi: 10.1001/jama.284.17.2242-JMS1101-3-1, https://jamanetwork.com/journals/jama/fullarticle/1843445;

C. Lee Ventola, "Direct-to-Consumer Pharmaceutical Advertising, Therapeutic or Toxic?" *P&T* 36, no. 10 (2011): 669-74, 681-4. https://www.ncbi.nlm.nih.gov/pmc/articles/PMC3278148/.

173 "Learned-Intermediary Doctrine Law and Legal Definition," US Legal, airSlate Legal Forms, accessed Oct. 15, 2019, https://definitions.uslegal.com/l/learned-intermediary-doctrine/.

174 "Handling the Angry Patient," HPSO, Affinity Insurance Services, accessed Oct. 15, 2019, http://www.hpso.com/risk-education/individuals/articles/Handling-the-Angry-Patient.

"Six Tips for Dealing with Difficult Patients," Jacksonville University, accessed Oct. 15, 2019, https://www.jacksonvilleu.com/blog/nursing/difficult-patients/.

175 Richard L. Kravitz et al., "Influends of Patients' requests for Directly Advertised Antidepressants: A Randomized Controlled Trial," *JAMA* 293, no. 16 (2005): 1995-2002, accessed Oct. 15, 2019. doi: 10.1001/jama.293.16.1995, https://www.ncbi.nlm.nih.gov/pmc/articles/PMC3155410/.

176 Lisa Morrise and Katy Jo Stevens, "Training Patient and Family Storytellers and patient and Family Faculty," *The Permanente Journal* 17, no. 3 (2013): e142-5, accessed Oct. 15, 2019. doi: 10.7812/TPP/12-059, https://www.ncbi.nlm.nih.gov/pmc/articles/PMC3783065/.

177 Suzanne Fiscella, "Are Patients Really the Problem," *Kevin MD* (blog), July 20,, 2017, https://www.kevinmd.com/blog/2017/07/patients-really-problem.html.

178 Meera Viswanathan et al., "Interventions to Improve Adherence to Self-administered Medications for Chronic Diseases in the United States: A Systematic Review," *Annals of Internal Medicine* 157, no. 11 (2012): 785-95, accessed Oct. 15, 2019. https://www.ncbi.nlm.nih.gov/pubmed/22964778.

179 Abby Alpert et al., "Prescription Drug Advertising and Drug Utilization: The Role of Medicare part D" (NBER Working Paper Series 21714, National Bureau of Economic Research, 2015), http://www.nber.org/papers/w21714.pdf.

180 Laura Entis, "DTC Pharma Ad Spending Slipped 4.6% in 2017: Kantar," *MM&M*, March 12, 2018, https://www.mmm-online.com/commercial/dtc-pharma-ad-spending-slipped-46-in-2017-kantar/article/750421/.

181 Sridhar Narayanan et al., "ROI Implications for Pharmaceutical Promotional Expenditures: The Role of Marketing Mix Interactions" (Forthcoming in *Journal of Marketing*, 2003), https://pdfs.semanticscholar.org/5bb3/6f34c96fb2748b69b948d12fea505ac45215.pdf.

182 W. David Bradford et al., "Effects of Direct-to-Consumer Advertising of Hydroxymethylglutarly Coenzyme a Reductase Inhibitors on Attainment of LDL-C Goals," *Clinical Therapeutics* 23, no. 12 (2006): 2105-118, accessed Oct. 15, 2019. doi: 10.1016/j.clinthera.2006.12.015, https://www.sciencedirect.com/science/article/pii/S0149291806003183;

"Sick of TV Drug Ads? Here's Why They Might be Good for You," *Wharton*, June 30, 2015, http://knowledge.wharton.upenn.edu/article/the-side-effects-of-prescription-drug-advertising/.

183 Justin Tinsley, "Twenty-Five Years Ago Today, Magic Johnson Announced he Had HIV," *The Undefeated*, Nov. 7, 2016, https://theundefeated.com/features/twenty-five-years-ago-today-magic-johnson-announced-he-had-hiv-los-angeles-lakers/.

184 Beth Snyder Bulik, "Gilead Pushes Hep C Testing in Baby Boomers as Its Blockbusters Plummet," *Fierce Pharma*, Feb. 22, 2017, https://www.fiercepharma.com/marketing/baby-boomers-targeted-gilead-hepatitis-c-awareness-campaign-even-as-drug-s-fortunes-drop.

185 Sherry Amatenstein, "Pseudobulbar Affect: I Wish People Knew How I felt," *PSY Com*, Oct. 1, 2018, https://www.psycom.net/mood-disorders/pseudobulbar-affect.

186 "Beyond Laughter and Tears: A Journey of Hope," IMDb, Amazon, accessed Oct. 15, 2019, https://www.imdb.com/title/tt4913290/.

187 Victoria Rees, "FDA Approves Nine Generics for Lyrica Drug," *European Pharmaceutical Review*, July 23, 2019, https://www.europeanpharmaceuticalreview.com/news/94953/fda-approves-nine-generics-for-lyrica-drug/.

188 AMA, *New PSA Campaign Urges Americans to Bring Hypertension Under Control,* Nov. 16, 2017, accessed Oct. 15, 2019, https://www.ama-assn.org/press-center/press-releases/new-psa-campaign-urges-americans-bring-hypertension-under-control.

189 "Health," AD Council, accessed Oct. 15, 2019, https://www.adcouncil.org/Our-Campaigns/Health

190 S. F. Kemp et al., "Epinephrine: The Drug of Choice for Anaphylaxis. A Statement of the World Allergy Organization," *European Journal of Allergy and Clinical Immunology* 63, no. 8 (2008): 1061-70, accessed Oct. 15, 2019. doi: 10.1111/j.1398-9995.2008.01733.x., https://www.ncbi.nlm.nih.gov/pubmed/18691308.

191 S. F. Kemp et al., "Epinephrine: The Drug of Choice for Anaphylaxis. A Statement of the World Allergy Organization," *European Journal of Allergy and Clinical Immunology* 63, no. 8 (2008): 1061-70, accessed Oct. 15, 2019. doi: 10.1111/j.1398-9995.2008.01733.x., https://www.ncbi.nlm.nih.gov/pubmed/18691308.

192 Cynthia Koons and Robert Langreth, "How Marketing Turned the EpiPen Into a Billion-Dollar Business," *Bloomberg Businessweek,* Set. 23, 2015, https://www.bloomberg.com/news/articles/2015-09-23/how-marketing-turned-the-epipen-into-a-billion-dollar-business.

193 Cythina Koons et al., "How EpiPen's Price Rose and Rose," *Bloomberg*, Sept. 1, 2016, https://www.bloomberg.com/graphics/2016-epipen-pricing/.

194 James Surowiecki, "How the Maker of the EpiPen Made Government Its Ally," *The New Yorker*, Sept. 22, 2016, https://www.newyorker.com/business/currency/how-the-maker-of-the-epipen-made-government-its-ally.

195 Carly Helfand, "FDA Swats Down Teva's EpiPen Copy, Putting Mylan in Cruise Control," *Fierce Pharma*, March 1, 2016, https://www.fiercepharma.com/sales-and-marketing/fda-swats-down-teva-s-epipen-copy-putting-mylan-cruise-control.

196 FDA, *FDA Alerts Consumers of Nationwide Voluntary Recall of EpiPen and EpiPen Jr.,* March 31, 2017, accessed Oct. 15, 2019, https://www.fda.gov/news-events/press-announcements/fda-alerts-consumers-nationwide-voluntary-recall-epipen-and-epipen-jr.

197 "Why Aren't Doctors Prescribing the Cheaper EpiPen Alternative?" *CBS News*, Nov. 6, 2016, https://www.cbsnews.com/news/why-arent-doctors-prescribing-the-cheaper-epipen-alternative/.

198 FDA, *FDA Alerts Consumers.*

199 Pauline Bartolone, "EpiPen's Dominance Driven By Competitors' Stumbles and Tragic Deaths," *Shot, Health News from NPR*, Sept. 7, 2016, https://www.npr.org/sections/health-shots/2016/09/07/492964464/epipen-s-dominance-driven-by-competitors-stumbles-and-tragic-deaths.

200 Steven Johnson, "Big Pharma Incentives Are Out of Whack: Why We Need an X-Prize for Drugs," *Wired*, Oct. 11, 2012, https://www.wired.com/2012/10/prescription-drug-crisis/.

201 Ross A. Pollack et al., "Impact of Bystander Automated External Defibrillator Use on Survival and Functional Outcomes in Shockable Observed Public Cardiac Arrests," *Circulation* 137, no. 20 (2018): 2104-113, accessed Oct. 15, 2019. doi: 10.1161/CIRCULATIONAHA.117.030700, https://www.ahajournals.org/doi/full/10.1161/CIRCULATIONAHA.117.030700.

202 "CPR/AED Laws," Sudden Cardiac Arrest Foundation, accessed Oct. 15, 2019, https://www.sca-aware.org/cpr-aed-laws.

203 Frederick Wolfe, "Fibromyalgia Wars," *The Journal of Rheumatology* 36, no. 4 (2009): 671-8, accessed Oct. 15, 2019. doi: 10.3899/jrheum.081180, http://www.jrheum.org/content/36/4/671.long.

204 "Reader Stories," The No Nut Traveler, accessed Oct. 15, 2019, http://nonuttraveler.com/reader-stories.

205 Kunal Srivastava, "Impact of Reducing Dosing Frequency on Adherence to Oral Therapies: A Literature Review and Meta-Analysis," *Patient Preference and Adherence* 7 (2013): 419-34, accessed Oct. 15, 2019. doi: 10.2147/PPA.S44646, https://www.ncbi.nlm.nih.gov/pmc/articles/PMC3669002/;

Dirk Kuypers et al., "Improved Adherence to Tacrolimus Once-Daily Formulation in Renal Recipients: A Randomized Controlled Trial Using Electronic Monitoring," *Transplantation Journal* 9 no. 2 (2013): 33-40, accessed Oct. 15, 2019. doi: 10.1097/TP.0b013e3182725532, https://www.ncbi.nlm.nih.gov/pubmed/23263559;

Kevin Haehl, "The Importance of Convenient Dosing Formulations for Elderly Patients," *American Pharmaceutical Review*, Jan. 31, 2016, https://www.americanpharmaceuticalreview.com/Featured-Articles/183038-The-Importance-of-Convenient-Dosing-Formulations-for-Elderly-Patients/.

206 Mayer B. Davidson, "Insulin Analogs—Is There a Compelling Case to Use Them? No!" *Diabetes Care* 37, no. 6 (2014): 1771-4, accessed Oct. 15, 2019. doi: 10.2337/dc13-2915, http://care.diabetesjournals.org/content/37/6/1771;

George Grunberger, "Insulin Analogs—Are They Work It? Yes!" *Diabetes Care* 37, no. 6 (2014): 1767-70, accessed Oct. 15, 2019. doi: 10.2337/dc14-0031, http://care.diabetesjournals.org/content/37/6/1767.

207 John LaMattina "Today's insulin isn't what Banting and Best developed. It's far, far better," *Stat*, November 14, 2019, https://www.statnews.com/2019/11/14/insulin-safer-better-easier-to-use/ accessed November 23, 2019.

208 Joyce Frieden, "Senators Probe 'Enormous' Insulin Price Spikes," *MedPage Today*, May 8, 2018, https://www.medpagetoday.com/endocrinology/type1diabetes/72771.

209 Diana I. Brixner and Carrie McAdam-Marx, "Cost-Effectiveness of Insulin Analogs," *The American Journal of Managed Care* 14, no. 11 (2008): 766-75, accessed Oct. 15, 2019. https://www.ncbi.nlm.nih.gov/pubmed/18999911?dopt=Abstract.

210 Amelia Dmowska and Payal Marathe, "FDA Approves Admelog, the First Biosimilar Mealtime Insulin," *diaTribe Learn*, Jan. 17, 2018, https://diatribe.org/fda-approves-admelog-first-biosimilar-mealtime-insulin;

ER/AJW, "FDA Approves New Insulin Glargine Basaglar—The First 'Biosimilar' Insulin in the US," *diaTribe Learn*, Jan. 11, 2016, https://diatribe.org/fda-approves-new-insulin-glargine-basaglar-first-biosimilar-insulin-us.

211 Silas W. Smith, "Chiral Toxicology: It's the Same Thing...Only Different," *Toxicological Sciences* 110, no. 1 (2009): 4 30, accessed Oct. 15, 2019. doi: 10.1093/toxsci/kfp097, https://academic.oup.com/toxsci/article/110/1/4/1668162.

212 "Development of New Stereoisomeric Drugs," FDA, updated March 21, 2018, https://www.fda.gov/regulatory-information/search-fda-guidance-documents/development-new-stereoisomeric-drugs.

213 Mateji Mikulic, "AstraZeneca's Revenue from Top Product Nexium 2006-2018, *Statista*, March 11, 2019, https://www.statista.com/statistics/266545/astrazenecas-revenue-from-top-product-nexium-since-2006/;

"Nexium: How Patent Shenanigans Cost Payers Billions," *Prescription Intelligence,* Dec. 30, 2015, https://prescriptionintelligence.com/nexium-how-patent-shenanigans-cost-payers-billions/.

214 R Paul, "Comparison of Racemic Ketamine and S-ketamine in Treatment-Resistant Major Depression: Report of Two Cases," *World Journal of Biol Psychiatry* 10, no. 3 (2009): 241-4, accessed Oct. 15, 2019. doi: 10/1080/15622970701714370, https://www.ncbi.nlm.nih.gov/m/pubmed/19224412/.

215   Marco A. Ramos et al., "Opinion: The New Ketamine-Based Antidepressant Is a Rip-Off," *Vice,* May 17, 2019, https://www.vice.com/en_us/article/pajkjy/opinion-the-new-ketamine-based-antidepressant-is-a-rip-off.

216   Wikipedia Contributors, "Orphan Drug Act of 1983," *Wikipedia, The Free Encyclopedia,* accessed Oct. 15, 2019, https://en.wikipedia.org/wiki/Orphan_Drug_Act_of_1983.

217   *Operating Plan for FY 2019* (National Institutes of Health, 2019), 1-2, https://officeofbudget.od.nih.gov/pdfs/FY20/cy/FY%202019%20NIH%20Operating%20Plan%202.8.19%20Web.pdf

218   *US Investments in Medical and Health Research and Development, 2013-2015* (Arlington, VA: Research America, 2016), https://www.researchamerica.org/sites/default/files/2016US_Invest_R&D_report.pdf.

219   Hamilton Moses III et al., "The Anatomy of Medical Research: US and International Comparisons," *JAMA* 313, no. 2 (2015): 174-89, accessed Oct. 15, 2019. doi: 10.1001/jama.2014.15939, https://www.ncbi.nlm.nih.gov/pubmed/25585329.

220   "Humira: The Highs and Lows of the World's Best-Selling Drug," *Pharmaceutical Technology,* Sept. 2018, https://www.pharmaceutical-technology.com/features/humira-abbvie-drug/.

221   AbbVie, *AbbVie Reports Full-Year and Fourth-Quarter 2018 Financial Results,* Jan. 25, 2019, https://news.abbvie.com/news/abbvie-reports-full-year-and-fourth-quarter-2018-financial-results.htm.

222   Kyle Blankenship, "The Top 20 Drugs By 2018 US Sales," *Fierce Pharma,* June 17, 2019, https://www.fiercepharma.com/special-report/top-20-drugs-by-2018-u-s-sales.

223   The Njardarson Group, *Top 200 Pharmaceutical Products by Retail Sales in 2018* (Tucson, AZ: The University of Arizona, 2018), https://njardarson.lab.arizona.edu/sites/njardarson.lab.arizona.edu/files/2018Top200PharmaceuticalRetailSalesPosterLowResFinalV2.pdf; This lists drugs by their global sales, so, to be more inclusive in my count, I conservatively estimated that US sales represented 60% of these values, though for some drugs 30-50% might be more appropriate.

224   Jing Wu, "While Kalydeco Sailed Through, Vertex's Orkambi Faces Strong Headwinds in Europe," *Decision Resources Group,* June 2, 2016, https://decisionresourcesgroup.com/blog/kalydeco-sailed-vertexs-orkambi-faces-strong-headwinds-europe/.

225   Ed Silverman, "Vertex CEO Complains to U.K. Prime Minister About Stalled Talks Over a Pricey Drug," *STAT,* July 6, 2018, https://www.statnews.com/pharmalot/2018/07/06/vertex-ceo-uk-prime-minister-drug/..

226   Eric Sagonowsky, "Vertex Cancels Plans for CF Triple Combo Testing in France, Citing Failed Orkambi Negotiations," *Fierce Pharma,* Feb. 15, 2018, https://www.fiercepharma.com/pharma/after-failed-orkambi-negotiations-vertex-pulls-plug-phase-3-triple-combo-testing-france.

227   Alexander Gaffney et al., "Regulatory Explainer: Everything You Need to Know About FDA'S Priority Review Vouchers," *Regulatory Focus,* Nov. 6, 2019, https://www.raps.org/regulatory-focus/news-articles/2017/12/regulatory-explainer-everything-you-need-to-know-about-fdas-priority-review-vouchers.

228   Paul J. Meis et al., "Prevention of Recurrent Preterm Delivery by 17 Aplha-Hydroxyprogesterone Caproate," *New England Journal of Medicine* 348 (2003): 2379-85, accessed Nov. 24, 2019. doi: 10.1056/NEJMoa035140, https://www.nejm.org/doi/full/10.1056/NEJMoa035140, accessed November 24, 2019.

229   Rob Stein, "Critics Slam Cost of FDA-Approved Drug to Prevent Preterm Births," *The Washington Post,* March 28, 2011, https://www.washingtonpost.com/national/fda-approval-of-drug-to-prevent-preemies-prompts-price-jump-from-10-to-1500/2011/03/04/AFmRo6qB_story.html?utm_term=.1d238d582cc9.

230   Ed Silverman, "FDA Statement About Makena Compounding Clouds KV Pharma's Future, *Forbes* June 18, 2012, https://www.forbes.com/sites/edsilverman/2012/06/18/fda-statement-about-makena-compounding-clouds-kv-pharmas-future/#68de5b5595d3.

231　Richard Knox, "Preemie Prevention Drug Costs 53 Times More Than Generic, But Researchers Find It's NO Better," *Common Health*, Oct. 3, 2017, https://www.wbur.org/commonhealth/2017/10/03/preterm-birth-prevention-drug-costs.

232　Wikipedia Contributors, "New England Compounding Center Meningitis Outbreak."

233　David B. Nelson et al., "17-Alpha Hydroxyprogesterone Caproate Did Not Reduce the Rate of Recurrent Preterm Birth in a Prospective Cohort Study," *American Journal of Obstetrics & Gynecology* 216, no. 6 (2017): 600, accessed Oct. 15, 2019. doi: 10.1016/j.ajog.2017.02.025, https://www.ncbi.nlm.nih.gov/pmc/articles/PMC5449222/.

234　*Transplant Activity Report Covering 2012-2016* (Center for International Blood and marrow Transplant Research, 2018), 1, https://bloodcell.transplant.hrsa.gov/research/transplant_data/transplant_activity_report/bycellsource_.pdf;

　　Michael S. Broder et al., "The Cost of Hematopoietic Stem-Cell Transplantation in the United States," *American Health & Drug Benefits* 10, no. 7 (2017): 366-74, accessed Oct. 15, 2019. https://www.ncbi.nlm.nih.gov/pmc/articles/PMC5726064/: (crudely: $250,000/allogeneic * 8,800 allogeneic transplants/year + 140,000/autologous * 12,800 autologous transplants/year = $4.3B)

235　Kyle Blankenship, "The Top 20 Drugs By 2018 US Sales."

236　Kayana Szymczak, "Drug Companies and Doctors Battle Over the Future of Fecal Transplants," *The New York Times*, March 3, 2019, https://www.nytimes.com/2019/03/03/health/fecal-transplants-fda-microbiome.html;

　　Jim Doyle, "KV Boosts Prenatal Drug Price 100-Fold," *St. Louis Post-Dispatch,* March 20, 2011, https://www.stltoday.com/business/local/article_55dbaf88-4ab0-11e0-ad73-0017a4a78c22.html.

237　Openbiome.org

238　GAO, "Prescription Drugs: OxyContin Abuse and Diversion and Efforts to Address the Problem," (report to Congressional requesters, Washington D.C., 2013), https://www.govinfo.gov/content/pkg/GAOREPORTS-GAO-04-110/pdf/GAOREPORTS-GAO-04-110.pdf;

　　Commonwealth of Massachusetts v. Purdue Pharma L.P. et al., 1184 C.V. 01808 (2019) (Mem.), https://www.documentcloud.org/documents/5684879-Mass-AGO-Pre-Hearing-Memo-and-Exhibits.html.

239　Patrick Radden Keefe, "The Family That Built an Empire of Pain," *The New Yorker*, Oct. 23, 2017, https://www.newyorker.com/magazine/2017/10/30/the-family-that-built-an-empire-of-pain.

240　United States General Accounting Office, "Prescription Drugs: OxyContin Abuse and Diversion and Efforts to Address the Problem" (report number GAO-04-110, Washington D.C., 2004), https://www.gao.gov/htext/d04110.html.

241　"Purdue Pharma Announces Agreement in Principle on Landmark Opioid Litigation Settlement," Purdue, Sept. 16, 2019, https://www.purduepharma.com/news/2019/09/16/purdue-pharma-announces-agreement-in-principle-on-landmark-opioid-litigation-settlement/.

242　Jonathan Stempel, "Drug Firms Must Face Trial Over Opioids, Judge Orders," *Insurance Journal*, Sept. 4, 2019, https://www.insurancejournal.com/news/national/2019/09/04/538781.htm.

243　Wikipedia Contributors, "List of Largest Pharmaceutical Settlements," *Wikipedia, The Free Encyclopedia,* accessed Oct. 15, 2019, https://en.wikipedia.org/wiki/List_of_largest_pharmaceutical_settlements.

244　Simon Kung et al., 'Treatment of Nightmares with Prazosin: A Systematic Review," *Mayo Clinic Proceedings* 87, no. 9 (2012): 890-900, Oct. 15, 2019. doi: 10.1016/j.mayocp.2012.05.015, https://www.ncbi.nlm.nih.gov/pmc/articles/PMC3538493/.

245　Murray A. Raskind, "The a1-Adrenergic Antagonist Prazosin Ameliorates Combat Trauma Nightmares in Veterans with Posttraumatic Stress Disorder: A Report of Four Cases," *The Journal of Clinical Psychiatry* 61, no. 2 (2000): 129-33, Oct. 15, 2019. https://www.ncbi.nlm.nih.gov/pubmed/10732660.

246   Pfizer Labs, *Minipress Capsules: Prazosin Hydrochloride* (New York: Pfizer Inc., 2019), https://www.accessdata.fda.gov/drugsatfda_docs/label/2009/017442s033lbl.pdf

247   "Food and Drug Administration Amendments Act (FDAAA) of 2007," US Food & Drug Administration, March 29, 2018, https://www.fda.gov/regulatory-information/selected-amendments-fdc-act/food-and-drug-administration-amendments-act-fdaaa-2007.

248   "Drug Facilitated Sexual Assault," Science Direct, Elsevier, accessed Oct. 15, 2019, https://www.sciencedirect.com/topics/medicine-and-dentistry/drug-facilitated-sexual-assault.

249   Trinka Porrata, "GHB Death Statistics," Project GHB, accessed Oct. 15, 2019, http://www.projectghb.org/content/ghb-death-statistics.

250   Wikipedia Contributors, "Date Rape Drug," *Wikipedia, The Free Encyclopedia,* accessed Oct. 15, 2019, https://en.wikipedia.org/wiki/Date_rape_drug

251   Reviewed by L. Anderson, "List of Schedule 1 Drugs," Drugs.com, updated May 18, 2018, https://www.drugs.com/article/csa-schedule-1.html.

252   XYREM, *Patient Quick Start Guide* (Jazz Pharmaceuticals, 2019), https://www.xyremrems.com/assets/files/Xyrem_REMS_Patient_Quick_Start_Guide_PDF_final_press.pdf.

253   Y. Grace Wang et al., "Safety Overview of Postmarketing and Clinical Experience of Sodium Oxybate (Xyrem): Abuse, Misuse, Dependence, and Diversion," *Journal of Clinical Sleep Medicine* 5, no. 4 (2009): 365-71, Oct. 15, 2019. https://www.ncbi.nlm.nih.gov/pmc/articles/PMC2725257/.

254   *Gamma Hydroxybutyric Acid* (Drug Enforcement Administration, 2018), https://www.deadiversion.usdoj.gov/drug_chem_info/ghb.pdf. ;
      Wikipedia Contributors, "Date Rape Drug."

255   "Narcolepsy Fast Facts," Narcolepsy Network, revised June 2015, https://narcolepsynetwork.org/about-narcolepsy/narcolepsy-fast-facts/;
      *Second Quarter 2019 Financial Results* (Jazz Pharmaceuticals, 2019), https://investor.jazzpharma.com/static-files/af719763-9e0a-4ada-8ab9-b22c52c8c22c;
      "Prevalence," National Fibromyalgia Association, accessed Oct. 15, 2019, http://www.fmaware.org/about-fibromyalgia/prevalence/.

256   Roland Staud, "Sodium Oxybate for the Treatment of Fibromyalgia," *Expert Opinion on Pharmacotherapy* 12, no. 11 (2011): 1789-98, accessed Oct. 15, 2019. doi: 10.1517/14656566.2011.589836, https://www.ncbi.nlm.nih.gov/pubmed/21679091.

257   Michael J. Brownstein, "A Brief History of Opiates, Opioid Peptides, and Opioid Receptors," *Proc. Natl. Acad. Sci.* 90 (1993): 5391-93, accessed Oct. 15, 2019. https://www.ncbi.nlm.nih.gov/pmc/articles/PMC46725/pdf/pnas01469-0022.pdf.

258   Chandrasekhar Krishnamurti and SSC Chakra Rao, "The Isolation of Morphine by Serturner," *Indian Journal of Anaesthesia* 60, no. 11 (2016): 861-2, accessed Oct. 15, 2019. doi: 10.4103/0019-5049.193696, https://www.ncbi.nlm.nih.gov/pmc/articles/PMC5125194/.

259   Leung et al., "Addiction Rare in Patients Treated with Narcotics," *New England Journal of Medicine* 302, no. 123 (1980), accessed Oct. 15, 2019. doi: 10.1056/NEJM198001103020221, https://www.nejm.org/doi/10.1056/NEJM198001103020221.

260   James N. Campbell, "APS 1995 Presidential Address" (speech, Los Angeles, Nov. 12, 1995) *The Journal of Pain,*, https://www.jpain.org/article/S1082-3174(96)80076-6/abstract.

261   "Timeline of Selected FDA Activities and Significant Events Addressing Opioid Misuse and Abuse," US Food & Drug Administration, updated Sept. 25, 2019, https://www.fda.gov/drugs/information-drug-class/timeline-selected-fda-activities-and-significant-events-addressing-opioid-misuse-and-abuse.

262   Marcia Angell, "Opioid Nation," *The New York Review of Books*, Dec. 6, 2018, https://www.nybooks.com/articles/2018/12/06/opioid-nation/.

263   GAO, "Prescription Drugs.";

Commonwealth of Massachusetts v. Purdue Pharma L.P. et al., 1184 C.V. 01808 (2019) (Mem.), https://www.documentcloud.org/documents/5684879-Mass-AGO-Pre-Hearing-Memo-and-Exhibits.html.

264  GAO, "Prescription Drugs."

265  GAO, "Prescription Drugs."

266  Wikipedia Contributors, "List of Largest Pharmaceutical Settlements."

267  Heather Won Tesoriero, "OxyContin Maker Pleads Guilty," *The Wall Street Journal,* May 11, 2007, https://www.wsj.com/articles/SB117880640850298612.

268  Patrick Radden Keefe, "The Family That Built an Empire of Pain."

269  James C. Crews and Donald D. Denson, "Recovery of Morphine From a Controlled-Release Preparation: A Source of Opioid Abuse," *Cancer* 66 (1990): 2642-4, accessed Oct. 15, 2019. https://onlinelibrary.wiley.com/doi/pdf/10.1002/1097-0142(19901215)66:12%3C2642::AID-CNCR2820661229%3E3.0.CO;2-B.

270  "Timeline of Selected FDA Activities," US Food & Drug Administration.

271  "Overdose Death Rates," National Institute on Drug Abuse, USA.Gov, updated Jan. 2019, https://www.drugabuse.gov/related-topics/trends-statistics/overdose-death-rates.

272  Marilyn Bulloch, "How Oxycodone Has Contributed to the Opioid Epidemic," *Pharmacy Times*, Aug. 2, 2018, https://www.pharmacytimes.com/contributor/marilyn-bulloch-pharmd-bcps/2018/08/how-oxycodone-has-contributed-to-the-opioid-epidemic.

273  "What New Opioid Laws Mean for Pain Relief," *Harvard Health Publishing*, Oct. 2018, https://www.health.harvard.edu/pain/what-new-opioid-laws-mean-for-pain-relief;

National Academies of Sciences, Engineering, and Medicine et al., *Pain Management and the Opioid Epidemic* (Washington, D.C.: The National Academies Press, 2017), https://www.ncbi.nlm.nih.gov/books/NBK458661/.

274  Ronald S. Litman et al., "Abuse-Deterrent Opioid Formulations," *Anesthesiology* 5, no. 128 (2018): 1015-26, accessed Oct. 15, 2019. doi: 10.1097/ALN.0000000000002031, https://anesthesiology.pubs.asahq.org/article.aspx?articleid=2667599;

"Study Finds 22 Percent Decrease in Opioid Prescriptions," *AAFP*, April 25, 2018, https://www.aafp.org/news/health-of-the-public/20180425opioidstudy.html.

275  Richard A. "Red" Lawhern, "Stop Persecuting Doctors for Legitimately Prescribing Opioids for Chronic Pain," *Stat*, June 28, 2019, https://www.statnews.com/2019/06/28/stop-persecuting-doctors-legitimately-prescribing-opioids-chronic-pain/;

"CDC Reiterates Limits of Opioid Prescribing Guideline," *PT In Motion News*, April 10, 2019, https://www.apta.org/PTinMotion/News/2019/04/10/CDCClarificationGuideline/: (read comments section).

276  Courtney Krueger, "Ask the Expert: Do NSAIDs Cause More Deaths Than Opioids?" *Practical Pain Management*, Nov./Dec., 2013, https://www.practicalpainmanagement.com/treatments/pharmacological/opioids/ask-expert-do-nsaids-cause-more-deaths-opioids.

277  William M. Lee, "Acetaminophen and the US Acute Liver Failure Study Group: Lowering the Risks of Hepatic Failure," *Heptology* 40, no. 1 (2004): 6-9, accessed Oct. 15, 2019. doi: 10.1002/hep.20293, https://www.ncbi.nlm.nih.gov/pubmed/15239078.

278  John J. Murphy, "A Pain Specialist's Perspective on the Opioid Epidemic: A Discussion with Dr. Mark Bailey," *MDLinx*, Aug. 5, 2017, https://www.mdlinx.com/pain-management/article/1019; *Caring for Opioid Dependent Women in the Hospital Setting* (Healthy Start Coalition of Flagler and Volusia Counties, Inc., 2016), https://www.healthystartfv.org/wp-content/uploads/2016/06/Opioid%20Addiction%20in%20Pregnancy%20and%20Postparum%20June%202016%20Final.pdf.

279  Ronald S. Litman et al., "Abuse-deterrent Opioid Formulations," 1015-26.

280 "Clincal Alert: Generic OxyContin Delayed Tlil 2025," *myMatrixx*, April 18, 2013, https://www.mymatrixx.com/clinical-alert-generic-OxyContin-delayed-till-2025/.

281 VM Kuma et al., "Impact of Abuse Deterrent Formulations of Opioids in Patients with Chronic Pain in the United States: A Cost-Effectiveness Model," *Value Health* 22, no. 4 (2019): 416-22, accessed Oct. 15, 2019. doi: 10.1016/j.jval.2018.12.005, https://www.ncbi.nlm.nih.gov/pubmed/30975392.

282 Alex Dasalla, "Collegium Provides Full-Year 2019 Financial Guidance," *P&T Community*, Jan. 7, 2019, https://www.ptcommunity.com/wire/collegium-provides-full-year-2019-financial-guidance.

283 Pradip K. Muhuri et al., "Associations of Nonmedical Pan Reliever Use and Initiation of Heroin use in the United States," *CBHSQ Data Review, SAMHSA*, Aug., 2013 https://www.samhsa.gov/data/sites/default/files/DR006/DR006/nonmedical-pain-reliever-use-2013.htm

284 "Overdose Death Rates," National Institute on Drug Abuse.

285 Abby Alpert et al., "Supply-Side Drug Policy in the Presence of Substitutes: Evidence from the Introduction of Abuse-Deterrent Opioids," (NBER Working Paper No. 23031, 2017), https://www.nber.org/papers/w23031.

286 William N. Evans and Ethan Lieber, "How the Reformulation of OxyContin Ignited the Heroin Epidemic," *Cato Institute,* Aug. 15, 2018, https://www.cato.org/publications/research-briefs-economic-policy/how-reformulation-OxyContin-ignited-heroin-epidemic.

287 Lindsey Vuolo, "The Federal Government Needs to Take Stronger Action to Prevent Discriminatory Coverage of Methadone," *Health Affairs*, April 25, 2019, https://www.healthaffairs.org/do/10.1377/hblog20190418.164447/full/.

288 German Lopez, "The Thousands of Lawsuits Against Opioid Companies, Explained," *Vox*, Oct. 17, 2019, https://www.vox.com/policy-and-politics/2017/6/7/15724054/opioid-epidemic-lawsuits-purdue-OxyContin.

289 Clive Bates and Andy Rowell, *Tobacco Explained* (WHO), https://www.who.int/tobacco/media/en/TobaccoExplained.pdf.

290 SAMHSA, *2017 NSDUH Annual National Report*, accessed Oct. 15, 2019, https://www.samhsa.gov/data/report/2017-nsduh-annual-national-report.

291 "Cigarette Health Warnings," US Food & Drug Administration, updated Nov. 8, 2019, https://www.fda.gov/tobacco-products/labeling-and-warning-statements-tobacco-products/cigarette-health-warnings.

292 Peter Kolchinsky, "America's Social Contract with the Biopharmaceutical Industry," *Biotech Social Contract,* Dec. 27, 2017, https://medium.com/the-biotech-social-contract/kolchinsky-tbsc-1-dafc2fe803e5.

293 Peter Kolchinsky, "When Drugs Can't Go Generic: Honoring Our End of the Contract with 'Synthetic' Genericization,'" *Biocentury,* Dec. 17, 2018, https://www.biocentury.com/biocentury/politics-policy-law/2018-12-17/kolchinsky-how-keep-social-contract-drugs-can%E2%80%99t-go-generic.

294 Preston Atteberry et al., "Biologics Are Natural Monopolies (Part 1)"; "Mark Trusheim et al., "Biologics Are Natural Monopolies (Part 2)."

295 Diana W. Shineman et al., "Overcoming Obstacles to Repurposing for Neurodegenerative Disease," *Annals of Clinical and Translational Neurology* 1, no. 7 (2014): 512-18, accessed Oct. 15, 2019. doi: 10.1002/acn3.76, https://onlinelibrary.wiley.com/doi/full/10.1002/acn3.76.

# INDEX

# ABOUT THE AUTHOR

**Peter Kolchinsky is a biotechnology investor and a scientist. He co-founded** and runs the Boston-based investment firm RA Capital Management, writes and teaches about biomedical entrepreneurship and its potential to transform global health, serves on the boards of several public and private drug development companies, and lives in Massachusetts with his historian/ equestrian wife, strong-willed children, and reasonably well-trained dog.

Printed in Poland
by Amazon Fulfillment
Poland Sp. z o.o., Wrocław

27632921R00167